Teacher Edition

Houghton
Mifflin
Harcourt

MATH
Expressions
Common Core

Dr. Karen C. Fuson

GRADE
K

Volume 2

This material is based upon work supported by the
National Science Foundation
under Grant Numbers
ESI-9816320, REC-9806020, and RED-935373.

Any opinions, findings, and conclusions, or recommendations expressed in this material
are those of the author and do not necessarily reflect the views of the National Science Foundation.

Printed in the U.S.A.

ISBN: 978-0-547-82493-2

10 0877 21 20 19 18 17 16 15 14

4500461511   A B C D E F G

MATH Expressions
Common Core

HOUGHTON MIFFLIN HARCOURT

COMPLETE
Common Core
Instruction

Math Expressions is a comprehensive Kindergarten – Grade 6 curriculum that offers new ways to teach and learn the rigorous mathematics in the Common Core State Standards.

By combining the most powerful elements of standards-based mathematics with the best of traditional approaches, *Math Expressions* emphasizes in-depth mathematics through real world problem situations, modeling, conceptual language and Math Talk to help students build mathematical ideas that make sense to them.

Focused and Coherent
to address today's Standards

Math Expressions' single focus is the Common Core State Standards. With this focus, students using Math Expressions study a small number of mathematical concepts. Therefore, they have the time to develop the knowledge to build in-depth understanding of major mathematical ideas.

"...the mathematics curriculum in the United States must become substantially more focused and coherent in order to improve mathematics achievement in this country."

Common Core State Standards for Mathematics
Introduction, p.3

With special emphasis on Mathematical Practices and Mathematical Progressions

In *Math Expressions*, teachers create an inquiry environment and encourage constructive discussion. Students invent, question, model, represent and explore, but also learn and practice important math strategies. Through daily Math Talk, students explain their methods and, in turn, become more fluent in them. Mathematics content and models connect and build across the grade levels in *Math Expressions* to provide a progression of teaching and learning that aligns precisely with the Common Core State Standards for Mathematics.

"The Standards for Mathematical Practice describe varieties of expertise that mathematics educators at all levels should seek to develop in their students. These practices rest on important "processes and proficiencies" with longstanding importance in mathematics education."

Common Core State Standards for Mathematics Introduction p.6

"The Common Core State Standards in mathematics were built on progressions: narrative documents describing the progression of a topic across a number of grade levels, informed both by research on children's cognitive development and by the logical structure of mathematics."

Progression Documents for the Common Core State Standards

Organized
for Success

Math Expressions provides many pathways to mathematical tasks. The program starts at the student's level and continually elicits thinking, provides visual and linguistic supports to move the student rapidly to understanding, and ends with extended fluency practice and application while continuing the emphasis on understanding and explaining.

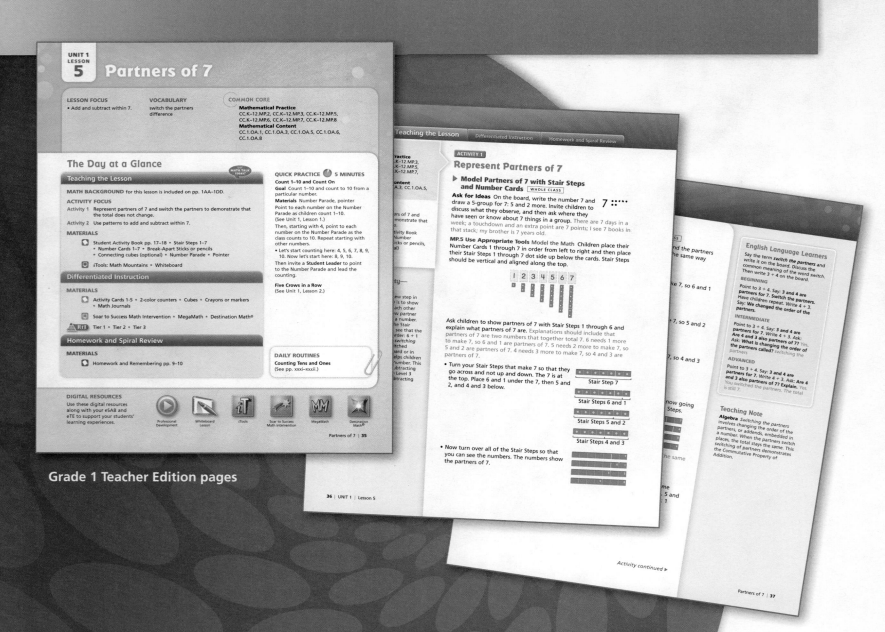

Grade 1 Teacher Edition pages

Differentiated for ALL Learners

Every *Math Expressions* lesson includes intervention, on-level, and challenge differentiation to support classroom needs. Leveled Math Writing Prompts provide opportunities for in-depth thinking and analysis, and help prepare students for important assessments. Support for English Language Learners is included in each lesson. A special Math Center Challenges Easel, with activities, projects, and puzzlers, helps the highest math achievers reach their potential.

Differentiated Instruction Activities appear in both the Teacher Edition and in a handy classroom kit.

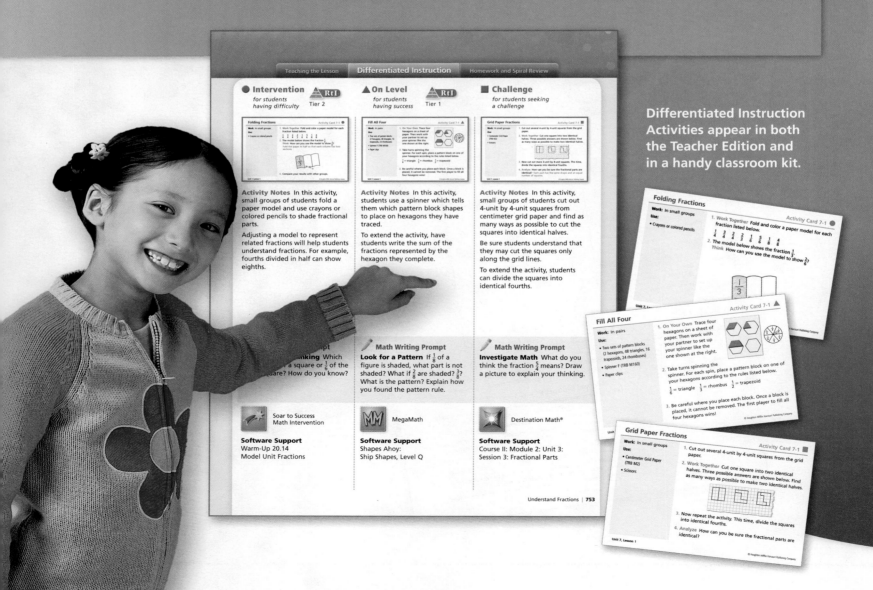

> "Activities and strategies should be developed and incorporated into instructional materials to assist teachers in helping all students become proficient in mathematics."

Adding It Up: Helping Children Learn Mathematics, National Research Council (2001), p. 421

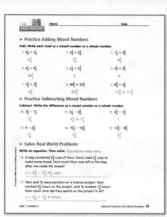

Student Activity Book page 15

▶ Practice Adding Mixed Numbers [PAIRS]

Student Pairs should work on Exercises 1–9 on Student Book page 15. These problems give students practice adding mixed numbers.

MP.6 Attend to Precision Verify Solutions Discuss the answers as a class.

▶ In Exercises 1–4, the total of the two fraction parts is less than 1. Students can solve these problems by using mental math.

▶ In Exercises 5 and 6, the fraction parts add to 1.

▶ In Exercises 7–9, the two fraction parts add to a number greater than 1.

English Language Learners

Write *regroup*. Write $5\frac{10}{7}$.

BEGINNING

Point and say: **When the numerator of the fraction part is greater than the denominator, we need to regroup.** Write $5\frac{10}{7} = 5 + \frac{7}{7} + \frac{3}{7} = 6\frac{3}{7}$. Say: **We regrouped $\frac{10}{7}$ to make $\frac{7}{7}$ plus $\frac{3}{7}$. $5\frac{10}{7}$ is regrouped to make $6\frac{3}{7}$.** Have students repeat.

INTERMEDIATE

Ask: **Why do we need to regroup?** because the numerator is greater than the denominator

ADVANCED

Ask students to describe how to regroup $5\frac{10}{7}$.

17 Time Zones

Start Different parts of the world are in different time zones.

In the United States, there are 6 different time zones. As you move from the East Coast to the West Coast, the time in the next time zone is one hour earlier.

What are the 6 different time zones?

1. New York is in the Eastern time zone. When it is 9:00 in New York, what time is it in California, which is in the Pacific time zone?

2. Colorado is in the Mountain time zone. When it is 2:00 in Colorado, what time is it in Texas, which is in the Central time zone?

3. Ask each other questions about time in different states. Use a United States map if you need to.

Time zones are all around the world. Look up time zones for 4 different countries.

4. If it is 8:00 in one of the countries, write what time it would be in the other 3 countries.

5. Analyze Why do you think there are different time zones?

Use after Unit 5, Lesson 2.

Unit 5: Time, Graphs, and Word Problems

A Comprehensive Approach to RtI

Math Expressions provides structured resources to help all students access the rigor of the Common Core State Standards. *Response to Intervention for the Common Core State Standards* provides focused instruction on the mathematics standards. Students work at different tiers based on their specific needs.

Teacher Edition

Teaching notes and instructional strategies to build understanding and skills using the tiered teaching lessons.

TIER 1 Lessons — Grade Level Content

Give students the opportunity to experience new instruction on grade level concepts they have not quite mastered.

TIER 2 Lessons — Prerequisite Skills

Give students the opportunity to experience new instruction in prerequisites necessary for success with grade level content.

TIER 3 Lessons — Scaffolded Activities

Use real world situations and carefully scaffolded examples to build the foundational knowledge necessary to achieve success with grade level content. Once success is achieved at Tier 3, students move to Tier 2 for more exposure to the topic and then to the Tier 1 activity for work on the grade level concept.

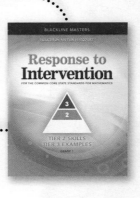

Soar to Success Math provides a digital path to intervention, with flexibility to address all three Tiers, along with an assessment, management and reporting system to keep track of student progress.

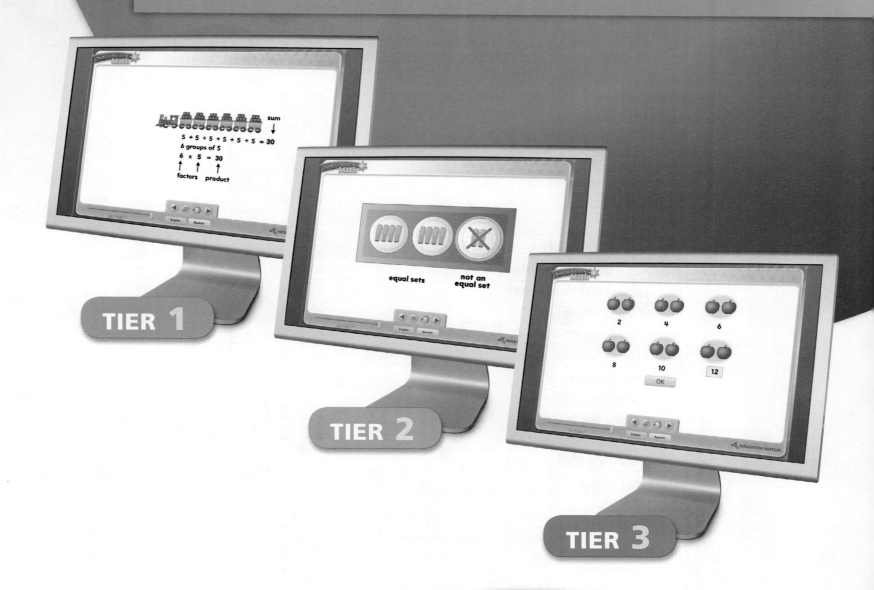

TIER **1**

TIER **2**

TIER **3**

"...all students must have the opportunity to learn and meet the same high standards if they are to access the knowledge and skills necessary in their post-school lives."

Common Core State Standards for Mathematics, Introduction

Components

	K	1	2	3	4	5	6
Core Components							
Teacher Edition	•	•	•	•	•	•	•
Student Activity Book*	•	•	•				•
Student Hardcover Book				•	•	•	•
Activity Workbook (Use with hardcover)				•	•	•	•
Homework and Remembering Book	•	•	•	•	•	•	•
Assessment Guide	•	•	•	•	•	•	•
MathBoards		•	•	•	•	•	•
Ready-Made Classroom Resources							
Individual Student Manipulatives Kit	•	•	•	•	•	•	•
Materials and Manipulatives Kit	•	•	•	•	•	•	•
Custom Manipulatives Kit	•	•	•	•	•	•	•
Teacher Modeling Kit	•	•	•	•	•	•	•
Math Center Challenges Easel	•	•	•	•	•	•	•
Teacher's Resource Book	•	•	•	•	•	•	•
Response to Intervention	•	•	•	•	•	•	•
Differentiated Instruction Activity Card Kit	•	•	•	•	•	•	•
Math Expressions Literature Library	•	•	•	•	•	•	•
Anno's Counting Book Big Book	•						
Technology							
eTeacher Edition	•	•	•	•	•	•	•
eStudent Activity Book	•	•	•	•	•	•	•
Lesson Planner	•	•	•	•	•	•	•
Online Assessment	•	•	•	•	•	•	•
MegaMath	•	•	•	•	•	•	•
Destination Math®	•	•	•	•	•	•	•
Soar to Success Math Intervention	•	•	•	•	•	•	•
Interactive Whiteboard Lessons	•	•	•	•	•	•	
*i*Tools (virtual manipulatives)	•	•	•	•	•	•	

*Grades K–6 available as consumable workbook; Grades 3–6 available as hardcover book.
The Activity Workbook is designed to be a companion piece to the hardcover books at Grades 3–6.

Welcome to MATH EXPRESSIONS!

History and Development

Math Expressions is a K–6 mathematics program, developed from the Children's Math Worlds (CMW) Research Project conducted by Dr. Karen Fuson, Professor Emerita at Northwestern University. This project was funded in part by the National Science Foundation. Grade 6 was primarily composed from Grade 5 units and from units piloted in CMW but not used in K–5 *Math Expressions*.

The Research Project

The project studied the ways students around the world understand mathematical concepts, approach problem solving, and learn to do computation; it included ten years of classroom research and incorporated the ideas of participating students and teachers into the developing curriculum.

The research focused on building conceptual supports that include special language, drawings, manipulatives, and classroom communication methods that facilitate mathematical competence.

Curriculum Design

Within the curriculum, a series of learning progressions reflect recent research regarding students' natural learning stages when mastering concepts such as addition, subtraction, multiplication, and problem solving. These learning stages help determine the order of concepts, the sequence of units, and the positioning of topics.

The curriculum is designed to help teachers apply the most effective conceptual supports so that each student progresses as rapidly as possible.

During the research, students showed increases in standardized test scores as well as in broader measures of student understanding. These results were found for a wide range of both urban and suburban students from a variety of socio-economic groups.

Philosophy

Math Expressions incorporates the best practices of both traditional and reform mathematics curricula. The program strikes a balance between promoting student-generated solution methods and introducing effective research-based methods.

The Common Core State Standards

The Common Core State Standards provide a coherent and streamlined progression of mathematical goals that relate to each other within a grade and build on the goals from the grades before. There is little repetition from grade to grade, so students need to master goals at their grade level. The number of goals has been reduced so that teachers will have more time to achieve both understanding and fluency for the core grade-level goals.

Math Expressions fits the learning progressions, the core grade-level goals, and the dual focus on understanding and fluency of the Common Core State Content Standards. This is because the Children's Math Worlds Research Project was designed to implement the same reports and international standards and approaches of high-achieving international programs that were used in the writing of the Common Core State Standards. Dr. Karen Fuson, along with Dr. Aki Murata, describe in research articles the Learning Path Teaching that underlies *Math Expressions*. These research articles summarize the national reports that provide the basis for the Common Core State Standards.

INTRODUCTION

Math Talk Community

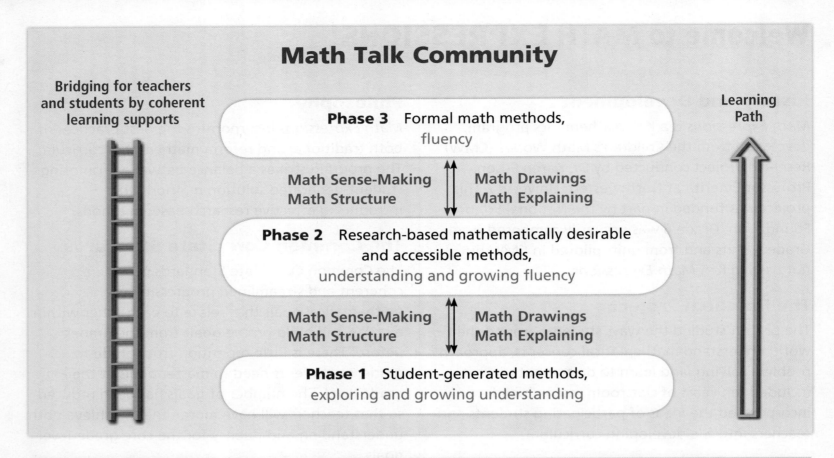

Bridging for teachers and students by coherent learning supports

Learning Path

Phase 3 Formal math methods, fluency

Math Sense-Making
Math Structure

Math Drawings
Math Explaining

Phase 2 Research-based mathematically desirable and accessible methods, understanding and growing fluency

Math Sense-Making
Math Structure

Math Drawings
Math Explaining

Phase 1 Student-generated methods, exploring and growing understanding

CCSS Mathematical Practices

Math Talk Community

Math Sense-Making	Math Structure	Math Drawings	Math Explaining
Make sense and use appropriate precision.	See structure and generalize.	Model and use tools.	Reason, explain, and question.
MP.1 Make sense of problems and persevere in solving them.	MP.7 Look for and make use of structure.	MP.4 Model with mathematics.	MP.2 Reason abstractly and quantitatively.
MP.6 Attend to precision.	MP.8 Look for and express regularity in repeated reasoning.	MP.5 Use appropriate tools strategically.	MP.3 Construct viable arguments and critique the reasoning of others.

Create a Nurturing Sense-Making Math Talk Community

The teacher orchestrates collaborative instructional conversations focused on the mathematical thinking of classroom members. Students and the teacher use seven responsive means of assistance that facilitate learning and teaching by all (several may be used together):

▸ engaging and involving
▸ managing

▸ coaching: modeling, cognitive restructuring and clarifying, instructing and explaining, questioning, feedback

The teacher supports the sense-making of all classroom members by using and assisting students to use and relate:

▸ coherent mathematical situations
▸ pedagogical supports
▸ cultural mathematical symbols and language

Teaching Model: An Inquiry Learning Path

The teacher leads students through teaching phases to help students move through their own learning paths.

Phase 1: Guided Introducing The teacher elicits and the class works with prior knowledge that students bring to a topic.

▸ Teacher and students discuss student ideas and methods.

▸ Teacher identifies different solution methods used by students as well as typical errors, and ensures that these are seen and discussed by the class.

Phase 2: Learning Unfolding (Major Sense-Making Phase) The teacher helps students form emergent conceptual networks and use mathematically desirable and accessible methods.

▸ Explanations of methods and mathematical issues include math drawings and other pedagogical supports to stimulate correct relating of concepts and symbols.

▸ Teacher focuses on or introduces mathematically desirable and accessible methods.

▸ Erroneous methods are analyzed and repaired with explanations.

▸ Advantages and disadvantages of various methods, including the current common method, are discussed so that central mathematical aspects of the topic become explicit.

Phase 3: Kneading Knowledge The teacher helps students gain fluency with desired methods.

▸ Students may choose a method.

▸ Fluency includes being able to explain the method.

▸ Some reflection and explaining still continue (kneading the individual conceptual networks).

Phase 4: Maintaining Fluency and Relating to Later Topics The teacher assists remembering by giving occasional problems and initiates and orchestrates instructional discussions to assist relating new topics to prior knowledge.

This model is a general model for all programs and all teachers. *Math Expressions* includes these phases and the mathematically desirable and accessible methods in the program.

For more about how a Learning Path Program is built upon and integrates the principles from both recent NRC reports and the NCTM Process Standards, see Karen C. Fuson & Aki Murata, Integrating NRC Principles and the NCTM Process Standards to Form a Class Learning Path Model That Individualizes Within Whole-Class Activities, *The National Council of Supervisors of Mathematics Journal of Mathematics Education Leadership*, 10 (1), 72–91(2007).

Math Talk `MATH TALK`

A significant part of the collaborative classroom culture is the frequent exchange of mathematical ideas and problem-solving strategies, or Math Talk. There are multiple benefits of Math Talk:

▸ Describing one's methods to another person can clarify one's own thinking as well as clarify the matter for others.

▸ Another person's approach can supply a new perspective, and frequent exposure to different approaches tends to engender flexible thinking.

▸ In the collaborative Math Talk classroom, students can ask for and receive help, and errors can be identified, discussed, and corrected.

▸ Student math drawings accompany early explanations in all domains, so that all students can understand and participate in the discussion.

▸ Math Talk permits teachers to assess students' understanding on an ongoing basis. It encourages students to develop their language skills, both in math and in everyday English.

▸ Math Talk enables students to become active helpers and questioners, creating student-to-student talk that stimulates engagement and community.

To encourage Math Talk, teachers can stand at the side or back of the classroom to help students interact more directly with each other. Teachers say that it is necessary for them to "bite their tongue" to keep from doing all of the talking. Student voices and explanations will emerge if you wait. For new topics, teachers may need to model explaining so that students learn to use new vocabulary; however, some students can usually explain even for a new topic.

The key supports for Math Talk are the various participant structures, or ways of organizing class members as they interact. The teacher always guides the activity to help students work both as a community and also independently. Descriptions of the most common participant structures follow.

Math Talk Participant Structures

Solve and Discuss (Solve, Explain, Question, and Justify) at the Board

The teacher selects 4 to 5 students (or as many as space allows) to go to the classroom board and solve a problem, using any method they choose. Their classmates work on the same problem at their desks. Then the teacher picks 2 or 3 students to explain their methods. Students at their desks are encouraged to ask questions and to assist their classmates in understanding.

Benefits: Board work reveals multiple methods of solving a problem, making comparisons possible, and communicating to students that different methods are acceptable. The teacher can select methods to highlight in subsequent discussions. Spontaneous helping occurs frequently by students working next to each other at the board. Time is used efficiently because everyone in the class is working. In addition, errors can be identified in a supportive way and corrected and understood by students.

Small Group Version of Solve and Discuss

Students can solve individually in small groups and then 2 or 3 students explain their method while the group members ask questions and help the explanation to be very clear. On the next problem different group members explain.

Benefits: Everyone gets a chance to explain and be helped in their explanation. This approach may work better for a given topic after whole-class discussions of the topic have taken place.

Student Pairs

Two students work together to solve a problem, to explain a solution method to each other, to role play within a mathematical situation (for example, buying and selling), to play a math game, or to help a partner. They are called Helping Pairs when more advanced students are matched with students who are struggling. Pairs may be organized formally, or they may occur spontaneously as help is needed. Initially, it is useful to model pair activities, contrasting effective and ineffective helping.

> **Benefits:** Pair work supports students in learning from each other, particularly in applying and practicing concepts introduced in whole-class discussion. Helping Pairs often foster learning by both students as the helper strives to adopt the perspective of the novice. Helping almost always enables the helper to understand more deeply.

Scenarios

The main purpose of scenarios in grades K–2 is to demonstrate mathematical relationships in a visual and memorable way. In scenario-based activities a group of students is called to the front of the classroom to act out a particular mathematical situation.

> **Benefits:** The scenario structure often fosters a sense of involvement among students. Scenarios also create meaningful contexts in which children can reason about numbers and relate math to their everyday lives.

Small Groups

Unstructured groups can form spontaneously if physical arrangements allow (for example, desks arranged in groups of four or more students working at tables).

Spontaneous helping between and among students as they work on problems individually can be encouraged.

For more structured projects, assign students to specific groups. It is usually a good idea to include a range of students and to have a strong reader in each group. Explain the problem or project and guide the groups as necessary. When students have finished, call a pair from each group to present and explain the results of their work or have the entire group present the results, with each member explaining one part of the solution or project. Having lower-performing students present first allows them to contribute, while higher-performing students expand on their efforts and give the fuller presentation.

> **Benefits:** Students learn different strategies from each other for approaching a problem or task. They are invested in their classmates' learning because the presentation will be on behalf of the whole group.

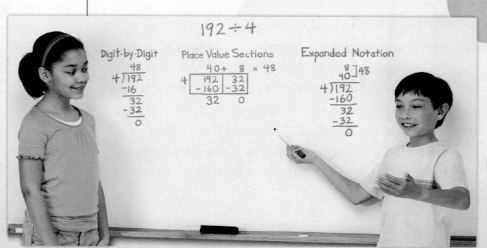

A Flexible Classroom

A Flexible Sense-Making Math Talk Community

A sense-making Math Talk community involves flexible grouping because students are often moving between reasoning and discussing their reasoning. Many teachers also prefer to allow grouping structures to be mixed, with some students working alone, some in helping or collaborative pairs, and some in small groups. Helping or working together may arise spontaneously as needed. When using the whole-class version of Solve and Discuss, the class moves between problem solving and discussion. When introducing or discussing a topic, the discussion may stop while students think about something individually.

Student Collaboration

The collaboration and peer helping that is a central part of *Math Expressions* classrooms deepens students' commitment to values such as responsibility and respect for others. As students reason about math situations or problems and collaboratively discuss their math thinking, they develop communication skills, sharpen their mathematical reasoning, and enhance their social awareness. Integrating students' social and cultural worlds into their emerging math worlds helps them to find their own voices and to connect real world experiences to math concepts. With the teacher's help, students' collaborative capacities will grow over the year.

Student Leadership

Student leadership is an equally important part of the *Math Expressions* classroom. Student Leaders play many roles in *Math Expressions* classrooms. They lead many of the vital Quick Practice routines that start each math class. They can help other students during problem solving. They can manage and help with handing out MathBoards or other learning materials.

During whole class or small group Math Talk, students can use these responsive means of assistance to help others learn:

▸ engaging and involving

▸ managing

▸ coaching: modeling, cognitive restructuring and clarifying, instructing and explaining, questioning, feedback

A vital role of the teacher is to support students to develop as Student Leaders throughout the year.

Common Core Mathematical Practices

All eight of the Mathematical Practices relate to and support each other.

Connections Among Math Sense-Making, Structure, Drawings, and Talk Using All Mathematical Practices

Making sense (MP.1) of mathematical situations and symbols is the foundation of math teaching and learning. Math drawings (MP.4 and MP.5) that model situations or quantities help students see mathematical structure and generalize across quantities and situations (MP.7 and MP.8). Making math drawings and engaging in Math Talk about them is an interactive and continual sense-making process (all eight Mathematical Practices). Having a math drawing that everyone can see during Math Talk supports the sense-making of everyone (all eight Mathematical Practices). Working within a Math Talk learning community (MP.1 through MP.8) means that help is available. This supports students to preserve the problem structure in problem solving, an important part of MP.1.

Students are always encouraged to say things in their own words during Math Talk (MP.2 and MP.3). The teacher relates student sense-making language to the precise math terms, which helps students make sense of the formal math language. Gradually students understand and use the precise terms (MP.1 and MP.6). Students also can improve the precision of their math drawings and Math Talk (all eight Mathematical Practices). Teachers and other students help everyone along this path toward precision (MP. 6).

Math drawings, equations, and the various steps used in paper and pencil problem solving are all tools that can be used strategically (MP.5). Modeling and using these tools (MP.4 and MP.5) with explanations (MP.3) help one's own, as well as others', learning process and sense-making (MP.1).

Math Expressions and the Common Core Standards

Many of the central features of the Common Core State Standards appeared in *Math Expressions* during its development and when it was first published. This is because *Math Expressions* drew on the same research base and international standards and programs used in the development of the CCSS. Therefore, the implementation of these central features of CCSS is well tested by the years of classroom development and by use in many classrooms in its published form. These are deeply and well developed in *Math Expressions*. A summary of these central features follows.

Math Drawings in the Common Core Standards

Math drawings (or diagrams) appear in standards in all domains in K–6 (OA, NBT, NF, MD, G). Students are encouraged to use math drawings to:

▸ represent and make sense of a situation or quantity
▸ relate the strategy to a written numerical method and explain the reasoning used (see below)

Students then transition to fluency with standard methods without drawings of quantities, but drawings of situations may continue to be needed and used for new or difficult problems.

The standards specify that drawings need not show details but should show the mathematics in the problem, i.e., they are math drawings. In later grades the CCSS use the term *diagram* instead of *drawing*.

Math Drawings are tools used in modeling (MP.4 and MP.5). They support sense-making, reasoning, and explaining (MP.1, MP.2, MP.3, MP.6). They require students to see structure and generalize (MP.7 and MP.8).

Reasoning Is Central in the Common Core Standards

Reasoning is explicitly and repeatedly mentioned in the standards as well as in the Mathematical Practices. Students are to reason about mathematical ideas. Importantly, such reasoning is supported by the visual/conceptual aspects of the standards discussed above and in the section on the Mathematical Practices. This enables age-appropriate learning paths to be developed by the teacher in the classroom.

Understanding and Fluency Are Both Crucial in the Common Core State Standards

Understanding and fluency are both mentioned repeatedly in various standards. Importantly, the standards are focused and coherent across grades so there is time to do both understanding and fluency. The *Math Expressions* learning path model of teaching and learning discussed earlier specifies how understanding and fluency can both be achieved.

Ambitious Algebraic Problems Appear in All Domains

The CCSS provide tables of core word problem types that describe different addition, subtraction, multiplication, and division situations. Importantly, any of the three quantities in each situation can be the unknown quantity. Some of these problem subtypes have a problem representation that differs from the solution representation or computation, so the original problem representation needs to be reflected on and re-represented. Students do this from Grade 1 on using informal reasoning rather than formal algebraic methods. But this process of representing the situation and then re-representing to find the solution is the same process used in algebra.

In *Math Expressions* students may do this representing with a situation equation, such as $n + 4 = 9$, and then re-represent this as a solution equation, $4 + n = 9$ or $9 - 4 = n$. Or, students may represent situations with a Math Drawing or a numerical diagram into which they put numbers. Or, they may use both. Using situation and solution equations and/or diagrams as representations is research based. These mathematically desirable and accessible methods are an integral part of the Teaching Model described previously. Students solve these problem types using different numbers and measures as well as two-step and multistep problems.

Students solve but also make up word problems. As a result, they become comfortable and flexible with mathematical language and can connect concepts and terminology with meaningful referents from their own lives.

Seeing and Using Equations of Many Forms

Many students in this country struggle with algebra because they think equations have to have one number alone on the right. The CCSS emphasize that students need to see equations of different forms even in the early grades. *Math Expressions* does this beginning in Kindergarten. The first equation students see is of the form $5 = 4 + 1$ to record decomposing 5 into two numbers. The equations and drawings record each decomposition. Students then discuss patterns across these decompositions. Students also write 8 related equations rather than just the usual 4 with one number on the right. They continue to work with many forms of equations as they represent and then re-represent problem situations.

Sarah picked 15 apples while her little brother Eli picked 3 apples. How many times as many apples did Sarah pick as her brother?

Sarah = 5 × Eli

Sarah | 3 | 3 | 3 | 3 | 3

Eli | 3 | Eli = $\frac{1}{5}$ Sarah

Levels of Addition/Subtraction Single-Digit Solution Strategies

Operations and Algebraic Thinking (OA) standards specify a learning path of levels of addition/subtraction strategies from Kindergarten through Grade 2: direct model, count on, and convert to a simpler problem (make a ten, doubles plus or minus 1, and other derived fact methods). *Math Expressions* has always supported students to learn these methods as rapidly as possible. The second and third levels are the research-based, mathematically desirable and accessible methods. These methods are then extended to form a learning path of levels of multiplication and division methods.

Math Expressions and the CCSS emphasize the importance of understanding subtraction as an unknown-addend situation and division as an unknown-factor situation. This enables students to solve a wider range of problems and to develop easier methods that go forward rather than backward.

Research-Based Mathematically Desirable and Accessible Multidigit Methods

The Number and Operations in Base Ten (NBT) standards specify that students develop, discuss, and use efficient, accurate, and generalizable methods including the standard algorithm. Students are to:

▸ use concrete models or drawings and strategies based on place value and properties of operations

▸ relate the strategy to a written method and explain the reasoning used (explanations may be supported by drawings or objects)

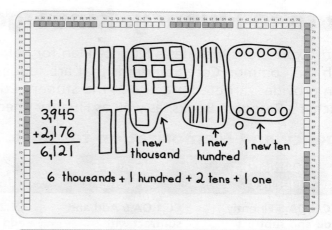

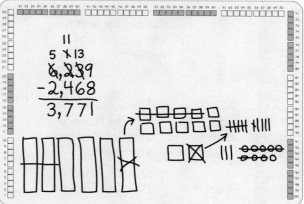

Math Expressions has always approached multidigit computation in this way. The MathBoards are designed to support understanding of multidigit numbers. They help students learn to make math drawings for multidigit quantities. Students invent methods, and they see and discuss research-based mathematically desirable and accessible methods. These methods connect to how students think, and they stimulate discussions of crucial aspects of computation. Most of these methods involve minor variations of the current common ways of writing the standard algorithms but are simpler for students to understand and carry out. These methods can also be considered standard algorithms because algorithms concern the big ideas underlying them and not minor variations in how they are written.

Path to Fluency: Kindergarten through Grade 5

Math Expressions includes a Fluency Plan for helping students achieve fluency with the Common Core Standards that are suggested for each grade. This plan provides targeted practice in the Student Editions, Teacher Editions, Teacher's Resource Books, as well as Fluency Checks in the Assessment Guide.

Fluency and Memorization for Basic Facts

Kindergarten Fluency	Grade 1 Fluency	Grade 2 Memorization	Grade 3 Memorization	Grades 3, 4 and 5 Intervention
CC.K.OA.5 Fluently **add and subtract** within 5.	**CC.1.OA.6 Add and subtract** within 20 demonstrating fluency for addition and subtraction within 10.	**CC.2.OA.2** Fluently **add and subtract** within 20 using mental strategies. By end of Grade 2 know from memory all sums of two one-digit numbers.	**CC.3.OA.7** Fluently **multiply and divide** within 100. By the end of Grade 3, **know from memory** all products of two one-digit numbers.	For those students who still need additional time for memorizing basic facts.
• Path to Fluency Practice (Student Edition) • Fluency Checks (Assessment Guide)	• Path to Fluency Practice (Student Edition) • Quick Practices (Teacher Edition) • Daily Routines (Teacher Edition) • Count-On Cards • Games • Fluency Checks (Assessment Guide)	• Path to Fluency Practice (Student Edition) • Quick Practices (Teacher Edition) • Daily Routines (Teacher Edition) • Math Mountain Cards • Strategy Cards • Fluency Checks (Assessment Guide)	• Path to Fluency Practice (Student Edition) • Quick Practices (Teacher Edition) • Practice Charts • Daily Study Plans • Study Sheets • Check Sheets • Dashes • Strategy Cards • Diagnostic Tests • Games • Fluency Checks (Assessment Guide)	Teacher's Resource Book: Grade 3: Addition and Subtraction Facts: • Diagnostic Quizzes • Practice Sheets Grade 4 and 5: Multiplication and Division Facts: • Diagnostic Quizzes • Practice Sheets

Fluency for Operations with Multidigit Numbers

Grade 2 Fluency	Grade 3 Fluency	Grade 4 Fluency	Grade 5 Fluency
CC2.NBT.5 Fluently **add and subtract** within 100.	**CC.3.NBT.2** Fluently **add and subtract** within 1,000.	**CC.4.NBT.4.** Fluently **add and subtract** multidigit whole numbers.	**CC.5.NBT.5** Fluently **multiply** multidigit whole numbers.
• Path to Fluency Practice (Student Edition) • Quick Practices (Teacher Edition) • Daily Routines (Teacher Edition) • Fluency Checks (Assessment Guide)	• Path to Fluency Practice (Student Edition) • Quick Practices (Teacher Edition) • Fluency Checks (Assessment Guide)	• Path to Fluency Practice (Student Edition) • Quick Practices (Teacher Edition) • Fluency Checks (Assessment Guide)	• Path to Fluency Practice (Student Edition) • Quick Practices (Teacher Edition) • Fluency Checks (Assessment Guide)

The Problem Solving Process

Using the Mathematical Practices

Throughout the program, *Math Expressions* integrates a research-based, algebraic problem-solving approach that focuses on problem types. Problem solving is a complex process that involves all eight of the CCSS Mathematical Practices. It is also an individual process that can vary considerably from one student to another. Students may conceptualize, represent, and explain a given problem in different ways.

Mathematical Practice	Student Actions
Understand the Problem Situation **MP.1** Make sense of the problem. **MP.2** Reason abstractly and quantitatively.	**Make Sense of the Language** Students use the problem language to conceptualize the real world situation.
Represent the Problem Situation **MP.4** Model with mathematics. **MP.7** Look for and make use of structure.	**Mathematize the Situation** Students focus on the mathematical aspects of the situation and make a math drawing and/or write a situation equation to represent the relationship of the numbers in the problem.
Solve the Problem **MP.5** Use appropriate tools. **MP.8** Use repeated reasoning.	**Find the Answer** Students use the math drawing and/or the situation equation to find the unknown.
Check That the Answer Makes Sense **MP.3** Critique the reasoning of others. **MP.6** Attend to precision.	**Check the Answer in the Context of the Problem** Students write the answer to the problem including a label. They explain and compare solutions with classmates.

Students are taught to make their own math drawings. Relating math drawings to equations helps them understand where in the drawing the total and the product are represented for each operation, and helps them solve equations with difficult unknowns.

Problem Types

This table shows how problem types are incorporated across the grades. A specific grade level problem types chart can be found at the back of each Student Book or Teacher Edition.

	Result Unknown	Change Unknown	Start Unknown
Add to	Six children were playing tag in the yard. Three more children came to play. How many children are playing in the yard now? *Situation and Solution Equation:* $6 + 3 = c$	Six children were playing tag in the yard. Some more children came to play. Now there are 9 children in the yard. How many children came to play? *Situation Equation:* $6 + c = 9$ *Solution Equation:* $9 - 6 = c$	Some children were playing tag in the yard. Three more children came to play. Now there are 9 children in the yard. How many children were in the yard at first? *Situation Equation:* $c + 3 = 9$ *Solution Equation:* $3 + c = 9$ or $9 - 3 = c$
Take from	Jake has 10 trading cards. He gave 3 to his brother. How many trading cards does he have left? *Situation and Solution Equation:* $10 - 3 = t$	Jake has 10 trading cards. He gave some to his brother. Now Jake has 7 trading cards left. How many cards did he give to his brother? *Situation Equation:* $10 - t = 7$ *Solution Equation:* $10 - 7 = t$	Jake has some trading cards. He gave 3 to his brother. Now Jake has 7 trading cards left. How many cards did he start with? *Situation Equation:* $t - 3 = 7$ *Solution Equation:* $7 + 3 = t$

	Total Unknown	Addend Unknown	Other Addend Unknown
Put Together/ Take Apart	Ana put 9 dimes and 4 nickels in her pocket. How many coins did she put in her pocket? *Situation and Solution Equation:* $9 + 4 = c$	Ana put 13 coins in her pocket. Nine coins are dimes and the rest are nickels. How many are nickels? *Situation Equation:* $13 = 9 + n$ *Solution Equation:* $13 - 9 = n$	Ana put 13 coins in her pocket. Some coins are dimes and 4 coins are nickels. How many coins are dimes? *Situation Equation:* $13 = d + 4$ *Solution Equation:* $13 - 4 = d$

	Difference Unknown	Bigger Unknown	Smaller Unknown
Compare[1]	Aki has 8 apples. Sofia has 14 apples. How many **more** apples does **Sofia** have than Aki? *Solution Equation:* $8 + a = 14$ or $14 - 8 = a$ Aki has 8 apples. Sofia has 14 apples. How many **fewer** apples does **Aki** have than Sofia? *Solution Equation:* $8 + a = 14$ or $14 - 8 = a$	**Leading Language** Aki has 8 apples. **Sofia** has **6 more** apples than Aki. How many apples does Sofia have? *Solution Equation:* $8 + 6 = a$ **Misleading Language** Aki has 8 apples. **Aki** has **6 fewer** apples than Sofia. How many apples does Sofia have? *Solution Equation:* $8 + 6 = a$	**Leading Language** Sofia has 14 apples. **Aki** has **6 fewer** apples than Sofia. How many apples does Aki have? *Solution Equation:* $14 - 6 = a$ or $6 + a = 14$ **Misleading Language** Sofia has 14 apples. **Sofia** has **6 more** apples than Aki. How many apples does Aki have? *Solution Equation:* $14 - 6 = a$ or $6 + a = 14$

[1]The comparing sentence can always be said in two ways: One uses more, and the other uses fewer. Misleading language suggests the wrong operation. For example, it says *Aki has 6 fewer apples than Sofia*, but you have to add 6 to Aki's 8 apples to get 14 apples.

	Unknown Product	Group Size Unknown	Number of Groups Unknown
Equal Groups	Seth has 5 bags with 2 apples in each bag. How many apples does Seth have in all? *Solution Equation:* $5 \cdot 2 = n$	Seth has 5 bags with the same number of apples in each bag. He has 10 apples in all. How many apples are in each bag? *Situation Equation:* $5 \cdot n = 10$ *Solution Equation:* $10 \div 5 = n$	Seth has some bags of apples. Each bag has 2 apples in it. He has 10 apples in all. How many bags of apples does Seth have? *Situation Equation:* $n \cdot 2 = 10$ *Solution Equation:* $10 \div 2 = n$

	Unknown Product	Unknown Factor	Unknown Factor
Arrays[2]	Jenna has 2 rows of stamps with 5 stamps in each row. How many stamps does Jenna have in all? *Solution Equation:* $2 \cdot 5 = s$	Jenna has 2 rows of stamps with the same number of stamps in each row. She has 10 stamps in all. How many stamps are in each row? *Situation Equation:* $2 \cdot s = 10$ *Solution Equation:* $10 \div 2 = s$	Jenna has a certain number of rows of stamps. There are 5 stamps in each row. She has 10 stamps in all. How many rows of stamps does Jenna have? *Situation Equation:* $r \cdot 5 = 10$ *Solution Equation:* $10 \div 5 = r$
Area	The floor of the kitchen is 2 meters by 5 meters. What is the area of the floor? *Solution Equation:* $2 \cdot 5 = a$	The floor of the kitchen is 2 meters long. The area of the floor is 10 square meters. How wide is the floor? *Situation Equation:* $2 \cdot s = 10$ *Solution Equation:* $10 \div 2 = s$	The width of the kitchen is 5 meters long. The area of the floor is 10 square meters. What is the length of the floor? *Situation Equation:* $r \cdot 5 = 10$ *Solution Equation:* $10 \div 5 = r$
Compare	Katie picked 5 times as many flowers as Benardo. Benardo picked 2 flowers. How many flowers did Katie pick? *Solution Equation:* $5 \cdot 2 = k$	Katie picked 5 times as many flowers as Benardo. Katie picked 10 flowers. How many flowers did Bernardo pick? *Situation Equation:* $5 \cdot b = 10$ *Solution Equation:* $10 \div 5 = b$	Katie picked 10 flowers. Bernardo picked 2 flowers. How many times as many flowers did Katie pick as Bernardo? *Situation Equation:* $m \cdot 2 = 10$ *Solution Equation:* $10 \div 2 = m$

[2]Array problems can also be stated using the number of rows and columns in the array: The apples in the grocery window are in 3 rows and 6 columns. How many apples are there?

Note: All of the division situations could also have the multiplication equation as the solution equation because you can solve division by finding the unknown factor.

Pacing Guide

This Pacing Guide includes additional days for longer lessons as well as formative and summative assessments.

Beginning of the Year Inventory This assessment tool, found in the Assessment Guide, is based on prekindergarten concepts and skills and will help you prepare for teaching each unit.

Fluency Checks These practice sheets, for addition and subtraction within 5, are provided in the Assessment Guide.

Quick Practice and **Daily Routines** Be sure to do these activities with Student Leaders to begin each lesson, as they provide needed practice on core grade-level skills.

Unit	Unit Focus	Pacing Suggestions	Days
1	**Understand Numbers 1–10** Children develop counting and cardinality skills for numbers 1–10. By using objects and making drawings they represent numbers and develop perceptual subitizing. Children learn to write the numbers 1–10. Addition and subtraction within 5 is introduced and numbers through 10 are compared. Children learn to identify circles, squares, and rectangles and use attributes to sort and compare these two-dimensional shapes.	18 Lessons: Lessons 1, 8, 10, 14 may take 2 days. 2 days: Unit Review/Test and Summative Assessment 2 days: Beginning of the Year Inventory	26
2	**5-Groups in Numbers 6–10** Children continue their study of numbers from 1 through 10 and simple shapes. They build on their knowledge of numbers 1 through 10 to understand the numbers 6–10 as composed of a 5-group and some ones. They explore number order, the +1 and −1 relationships, and partners for the numbers 1–10. Children learn and use the attributes of triangles and hexagons.	20 Lessons: Lessons 1, 3, 9, 13, 17 may take 2 days. 2 days: Unit Review/Test and Summative Assessment	27
3	**Teen Numbers as Tens and Ones** Children develop counting and cardinality skills for numbers 11–20 and learn to show teen numbers as ten ones and some more ones. They deepen their understanding of addition and subtraction, develop conceptual subitizing and fluency with 5, tell and solve addition and subtraction story problems, and show expressions that represent the problems. Children compose new shapes with two-dimensional shapes. They classify items according to attributes and compare the categories.	21 Lessons: Lessons 3, 4, 5, 9, 10, 12, 20, 21 may take 2 days. 2 days: Unit Review/Test and Summative Assessment	31
4	**Partners, Problem Drawings, and Tens** Children continue to develop skills with addition and subtraction, telling story problems and representing them with drawings, expressions, and equations. Children decompose numbers within 10 by finding partners. Children identify, describe, and name three-dimensional shapes including cubes, cones, cylinders, and spheres as well as describe relative positions of shapes.	22 Lessons: Lessons 1, 6, 8, 16, 20 may take 2 days. 2 days: Fluency Checks 2 days: Unit Review/Test and Summative Assessment	31
5	**Consolidation of Concepts** Children deepen their understanding of addition and subtraction story problems, analyzing problems and solutions. They compare groups and numerals. Children are introduced to and compare the measurable attributes of length, height, weight, and capacity.	23 Lessons: Lessons 2, 6, 9, 13, 15, 19, 22, 23 may take 2 days. 2 days: Fluency Checks 2 days: Unit Review/Test and Summative Assessment	35
		Total Days	150

Daily Routines for Volume 2

See pages T8 and T9 for information about materials for Daily Routines.

Counting Tens and Ones
(Use with Units 4–5.)

Materials: 120 Poster, pointer, Counting Tens and Ones Flip Chart, sticky notes, Giant Number Cards, sticky board

Continue with Counting Tens and Ones started in Unit 1. This will reinforce children's counting and number concepts. These activities should now move quickly, with three Student Leaders each day.

Using the 120 Poster

Student Leader 1 draws a new circle on the 120 Poster to represent adding 1 and, if there is a new ten, erases the circles and makes a bracket on the bottom of the column as before.

New Total 66:

1	11	21	31	41	51	61	71	81	91	101	111
2	12	22	32	42	52	62	72	82	92	102	112
3	13	23	33	43	53	63	73	83	93	103	113
4	14	24	34	44	54	64	74	84	94	104	114
5	15	25	35	45	55	65	75	85	95	105	115
6	16	26	36	46	56	66	76	86	96	106	116
7	17	27	37	47	57	67	77	87	97	107	117
8	18	28	38	48	58	68	78	88	98	108	118
9	19	29	39	49	59	69	79	89	99	109	119
10	20	30	40	50	60	70	80	90	100	110	120

$$66 = 60 + 6$$

New Total 82:

1	11	21	31	41	51	61	71	81	91	101	111
2	12	22	32	42	52	62	72	82	92	102	112
3	13	23	33	43	53	63	73	83	93	103	113
4	14	24	34	44	54	64	74	84	94	104	114
5	15	25	35	45	55	65	75	85	95	105	115
6	16	26	36	46	56	66	76	86	96	106	116
7	17	27	37	47	57	67	77	87	97	107	117
8	18	28	38	48	58	68	78	88	98	108	118
9	19	29	39	49	59	69	79	89	99	109	119
10	20	30	40	50	60	70	80	90	100	110	120

$$82 = 80 + 2$$

Count to the New Total Student Leader 1 then leads the class to count to the new total by tens and ones. For example, to count to 95, children say 10, 20, 30, 40, 50, 60, 70, 80, 90, *freeze*, 91, 92, 93, 94, 95. Children flash ten fingers all at once for each ten and show one finger for each one they count after that.

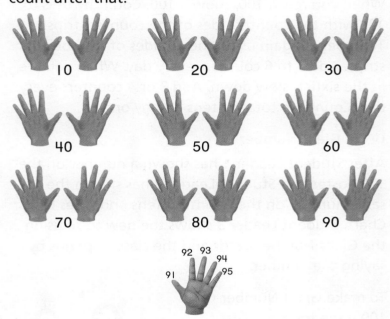

As the class counts, the Student Leader moves the pointer down each column and then points to each single number. When you reach 100, you can stop this part of the routine or have the class choose a number each day and count up to it by tens and ones.

Some children may comment on the numbers greater than 100 and notice how the numbers in the last two columns are like those in the first two columns. Children will use the part of the poster including numbers 101 to 120 in Grade 1.

Using the Counting Tens and Ones Flip Chart

Student Leader 2 leads the next part of the routine. Continue to use the Counting Tens and Ones Flip Chart with uncounted columns still covered with sticky notes. Each day a new counter is uncovered to make the new total to match the number on the 120 Poster. Write the number of counters uncovered in a column at the bottom of that column.

When you reach 100, show a 100. Count by tens to 100 with the counter sides of the counter strips. Then begin again using the 10 sides of the counter strips. Add 3 to 6 counters every day. When you are in the sixties, slow down. Add 3 or 4 counters every day. Count the total by tens and by ones.

Using Giant Number Cards

After Student Leader 1 has shown a number on the 120 Poster and Student Leader 2 has shown the same number on the Counting Tens and Ones Flip Chart, Student Leader 3 shows the new total using the Giant Number Cards and the class responds by saying the number.

To make Giant Number Card 100, tape together Giant Number Cards 10 and 0.

Making Teen Numbers

During **Unit 4,** you can also make teen numbers using a 10-Counter Strip, a 5-Counter Strip, and counters. Make one teen number each day starting with Lesson 1. Have all counters showing.

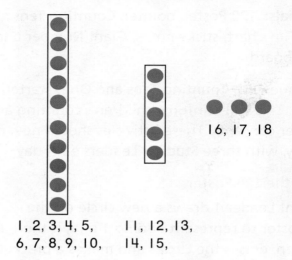

1, 2, 3, 4, 5,   11, 12, 13,
6, 7, 8, 9, 10,   14, 15,

16, 17, 18

VOLUME 1

UNIT 1

Understanding Numbers 1–10

REAL WORLD PROBLEM SOLVING

BIG IDEA 1   Counting and Cardinality 1–5

Common Core State Standards CC.K.CC.4a, CC.K.CC.4b

BIG IDEA 2   Adding, Subtracting, and Comparing Through 5

Common Core State Standards CC.K.CC.2, CC.K.CC.4a, CC.K.CC.4b, CC.K.CC.6, CC.K.OA.1, CC.K.MD.3, CC.K.G.1, CC.K.G.2, CC.K.G.5

CONTENTS

UNIT 2   5-Groups in Numbers 6–10

REAL WORLD
PROBLEM SOLVING

BIG IDEA 1   5-Groups in Numbers 6 to 10

Common Core State Standards CC.K.CC.1, CC.K.CC.3, CC.K.CC.4a, CC.K.CC.5, CC.K.CC.6, CC.K.OA.1, CC.K.OA.2, CC.K.OA.3, CC.K.OA.5

BIG IDEA 2   Addition and Subtraction Stories

Common Core State Standards CC.K.CC.1, CC.K.CC.2, CC.K.CC.3, CC.K.CC.4a, CC.K.CC.4b, CC.K.CC.5, CC.K.CC.6, CC.K.CC.7, CC.K.OA.1, CC.K.OA.2, CC.K.OA.3, CC.K.OA.4, CC.K.OA.5

CONTENTS

BIG IDEA 3   Practice Numbers 1 Through 10, the + Pattern

Common Core State Standards CC.K.CC.1, CC.K.CC.2, CC.K.CC.3, CC.K.CC.4a, CC.K.CC.4b, CC.K.CC.4c, CC.K.CC.5, CC.K.OA.1, CC.K.OA.2, CC.K.OA.3, CC.K.OA.4, CC.K.OA.5, CC.K.MD.3, CC.K.G.1, CC.K.G.3, CC.K.G.5

BIG IDEA 4   Numbers 1 Through 10, the – Pattern

Common Core State Standards CC.K.CC.1, CC.K.CC.2, CC.K.CC.3, CC.K.CC.4, CC.K.CC.4a, CC.K.CC.4c, CC.K.CC.5, CC.K.CC.7, CC.K.OA.1, CC.K.OA.2, CC.K.OA3, CC.K.OA.4, CC.K.MD.3, CC.K.G.1, CC.K.G.2, , CC.K.G.3, CC.K.G.5

Teen Numbers as Tens and Ones

Overview **203A**

REAL WORLD
PROBLEM SOLVING

| BIG IDEA 1 | Partners of 5 and 6 |

Common Core State Standards CC.K.CC.1, CC.K.CC.2, CC.K.CC.3, CC.K.CC.4a, CC.K.CC.4b, CC.K.CC.4c, CC.K.CC.5, CC.K.OA.1, CC.K.OA.2, CC.K.OA.3, CC.K.OA.5, CC.K.NBT.1, CC.K.G.2, CC.K.G.6

CONTENTS

BIG IDEA 2   **Classifying**

Common Core State Standards CC.K.CC.2, CC.K.CC.3, CC.K.CC.4c, CC.K.CC.5, CC.K.CC.6, CC.K.CC.7, CC.K.OA.1, CC.K.OA.2, CC.K.OA.5, CC.K.MD.3, CC.K.G.1, CC.K.G.2

BIG IDEA 3   **Tens in Teen Numbers**

Common Core State Standards CC.K.CC.3, CC.K.CC.4, CC.K.CC.5, CC.K.CC.7, CC.K.OA.1, CC.K.OA.2, CC.K.OA.3, CC.K.OA.5, CC.K.NBT.1

BIG IDEA 4   **Build Teen Numbers**

Common Core State Standards CC.K.CC.3, CC.K.CC.4, CC.K.CC.4b, CC.K.CC.5, CC.K.OA.1, CC.K.OA.3, CC.K.OA.5, CC.K.NBT.1, CC.K.MD.3, CC.K.G.1, CC.K.G.2, CC.K.G.4

 **FAMILY LETTER**

VOLUME 2

UNIT 4

Partners, Problem Drawings, and Tens

REAL WORLD
PROBLEM SOLVING

BIG IDEA 1 — Story Problems and Equations

Common Core State Standards CC.K.CC.3, CC.K.CC.4a, CC.K.CC.4b, CC.K.CC.4c, CC.K.OA.1, CC.K.OA.2, CC.K.OA.3, CC.K.OA.4, CC.K.OA.5, CC.K.NBT.1, CC.K.MD.3, CC.K.G.1

FAMILY LETTER

BIG IDEA 2 — Practice with Comparing

Common Core State Standards CC.K.CC.3, CC.K.CC.4, CC.K.CC.4c, CC.K.CC.5, CC.K.CC.6, CC.K.CC.7, CC.K.OA.1, CC.K.OA.2, CC.K.OA.3, CC.K.OA.4, CC.K.NBT.1

FAMILY LETTER

BIG IDEA 3   Equations and Teen Numbers

Common Core State Standards CC.K.CC.2, CC.K.CC.4a, CC.K.CC.4b, CC.K.CC.4c, CC.K.CC.6, CC.K.CC.7, CC.K.OA.1, CC.K.OA.2, CC.K.OA.3, CC.K.OA.4, CC.K.OA.5, CC.K.NBT.1, CC.K.MD.3, CC.K.G.1, CC.K.G.2, CC.K.G.3, CC.K.G.4

BIG IDEA 4   Equations for Partners

Common Core State Standards CC.K.CC.1, CC.K.CC.2, CC.K.CC.3, CC.K.CC.4a, CC.K.CC.4b, CC.K.CC.5, CC.K.CC.6, CC.K.CC.7, CC.K.OA.1, CC.K.OA.3, CC.K.OA.4, CC.K.OA.5, CC.K.NBT.1, CC.K.MD.3, CC.K.G.1, CC.K.G.2, CC.K.G.3, CC.K.G.4, CC.K.G.6

CONTENTS

UNIT 5

Consolidation of Concepts

REAL WORLD PROBLEM SOLVING

BIG IDEA 1 | **More Partners of 10**

Common Core State Standards CC.K.CC.1, CC.K.CC.3, CC.K.CC.5, CC.K.CC.7, CC.K.OA.2, CC.K.OA.3, CC.K.OA.4, CC.K.OA.5, CC.K.NBT.1

FAMILY LETTER

FAMILY LETTER

CONTENTS

BIG IDEA 4   **More Story Problems and Equations**

Common Core State Standards CC.K.CC.3, CC.K.CC.4, CC.K.CC.4c, CC.K.CC.5, CC.K.CC.6, CC.K.CC.7, CC.K.OA.1, CC.K.OA.2, CC.K.C.OA.3, CC.K.OA.4, CC.K.OA.5, CC.K.NBT.1, CC.K.MD.1, CC.K.MD.2

Appendix

CONTENTS

Common Core State Standards for Mathematical Content

CC.K.CC Counting and Cardinality

Know number names and the count sequence.

CC.K.CC.1	Count to 100 by ones and by tens.	Unit 1 Lesson 17; Unit 2 Lessons 1, 2, 6, 7, 8, 10, 11, 12, 15, 16, 18, 19; Unit 3 Lessons 1, 2, 3; Unit 4 Lesson 17; Unit 5 Lessons 2, 3, 5, 13 **Daily Routine:** Counting Tens and Ones Routine **Quick Practice:** Oral Counting 1–10, Show Fingers 1–10, Giant Number Cards 1–5, Count by Ones from 20 Through 60
CC.K.CC.2	Count forward beginning from a given number within the known sequence (instead of having to begin at 1).	Unit 1 Lesson 7; Unit 2 Lessons 9, 12, 15, 16, 18, 19; Unit 3 Lessons 5, 7, 11; Unit 4 Lessons 15, 20; Unit 5 Lesson 13 **Daily Routine:** Counting Tens and Ones Routine **Quick Practice:** Saying and Showing the 5-Group Pattern, Seeing and Hearing the 5-Group Pattern, The 5-Group Pattern for 6–10, Connect the 5-Group Pattern to Fingers, Count from 10 Through 20 Using Finger Freeze, Say Numbers 11 Through 20 in Order, Count by Ones from 20 Through 60
CC.K.CC.3	Write numbers from 0 to 20. Represent a number of objects with a written numeral 0–20 (with 0 representing a count of no objects).	Unit 1 Lessons 14, 16; Unit 2 Lessons 1, 2, 5, 7, 8, 9, 10, 11, 12, 14, 15, 16, 18, 19; Unit 3 Lessons 1, 4, 5, 6, 7, 11, 12, 13, 14, 18; Unit 4 Lessons 3, 8, 16, 18, 20; Unit 5 Lessons 2, 4, 5, 7, 8, 10, 11, 14, 16, 17, 20, 23 **Daily Routine:** Counting Tens and Ones Routine **Quick Practice:** Giant Number Cards 1–5, Giant Number Cards 6–10

Count to tell the number of objects.

CC.K.CC.4a	Understand the relationship between numbers and quantities; connect counting to cardinality. a. When counting objects, say the number names in the standard order, pairing each object with one and only one number name and each number name with one and only one object.	Unit 1 Lessons 1, 2, 3, 4, 5, 6, 7, 8, 9, 11, 12, 13, 14, 15, 16, 17; Unit 2 Lessons 3, 6, 8, 10, 11, 15, 18; Unit 3 Lesson 2; Unit 4 Lessons 1, 3, 12, 16, 20; Unit 5 Lesson 3 **Daily Routine:** Counting Tens and Ones Routine **Quick Practice:** Oral Counting 1–10, Show Fingers 1–10, Giant Number Cards 1–5, Giant Number Cards 6–10

CC.K.CC Counting and Cardinality (continued)

CC.K.CC.4b	Understand the relationship between numbers and quantities; connect counting to cardinality. b. Understand that the last number name said tells the number of objects counted. The number of objects is the same regardless of their arrangement or the order in which they were counted.	Unit 1 Lessons 1, 2, 3, 4, 5, 6, 7, 8, 9, 11, 12, 13, 14, 15, 16, 17; Unit 2 Lessons 8, 10, 11, 15; Unit 3 Lessons 2, 15, 18, 19, 20; Unit 4 Lessons 1, 3, 12, 20 **Daily Routine:** Counting Tens and Ones Routine **Quick Practice:** Show Fingers 1–10, Giant Number Cards 1–5, Giant Number Cards 6–10
CC.K.CC.4c	Understand the relationship between numbers and quantities; connect counting to cardinality. c. Understand that each successive number name refers to a quantity that is one larger.	Unit 2 Lessons 12, 14, 16, 19; Unit 3 Lessons 5, 7, 12, 20; Unit 4 Lessons 3, 5, 7, 12, 15; Unit 5 Lessons 7, 15, 19, 23 **Daily Routine:** Counting Tens and Ones Routine **Quick Practice:** Oral Counting 1–10, Show Fingers 1–10, Giant Number Cards 1–5, Creative Movement and Sounds
CC.K.CC.5	Count to answer "how many?" questions about as many as 20 things arranged in a line, a rectangular array, or a circle, or as many as 10 things in a scattered configuration; given a number from 1–20, count out that many objects.	Unit 1 Lessons 13, 15, 16; Unit 2 Lessons 1, 2, 3, 4, 5, 7, 8, 9, 10, 12, 14, 16, 18, 20; Unit 3 Lessons 1, 2, 8, 10, 11, 12, 13, 14, 15, 18, 19, 20, 21; Unit 4 Lessons 5, 6, 7, 8, 16; Unit 5 Lessons 1, 2, 3, 4, 7, 14, 15, 16, 17, 19, 20 **Daily Routine:** Counting Tens and Ones Routine **Quick Practice:** Giant Number Cards 1–5, Giant Number Cards 6–10

Compare numbers.

CC.K.CC.6	Identify whether the number of objects in one group is greater than, less than, or equal to the number of objects in another group, e.g., by using matching and counting strategies.	Unit 1 Lessons 9, 11, 12, 13, 15, 16, 17; Unit 2 Lessons 4, 9; Unit 3 Lessons 10, 12; Unit 4 Lessons 6, 10, 20; Unit 5 Lessons 16, 17, 20 **Daily Routine:** Counting Tens and Ones Routine
CC.K.CC.7	Compare two numbers between 1 and 10 presented as written numerals.	Unit 2 Lessons 9, 18; Unit 3 Lessons 12, 14; Unit 5 Lessons 2, 17, 20 **Daily Routine:** Counting Tens and Ones Routine

CC.K.OA Operations and Algebraic Thinking

Understand addition as putting together and adding to, and understand subtraction as taking apart and taking from.

CC.K.OA.1	Represent addition and subtraction with objects, fingers, mental images, drawings, sounds (e.g., claps), acting out situations, verbal explanations, expressions, or equations.	Unit 1 Lessons 6, 7, 21; Unit 2 Lessons 2, 3, 5, 6, 7, 9, 10, 11, 12, 14, 15, 16, 19; Unit 3 Lessons 3, 6, 7, 11, 15, 16, 17, 18, 19, 20; Unit 4 Lessons 1, 2, 3, 4, 5, 6, 7, 10, 12, 13, 15, 17, 19; Unit 5 Lessons 3, 6, 7, 8, 10, 14, 15, 16, 19 **Quick Practice:** Practice + 1, Practice + 1 Orally
CC.K.OA.2	Solve addition and subtraction word problems, and add and subtract within 10, e.g., by using objects or drawings to represent the problem.	Unit 1 Lesson 14; Unit 2 Lessons 1, 2, 4, 6, 9, 10, 11, 12, 14, 15, 16, 19; Unit 3 Lessons 1, 3, 4, 7, 11, 16; Unit 4 Lessons 2, 4, 5, 6, 7, 10, 12, 15; Unit 5 Lessons 1, 3, 4, 6, 7, 10, 12, 13, 15, 16, 19
CC.K.OA.3	Decompose numbers less than or equal to 10 into pairs in more than one way, e.g., by using objects or drawings, and record each decomposition by a drawing or equation (e.g., $5 = 2 + 3$ and $5 = 4 + 1$).	Unit 2 Lessons 2, 5, 10, 12, 14, 16, 19, 20; Unit 3 Lessons 3, 4, 6, 16, 17, 18; Unit 4 Lessons 2, 4, 5, 7, 8, 11, 13, 18, 19; Unit 5 Lessons 3, 4, 5, 6, 7, 8, 9, 10, 11, 12, 13, 14, 15, 18
CC.K.OA.4	For any number from 1 to 9, find the number that makes 10 when added to the given number, e.g. by using objects or drawings, and record the answer with a drawing or equation.	Unit 2 Lessons 10, 12, 14, 16, 19; Unit 4 Lessons 2, 4, 8, 11, 13, 18, 19; Unit 5 Lessons 2, 3, 4, 6, 8, 9, 11, 12, 13, 18 **Quick Practice:** The Partner Peek on the 10-Partner Showcase
CC.K.OA.5	Fluently add and subtract within 5.	Unit 2 Lessons 4, 6, 9, 10, 15; Unit 3 Lessons 4, 5, 6, 7, 12, 14, 18, 19; Unit 4 Lessons 3, 12, 15, 17; Unit 5 Lessons 1, 3, 7, 12, 13, 14, 15, 18

CC.K.NBT Number and Operations in Base Ten

Work with numbers 11–19 to gain foundations for place value.

CC.K.NBT.1	Compose and decompose numbers from 11 to 19 into ten ones and some further ones, e.g., by using objects or drawings, and record each composition or decomposition by a drawing or equation (e.g., $18 = 10 + 8$); understand that these numbers are composed of ten ones and one, two, three, four, five, six, seven, eight, or nine ones.	Unit 3 Lessons 2, 3, 5, 6, 8, 13, 15, 17, 18, 19, 20; Unit 4 Lessons 3, 5, 7, 12, 16, 18, 20; Unit 5 Lessons 1, 3, 4, 5, 6, 7, 9, 10, 15, 17, 18, 19, 20, 23 **Quick Practice:** 10 and 1 Make 11…, Show, Say, and See 11–19

CC.K.MD Measurement and Data

Describe and compare measurable attributes.

CC.K.MD.1	Describe measurable attributes of objects, such as length or weight. Describe several measurable attributes of a single object.	Unit 5 Lessons 21, 22, 23
CC.K.MD.2	Directly compare two objects with a measurable attribute in common, to see which object has "more of"/"less of" the attribute, and describe the difference.	Unit 5 Lessons 21, 22, 23

Classify objects and count the number of objects in each category.

CC.K.MD.3	Classify objects into given categories; count the numbers of objects in each category and sort the categories by count.	Unit 1 Lesson 10; Unit 2 Lessons 13, 17, 20; Unit 3 Lessons 10, 12, 21; Unit 4 Lessons 1, 9, 22

CC.K.G Geometry

Identify and describe shapes (squares, circles, triangles, rectangles, hexagons, cubes, cones, cylinders, and spheres).

CC.K.G.1	Describe objects in the environment using names of shapes, and describe the relative positions of these objects using terms such as *above, below, beside, in front of, behind,* and *next to.*	Unit 1 Lessons 8, 10, 18; Unit 2 Lessons 13, 17, 20: Unit 3 Lessons 10, 12, 21; Unit 4 Lessons 1, 9, 14, 21, 22
CC.K.G.2	Correctly name shapes regardless of their orientations or overall size.	Unit 1 Lessons 8, 10, 18; Unit 2 Lessons 13, 17, 20: Unit 3 Lessons 9, 10, 12, 21; Unit 4 Lessons 9, 14, 21, 22
CC.K.G.3	Identify shapes as two-dimensional (lying in a plane, "flat") or three-dimensional ("solid").	Unit 1 Lesson 18; Unit 4 Lessons 9, 14, 21

Analyze, compare, create, and compose shapes.

CC.K.G.4	Analyze and compare two- and three-dimensional shapes, in different sizes and orientations, using informal language to describe their similarities, differences, parts (e.g., number of sides and vertices/"corners") and other attributes (e.g., having sides of equal length).	Unit 1 Lesson 18; Unit 2 Lessons 13, 17, 20; Unit 3 Lesson 21; Unit 4 Lessons 9, 14, 22
CC.K.G.5	Model shapes in the world by building shapes from components (e.g., sticks and clay balls) and drawing shapes.	Unit 1 Lessons 8, 10; Unit 4 Lesson 9
CC.K.G.6	Compose simple shapes to form larger shapes.	Unit 3 Lesson 9; Unit 4 Lesson 21

UNIT 4 Partners, Problem Drawings, and Tens

Learning Progressions for the Common Core Standards
Counting and Cardinality, Operations and Algebraic Thinking, and Number and Operations in Base Ten

In Grade K, children will	In Grade 1, children will
• recognize that a collection of objects is composed of two subcollections and combine their cardinalities to find the cardinality of the collection (conceptual subitizing). • identify which of two groups has more than (or fewer than, or the same amount as) the other. • act out adding and subtracting situations by representing quantities with objects, their fingers, and math drawings. • compose and decompose numbers from 11 to 19 into ten ones and some further ones (the first step in understanding base-ten notation).	• see the first addend as embedded in the total, using counting on as a strategy. • compare two quantities to find "How many more" or "How many less." • represent problems with equations, called situation equations. • learn to view ten ones as a unit called a ten and to view the numbers 11 to 19 as composed of 1 ten and some ones.

Content Standards Across the Grades

Grade K	Grade 1
• Know number names and the count sequence. [CC.K.CC.1, 3] • Count to tell the number of objects. [CC.K.CC.4a, 4b, 4c, 5] • Compare numbers. [CC.K.CC.6, 7] • Understand addition as putting together and adding to, and understand subtraction as taking apart and taking from. [CC.K.OA 1, 2, 3, 4, 5] • Work with numbers 11–19 to gain foundations for place value (CC.K.NBT.1) • Identify and describe shapes (squares, circles, triangles, rectangles, hexagons, cubes, cones, cylinders, and spheres). [CC.K.G 1, 2] • Analyze, compare, create, and compose shapes. [CC.K.G 4]	• Represent and solve problems involving addition and subtraction. [CC.1.OA.1] • Understand and apply properties of operations and the relationship between addition and subtraction. [CC.1.OA.3] • Add and subtract within 20. [CC.1.OA.5, 6] • Work with addition and subtraction equations. [CC.1.OA.7, 8] • Extend the counting sequence. [CC.1.NBT.1] • Understand place value. [CC.1.NBT.2, 2a, 2b, 2c, 3] • Use place value understanding and properties of operation to add and subtract. [CC.1.NBT.5] • Represent and interpret data. [CC.1.MD.4] • Reason with shapes and their attributes. [CC.1.G.1, 2]

UNIT 4 PARTNERS, PROBLEM DRAWINGS, AND TENS

REAL WORLD
PROBLEM SOLVING

BIG IDEA 1   Story Problems and Equations

Common Core State Standards CC.K.CC.3, CC.K.CC.4a, CC.K.CC.4b, CC.K.CC.4c, CC.K.OA.1, CC.K.OA.2, CC.K.OA.3, CC.K.OA.4, CC.K.OA.5, CC.K.NBT.1, CC.K.MD.3, CC.K.G.1

REAL WORLD
PROBLEM SOLVING

BIG IDEA 2   Practice with Comparing

Common Core State Standards CC.K.CC.3, CC.K.CC.4, CC.K.CC.4b, CC.K.CC.4c, CC.K.CC.5, CC.K.CC.6, CC.K.CC.7, CC.K.OA.1, CC.K.OA.2, CC.K.OA.3, CC.K.OA.4, CC.K.NBT.1

REAL WORLD
PROBLEM SOLVING

BIG IDEA 3	Equations and Teen Numbers

Common Core State Standards CC.K.CC.2, CC.K.CC.4a, CC.K.CC.4b, CC.K.CC.4c, CC.K.CC.6, CC.K.CC.7, CC.K.OA.1, CC.K.OA.2, CC.K.OA.3, CC.K.OA.4, CC.K.OA.5, CC.K.NBT.1, CC.K.MD.3, CC.K.G.1, CC.K.G.2, CC.K.G.3, CC.K.G.4

UNIT 4 CONTENTS

REAL WORLD
PROBLEM SOLVING

BIG IDEA 4	**Equations for Partners**

Common Core State Standards CC.K.CC.1, CC.K.CC.2, CC.K.CC.3, CC.K.CC.4a, CC.K.CC.4b, CC.K.CC.5, CC.K.CC.6, CC.K.CC.7, CC.K.OA.1, CC.K.OA.3, CC.K.OA.4, CC.K.OA.5, CC.K.NBT.1, CC.K.MD.3, CC.K.G.1, CC.K.G.2, CC.K.G.3, CC.K.G.4, CC.K.G.6

Assessment

Math Expressions provides Diagnostic Tools for both Formative Assessment and Summative Assessment as well as Review Opportunities to support the learning needs of your children.

 Unit 4 Test Objectives

4A   Count objects and compare the number of objects in groups. [CC.K.CC.1, CC.K.CC.3, CC.K.CC.4, CC.K.CC.4a, CC.K.CC.4b, CC.K.CC.4c, CC.K.CC.5, CC.K.CC.6, CC.K.CC.7]

4B   Add and subtract within 10 by composing and decomposing numbers. [CC.K.OA.1, CC.K.OA.2, CC.K.OA.3, CC.K.OA.4, CC.K.OA.5]

4C   Decompose teen numbers into a group of ten ones and extra ones. [CC.K.NBT.1]

4D   Identify and describe three-dimensional shapes, and describe shapes in relative positions. [CC.K.G.1, CC.K.G.2, CC.K.G.3, CC.K.G.5, CC.K.G.6]

Assessment and Review Resources

DIAGNOSTIC TOOLS

Student Activity Book
- Unit Review and Test (pp. 201–204)

Assessment Guide
- Test A—Open Response
- Unit 4—Observational Assessment
- Performance Task

Online Test Generator
- Open Response Test
- Multiple Choice Test
- Test Bank Items

FORMATIVE ASSESSMENT

Teacher Edition
- Check Understanding (in every lesson)
- Quick Practice (in every lesson)
- Math Talk (in every lesson)
- Portfolio Suggestions (pp. 346, 378, 390, 436)

SUMMATIVE ASSESSMENT

Assessment Guide
- Test A—Open Response
- Unit 4—Observational Assessment
- Performance Task

REVIEW OPPORTUNITIES

Homework and Remembering
- Review of recently taught topics
- Spiral Review

Teacher Edition
- Unit Review and Test (pp. 455–459)

Assessment Guide
- Fluency Check (in every Big Idea)

Online Test Generator
- Custom review sheets

PLANNING GUIDE FOR UNIT 4

Partners, Problem Drawings, and Tens

LESSONS	Print Resources	Materials
BIG IDEA 1 Story Problems and Equations		
1 Numbers 1–10 and Math Stories: Grocery Store Scenario Common Core State Standards CC.K.CC.4a, CC.K.CC.4b, CC.K.OA.1, CC.K.MD.3, CC.K.G.1 FOCUS Experience adding and subtracting situations in the real world; Define way to sort objects.	TE pp. 329–334 SAB pp. 149–156 AC 4-1	Crayons or markers Scissors
2 Find Partners of 10 Common Core State Standards CC.K.OA.1, CC.K.OA.2, CC.K.OA.3, CC.K.OA.4 FOCUS Identify partners of 6, 7, and 10.	TE pp. 335–340 SAB pp. 157–158 H&R pp. 67–68 AC 4-2	✓ Counting Mats ✓ Number Tiles 1–7 ✓ +/− Tiles ✓ Centimeter cubes Break-Apart Sticks Chart paper Crayons or markers (optional)
3 Teen Numbers and Equations Common Core State Standards CC.K.CC.3, CC.K.CC.4a, CC.K.CC.4b, CC.K.CC.4c, CC.K.OA.1, CC.K.OA.5, CC.K.NBT.1 FOCUS Show teen numbers as a group of ten ones and extra ones and as 10 + a 1-digit number.	TE pp. 341–346 SAB pp. 159–162 H&R pp. 69–70 AC 4-3 MCC 13	✓ 1–20 Boards (back) ✓ 10-sticks ✓ Centimeter cubes Scissors
4 Addition and Subtraction Stories: Grocery Store Scenario Common Core State Standards CC.K.OA.1, CC.K.OA.2, CC.K.OA.3, CC.K.OA.4 FOCUS Explore and express addition and subtraction story problems in buying and selling experiences.	TE pp. 347–352 H&R pp. 71–72 AC 4-4	Grocery store fruit display ✓ Square-Inch Tiles Break-Apart Sticks
BIG IDEA 2 Practice with Comparing		
5 Practice with Teen Numbers and Partners Common Core State Standards CC.K.CC.4, CC.K.CC.4c, CC.K.CC.5, CC.K.OA.1, CC.K.OA.2, CC.K.OA.3, CC.K.NBT.1 FOCUS Show teen numbers as a group of ten ones and extra ones and as 10 + a 1-digit number; Decompose numbers up to 7 into pairs in more than one way and record the pairs.	TE pp. 353–358 SAB pp. 163–164 AC 4-5	✓ 1–20 Boards (back) ✓ 10-sticks ✓ Centimeter cubes Teen Equation Cards ✓ Counting Mats ✓ Number Tiles 1–7 ✓ +/− Tiles Break-Apart Sticks
6 Count, Match, and Compare Common Core State Standards CC.K.CC.4, CC.K.CC.5, CC.K.CC.6, CC.K.CC.7, CC.K.OA.1, CC.K.OA.2 FOCUS Use drawings and write expressions to solve addition and subtraction story problems; Use matching and counting as strategies for comparing the number of objects in groups.	TE pp. 359–364 SAB pp. 165–166 AC 4-6	Grocery store fruit display Crayons or markers Paper

Digital Resources

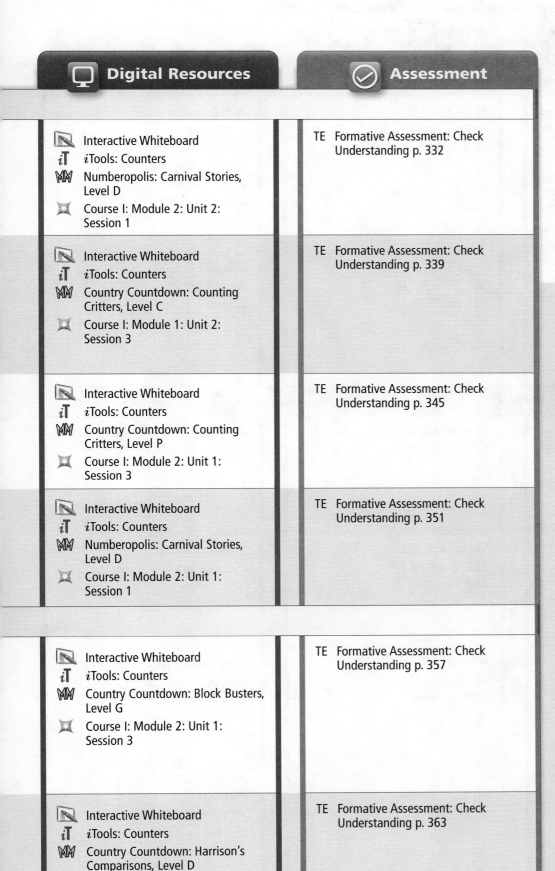

Interactive Whiteboard
*i*Tools: Counters
Numberopolis: Carnival Stories, Level D
Course I: Module 2: Unit 2: Session 1

Interactive Whiteboard
*i*Tools: Counters
Country Countdown: Counting Critters, Level C
Course I: Module 1: Unit 2: Session 3

Interactive Whiteboard
*i*Tools: Counters
Country Countdown: Counting Critters, Level P
Course I: Module 2: Unit 1: Session 3

Interactive Whiteboard
*i*Tools: Counters
Numberopolis: Carnival Stories, Level D
Course I: Module 2: Unit 1: Session 1

Interactive Whiteboard
*i*Tools: Counters
Country Countdown: Block Busters, Level G
Course I: Module 2: Unit 1: Session 3

Interactive Whiteboard
*i*Tools: Counters
Country Countdown: Harrison's Comparisons, Level D
Course I: Module 2: Unit 1: Session 2

Assessment

TE Formative Assessment: Check Understanding p. 332

TE Formative Assessment: Check Understanding p. 339

TE Formative Assessment: Check Understanding p. 345

TE Formative Assessment: Check Understanding p. 351

TE Formative Assessment: Check Understanding p. 357

TE Formative Assessment: Check Understanding p. 363

COMMON CORE STATE STANDARDS FOR MATHEMATICAL CONTENT KEY

CC.K.CC Counting and Cardinality

CC.K.OA Operations and Algebraic Thinking

CC.K.NBT Number and Operations in Base Ten

CC.K.MD Measurement and Data

CC.K.G Geometry

PRINT KEY

TE: Teacher Edition

SAB: Student Activity Book

H&R: Homework and Remembering

AC: Activity Cards

MCC: Math Center Challenge

AG: Assessment Guide

TRB: Teacher's Resource Book

✓: Grade K kits

DIGITAL KEY

*i*T *i*Tools

Soar to Success Math Intervention*

HMH MegaMath

Destination Math®

Interactive Whiteboard

Online Assessment

EV ExamView

* See RtI p. 329R

PLANNING UNIT 4: Partners, Problem Drawings, and Tens (continued)

LESSONS	Print Resources	Materials
BIG IDEA 2 Practice with Comparing (continued)		
7 **Practice Teen Numbers and Equations** Common Core State Standards CC.K.CC.4, CC.K.CC.4c, CC.K.CC.5, CC.K.OA.1, CC.K.OA.2, CC.K.OA.3, CC.K.NBT.1 FOCUS Show teen numbers as a group of ten ones and extra ones and as 10 + a 1-digit number; Decompose numbers up to 7 into pairs in more than one way and record the pairs.	TE pp. 365–370 H&R pp. 73–74 AC 4-7	✓ 1–20 Boards (back) ✓ 10-sticks ✓ Centimeter cubes Teen Equation Cards ✓ Counting Mats ✓ Number Tiles 1–7 ✓ +/− Tiles Break-Apart Sticks
8 **Break-Apart Numbers for 10** Common Core State Standards CC.K.CC.3, CC.K.CC.5, CC.K.OA.3, CC.K.OA.4 FOCUS Find sets of partners for 10; Record sets of partners for 5–7 and 10.	TE pp. 371–378 SAB 167–170 H&R pp. 75–76 AC 4-8 MCC 14	✓ Square-Inch Tiles Break-Apart Sticks Crayons or markers
BIG IDEA 3 Equations and Teen Numbers		
9 **Attributes of 3-Dimensional Shapes** Common Core State Standards CC.K.MD.3, CC.K.G.1, CC.K.G.2, CC.K.G.3, CC.K.G.4 FOCUS Describe and classify three-dimensional shapes.	TE pp. 379–384 AC 4-9	✓ Rectangles, squares, triangles, circles, hexagons, spheres, cubes, cones, cylinders ✓ Comparing Mat ✓ Square-Inch Tiles
10 **Addition and Subtraction Drawings: Grocery Store Scenario** Common Core State Standards CC.K.CC.6, CC.K.CC.7, CC.K.OA.1, CC.K.OA.2 FOCUS Tell, draw, and solve addition and subtraction story problems; Compare numbers of objects in a group using matching and counting strategies.	TE pp. 385–390 SAB pp. 171–172 H&R pp. 77–78 AC 4-10	Grocery store vegetable display Crayons or markers ✓ Square-Inch Tiles (optional)
11 **Partners of 10 with 5-Groups** Common Core State Standards CC.K.OA.3, CC.K.OA.4 FOCUS Find partners of 10 in 5-groups; Record sets of partners for 10, 6, 5, 4, 3, and 2.	TE pp. 391–396 SAB pp. 173–174 H&R pp. 79–80 AC 4-11	✓ Square-Inch Tiles Crayons
12 **Addition Equations** Common Core State Standards CC.K.CC.4a, CC.K.CC.4b, CC.K.CC.4c, CC.K.OA.1, CC.K.OA.2, CC.K.OA.5, CC.K.NBT.1 FOCUS Show teen numbers as a group of ten ones and extra ones and as 10 and a 1-digit number; Add within 6 through 10 and practice addition and subtraction fluency within 5.	TE pp. 397–402 SAB pp. 175–178 AC 4-12	✓ 1–20 Boards ✓ 10-sticks ✓ Centimeter cubes Teen Equation Cards

Digital Resources

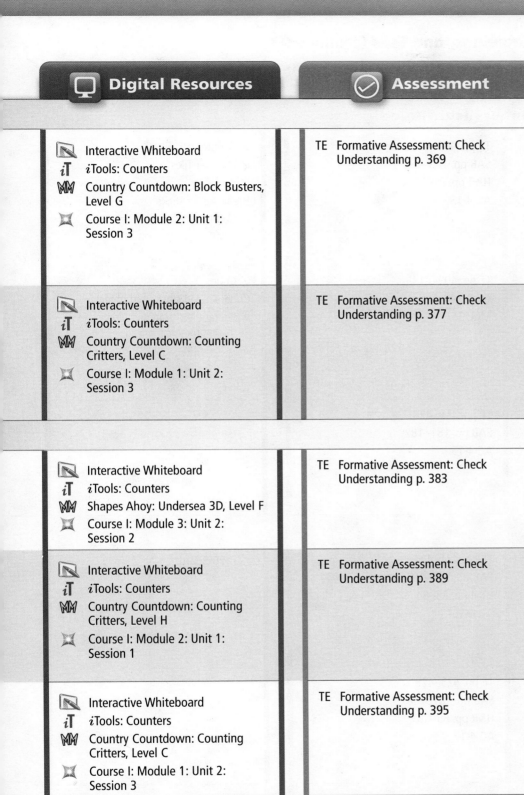

Interactive Whiteboard
*i*T *i*Tools: Counters
MM Country Countdown: Block Busters, Level G
Course I: Module 2: Unit 1: Session 3

Interactive Whiteboard
*i*T *i*Tools: Counters
MM Country Countdown: Counting Critters, Level C
Course I: Module 1: Unit 2: Session 3

Interactive Whiteboard
*i*T *i*Tools: Counters
MM Shapes Ahoy: Undersea 3D, Level F
Course I: Module 3: Unit 2: Session 2

Interactive Whiteboard
*i*T *i*Tools: Counters
MM Country Countdown: Counting Critters, Level H
Course I: Module 2: Unit 1: Session 1

Interactive Whiteboard
*i*T *i*Tools: Counters
MM Country Countdown: Counting Critters, Level C
Course I: Module 1: Unit 2: Session 3

Interactive Whiteboard
*i*T *i*Tools: Counters
MM Country Countdown: Block Busters, Level G
Course I: Module 2: Unit 1: Session 3

Assessment

TE Formative Assessment: Check Understanding p. 369

TE Formative Assessment: Check Understanding p. 377

TE Formative Assessment: Check Understanding p. 383

TE Formative Assessment: Check Understanding p. 389

TE Formative Assessment: Check Understanding p. 395

TE Formative Assessment: Check Understanding p. 401

COMMON CORE STATE STANDARDS FOR MATHEMATICAL CONTENT KEY

CC.K.CC Counting and Cardinality

CC.K.OA Operations and Algebraic Thinking

CC.K.NBT Number and Operations in Base Ten

CC.K.MD Measurement and Data

CC.K.G Geometry

PRINT KEY

TE: Teacher Edition

SAB: Student Activity Book

H&R: Homework and Remembering

AC: Activity Cards

MCC: Math Center Challenge

AG: Assessment Guide

TRB: Teacher's Resource Book

✓: Grade K kits

DIGITAL KEY

*i*T *i*Tools

Soar to Success Math Intervention*

MM HMH MegaMath

Destination Math®

Interactive Whiteboard

✓ Online Assessment

EV ExamView

*   See RtI p. 329R

PLANNING UNIT 4: **Partners, Problem Drawings, and Tens** (continued)

LESSONS	Print Resources	Materials
BIG IDEA 3 Equations and Teen Numbers (continued)		
13 **More Partners of 10 with 5-Groups** Common Core State Standards CC.K.OA.1, CC.K.OA.3, CC.K.OA.4 FOCUS Find partners of 10 and review partners of 7, 8, and 9.	TE pp. 403–408 SAB pp. 179–180 H&R pp. 81–82 AC 4-13	✓ Square-Inch Tiles ✓ Number Tiles ✓ +/– Tiles Break-Apart Sticks ✓ Counting Mats
14 **Identify Cubes** Common Core State Standards CC.K.G.1, CC.K.G.2, CC.K.G.3, CC.K.G.4 FOCUS Describe a cube and identify relative positions of shapes.	TE pp. 409–414 AC 4-14 MCC 15	✓ Cubes Cube-shaped classroom objects ✓ Rectangles, triangles, circles, hexagons
15 **Addition and Subtraction Equations** Common Core State Standards CC.K.CC.2, CC.K.CC.4c, CC.K.OA.1, CC.K.OA.2, CC.K.OA.5 FOCUS Create and solve addition and subtraction story problems and equations for numbers within 6–10 and for fluency within 5; Order numbers 1 through 20.	TE pp. 415–420 SAB pp. 181–182 AC 4-15	
BIG IDEA 4 Equations for Partners		
16 **Teen Number Book** Common Core State Standards CC.K.CC.3, CC.K.CC.4a, CC.K.CC.5, CC.K.NBT.1 FOCUS Model teen numbers as a group of ten ones and extra ones and order numbers 1–19.	TE pp. 421–424 SAB pp. 183–186 H&R pp. 83–84 AC 4-16	✓ 1–20 Board
17 **Addition Equations** Common Core State Standards CC.K.CC.1, CC.K.OA.1, CC.K.OA.5 FOCUS Solve addition equations within 5 and explore addition strategies.	TE pp. 425–428 SAB pp. 187–188 H&R pp. 85–86 AC 4-17	
18 **Partners and Equations** Common Core State Standards CC.K.CC.3, CC.K.OA.3, CC.K.OA.4, CC.K.NBT.1 FOCUS Write equations for partners; Show teen numbers as a group of ten ones and extra ones.	TE pp. 429–432 SAB pp. 189–192 AC 4-18	✓ 1–20 Boards (back)

Digital Resources

Assessment

Digital Resources	Assessment
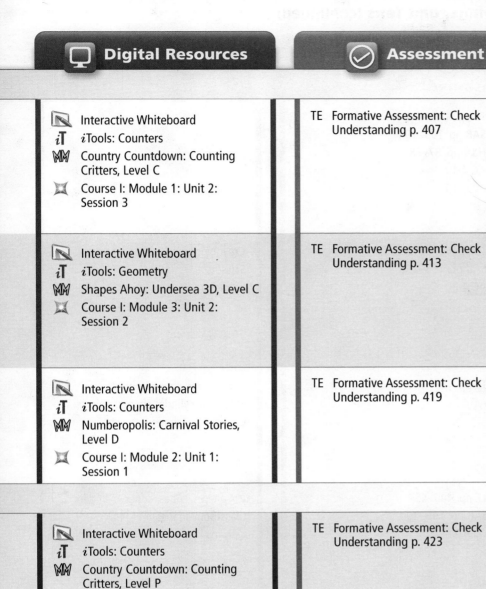 Interactive Whiteboard *i*Tools: Counters Country Countdown: Counting Critters, Level C Course I: Module 1: Unit 2: Session 3	TE Formative Assessment: Check Understanding p. 407
Interactive Whiteboard *i*Tools: Geometry Shapes Ahoy: Undersea 3D, Level C Course I: Module 3: Unit 2: Session 2	TE Formative Assessment: Check Understanding p. 413
Interactive Whiteboard *i*Tools: Counters Numberopolis: Carnival Stories, Level D Course I: Module 2: Unit 1: Session 1	TE Formative Assessment: Check Understanding p. 419
Interactive Whiteboard *i*Tools: Counters Country Countdown: Counting Critters, Level P Course I: Module 2: Unit 1: Session 3	TE Formative Assessment: Check Understanding p. 423
Interactive Whiteboard *i*Tools: Counters Country Countdown: Counting Critters, Level G Course I: Module 2: Unit 1: Session 1	TE Formative Assessment: Check Understanding p. 427
Interactive Whiteboard *i*Tools: Counters Country Countdown: Counting Critters, Level P Course I: Module 2: Unit 1: Session 3	TE Formative Assessment: Check Understanding p. 431

COMMON CORE STATE STANDARDS FOR MATHEMATICAL CONTENT KEY

CC.K.CC Counting and Cardinality

CC.K.OA Operations and Algebraic Thinking

CC.K.NBT Number and Operations in Base Ten

CC.K.MD Measurement and Data

CC.K.G Geometry

PRINT KEY

TE: Teacher Edition

SAB: Student Activity Book

H&R: Homework and Remembering

AC: Activity Cards

MCC: Math Center Challenge

AG: Assessment Guide

TRB: Teacher's Resource Book

✓: Grade K kits

DIGITAL KEY

*i*T *i*Tools

Soar to Success Math Intervention*

HMH MegaMath

Destination Math®

Interactive Whiteboard

Online Assessment

EV ExamView

* See RtI p. 329R

PLANNING UNIT 4: Partners, Problem Drawings, and Tens (continued)

LESSONS	Print Resources	Materials
BIG IDEA 4 Equations for Partners (continued)		
19 **Write Addition Equations** Common Core State Standards CC.K.OA.1, CC.K.OA.3, CC.K.OA.4 **FOCUS** Find and write equations for partners; Solve subtraction equations within 6 to 10.	TE pp. 433–436 SAB pp. 193–194 H&R pp. 87–88 AC 4-19 MCC 16	
20 **Teen Number Book** Common Core State Standards CC.K.CC.2, CC.K.CC.3, CC.K.CC.4a, CC.K.CC.4b, CC.K.CC.6, CC.K.CC.7, CC.K.NBT.1 **FOCUS** Model teen numbers as a group of ten ones and extra ones; Match pictures to numbers, compare groups, and practice addition within 10.	TE pp. 437–442 SAB pp. 195–198 AC 4-20	Crayons or markers Scissors Stapler
21 **Identify Cones and Cylinders** Common Core State Standards CC.K.G.1, CC.K.G.2, CC.K.G.3, CC.K.G.6 **FOCUS** Describe cones and cylinders and compose three-dimensional shapes.	TE pp. 443–448 AC 4-21	Cones, cone-shaped objects Cylinders, cylinder-shaped objects Cubes, cube-shaped objects
22 **Focus on Mathematical Practices** Common Core State Standards CC.K.MD.3, CC.K.G.1, CC.K.G.2, CC.K.G.4 **FOCUS** Use the Common Core Content Standards and Practices in a variety of real world problem solving situations.	TE pp. 449–454 SAB pp. 199–200 AC 4-22	✓ Spheres, cubes, cones, cylinders Classroom shapes Crayons
UNIT REVIEW/TEST	TE Unit 4 Review and Test, pp. 455–459 SAB Unit 4 Review and Test, pp. 201–204	

Digital Resources

	Assessment
![icon] Interactive Whiteboard *i*T *i*Tools: Counters MM Country Countdown: Counting Critters, Level G ✶ Course I: Module 2: Unit 1: Session 1	TE Formative Assessment: Check Understanding p. 435
![icon] Interactive Whiteboard *i*T *i*Tools: Counters MM Country Countdown: Counting Critters, Level P ✶ Course I: Module 2: Unit 1: Session 3	TE Formative Assessment: Check Understanding p. 441
![icon] Interactive Whiteboard *i*T *i*Tools: Geometry MM Shapes Ahoy: Undersea 3D, Level C ✶ Course I: Module 3: Unit 2: Session 2	TE Formative Assessment: Check Understanding p. 447
![icon] Interactive Whiteboard *i*T *i*Tools: Geometry MM Shapes Ahoy: Undersea 3D, Level F ✶ Course I: Module 3: Unit 2: Session 2	TE Formative Assessment: Check Understanding p. 453
✔ Online Assessment EV ExamView	AG Unit 4 Test A—Open Response AG Unit 4 Test B—Multiple Choice AG Unit 4 Performance Assessment

COMMON CORE STATE STANDARDS FOR MATHEMATICAL CONTENT KEY

CC.K.CC Counting and Cardinality

CC.K.OA Operations and Algebraic Thinking

CC.K.NBT Number and Operations in Base Ten

CC.K.MD Measurement and Data

CC.K.G Geometry

PRINT KEY

TE: Teacher Edition

SAB: Student Activity Book

H&R: Homework and Remembering

AC: Activity Cards

MCC: Math Center Challenge

AG: Assessment Guide

TRB: Teacher's Resource Book

✓: Grade K kits

DIGITAL KEY

*i*T *i*Tools

✶ Soar to Success Math Intervention*

MM HMH MegaMath

✶ Destination Math®

![icon] Interactive Whiteboard

✔ Online Assessment

EV ExamView

* See RtI p. 329R

Common Core State Standards for Mathematics

Math Expressions integrates the Mathematical Practices throughout every teaching lesson. This program correlates fully to the concepts, skills, and problems listed in the Common Core Content Standards.

Common Core State Standards for Mathematical Practices in This Unit

CC.K–12.MP.1	Make sense of problems and persevere in solving them.	Lessons 2, 3, 4, 5, 6, 9, 10, 12, 14, 15, 21, 22
CC.K–12.MP.2	Reason abstractly and quantitatively.	Lessons 1, 2, 5, 6, 7, 9, 12, 16, 17, 18, 19, 22
CC.K–12.MP.3	Construct viable arguments and critique the reasoning of others.	Lessons 1, 8, 9, 11, 13, 14, 17, 19, 21, 22
CC.K–12.MP.4	Model with mathematics.	Lessons 2, 4, 6, 8, 12, 14, 20, 21, 22
CC.K–12.MP.5	Use appropriate tools strategically.	Lessons 5, 7, 9, 14, 20, 21, 22
CC.K–12.MP.6	Attend to precision.	Lessons 1, 3, 4, 5, 7, 8, 9, 10, 11, 12, 13, 14, 15, 17, 18, 19, 20, 21, 22
CC.K–12.MP.7	Look for and make use of structure.	Lessons 1, 2, 4, 5, 6, 7, 8, 9, 11, 12, 13, 14, 15, 16, 20, 21, 22
CC.K–12.MP.8	Look for and express regularity in repeated reasoning.	Lessons 5, 6, 7, 9, 13, 15, 22

Common Core State Standards for Mathematical Content in This Unit

CC.K.CC Counting and Cardinality

Know number names and the count sequence.

CC.K.CC.1	Count to 100 by ones and by tens.	Lesson 17
CC.K.CC.2	Count forward beginning from a given number within the known sequence (instead of having to begin at 1).	Lessons 15, 20
CC.K.CC.3	Write numbers from 0 to 20. Represent a number of objects with a written numeral 0–20 (with 0 representing a count of no objects).	Lessons 3, 8, 16, 18, 20

Count to tell the number of objects.

CC.K.CC.4	Understand the relationship between numbers and quantities; connect counting to cardinality.	Lessons 5, 6, 7
CC.K.CC.4a	When counting objects, say the number names in the standard order, pairing each object with one and only one number name and each number name with one and only one object.	Lessons 1, 3, 12, 16, 20
CC.K.CC.4b	Understand that the last number name said tells the number of objects counted. The number of objects is the same regardless of their arrangement or the order in which they were counted.	Lessons 1, 3, 12, 20

Common Core State Standards for Mathematical Content in This Unit (continued)

CC.K.CC.4c	Understand that each successive number name refers to a quantity that is one larger.	Lessons 3, 5, 7, 12, 15
CC.K.CC.5	Count to answer "how many?" questions about as many as 20 things arranged in a line, a rectangular array, or a circle, or as many as 10 things in a scattered configuration; given a number from 1–20, count out that many objects.	Lessons 5, 6, 7, 8, 16
CC.K.CC.6	Identify whether the number of objects in one group is greater than, less than, or equal to the number of objects in another group, e.g., by using matching and counting strategies.	Lessons 6, 10, 20
CC.K.CC.7	Compare two numbers between 1 and 10 presented as written numerals.	Lessons 6, 10, 20

CC.K.OA Operations and Algebraic Thinking

Understand addition as putting together and adding to, and understand subtraction as taking apart and taking from.

CC.K.OA.1	Represent addition and subtraction with objects, fingers, mental images, drawings, sounds (e.g., claps), acting out situations, verbal explanations, expressions, or equations.	Lessons 1, 2, 3, 4, 5, 6, 7, 10, 12, 13, 15, 17, 19
CC.K.OA.2	Solve addition and subtraction word problems, and add and subtract within 10, e.g., by using objects or drawings to represent the problem.	Lessons 2, 4, 5, 6, 7, 10, 12, 15
CC.K.OA.3	Decompose numbers less than or equal to 10 into pairs in more than one way, e.g., by using objects or drawings, and record each decomposition by a drawing or equation (e.g., $5 = 2 + 3$ and $5 = 4 + 1$).	Lessons 2, 4, 5, 7, 8, 11, 13, 18, 19
CC.K.OA.4	For any number from 1 to 9, find the number that makes 10 when added to the given number, e.g., by using objects or drawings, and record the answer with a drawing or equation.	Lessons 2, 4, 8, 11, 13, 18, 19
CC.K.OA.5	Fluently add and subtract within 5.	Lessons 3, 12, 15, 17

CC.K.NBT Number and Operations in Base Ten

Work with numbers 11–19 to gain foundations for place value.

CC.K.NBT.1	Compose and decompose numbers from 11 to 19 into ten ones and some further ones, e.g., by using objects or drawings, and record each composition or decomposition by a drawing or equation (e.g., $18 = 10 + 8$); understand that these numbers are composed of ten ones and one, two, three, four, five, six, seven, eight, or nine ones.	Lessons 3, 5, 7, 12, 16, 18, 20

CC.K.MD Measurement and Data

Classify objects and count the number of objects in each category.

CC.K.MD.3	Classify objects into given categories; count the numbers of objects in each category and sort the categories by count.	Lessons 1, 9, 22

CC.K.G Geometry

Identify and describe shapes (squares, circles, triangles, rectangles, hexagons, cubes, cones, cylinders, and spheres).

CC.K.G.1	Describe objects in the environment using names of shapes, and describe the relative positions of these objects using terms such as *above, below, beside, in front of, behind,* and *next to.*	Lessons 1, 9, 14, 21, 22
CC.K.G.2	Correctly name shapes regardless of their orientations or overall size.	Lessons 9, 14, 21, 22
CC.K.G.3	Identify shapes as two-dimensional (lying in a plane, "flat") or three-dimensional ("solid").	Lessons 9, 14, 21

Analyze, compare, create, and compose shapes.

CC.K.G.4	Analyze and compare two- and three-dimensional shapes, in different sizes and orientations, using informal language to describe their similarities, differences, parts (e.g., number of sides and vertices/"corners") and other attributes (e.g., having sides of equal length).	Lessons 9, 14, 22
CC.K.G.6	Compose simple shapes to form larger shapes.	Lesson 21

NOTES:

_____

_____

_____

_____

_____

_____

_____

_____

_____

_____

_____

_____

_____

_____

_____

_____

_____

UNIT 4

CONTENTS

Differentiated Instruction

Math Expressions lessons are designed to accommodate a wide range of student learning styles and academic skills. A variety of lesson features and program resources incorporate strategies and opportunities for differentiating instruction.

English Language Learners

Present this problem to all children. Offer the different levels of support to meet children's levels of language proficiency.

Objective Represent addition with an equation.

Problem Say: **Cara drew 4 circles and 1 triangle. How many shapes did Cara draw?** Draw the shapes on the board. Write 4 + 1 = 5 and the word *equation*.

BEGINNING

Point to the addition sign. Ask: **What are the partners?** 4 and 1 Point to the equal sign. Ask: **How many shapes in all?** 5 Say: **The equation 4 + 1 = 5 shows the addition story.** Ask children to repeat *equation*.

INTERMEDIATE

Point to the *equation* on the board. Guide children to answer "addition sign, partners 4 and 1, and equal sign" as you point to the parts of the *equation*. Ask: **What is 4 + 1 = 5?** an *equation*

ADVANCED

Point to the board. Ask: **Which of these shows the addition story?** The *equation* 4 + 1 = 5 shows the addition story. Ask children to say the parts of the *equation* as you circle each part. addition sign, partners 4 and 1, and equal sign

Differentiated Instruction: Individualizing Instruction Activities

Differentiated Instruction Cards	*On Level • Challenge in every lesson*
Math Writing Prompts	*On Level • Challenge in every lesson*
Math Center Challenges	*Advanced: 4 in every unit*
English Language Learners	*In every lesson*

Ready-Made Math Challenge Centers

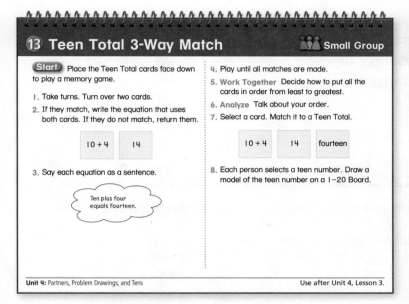

13 Teen Total 3-Way Match — Small Group

Start Place the Teen Total cards face down to play a memory game.

1. Take turns. Turn over two cards.
2. If they match, write the equation that uses both cards. If they do not match, return them.

10 + 4   14

3. Say each equation as a sentence.

Ten plus four equals fourteen.

4. Play until all matches are made.
5. **Work Together** Decide how to put all the cards in order from least to greatest.
6. **Analyze** Talk about your order.
7. Select a card. Match it to a Teen Total.

10 + 4   14   fourteen

8. Each person selects a teen number. Draw a model of the teen number on a 1–20 Board.

Unit 4: Partners, Problem Drawings, and Tens   Use after Unit 4, Lesson 3.

Grouping Small Group
Materials Teen Total Cards (TRB M46), 1–20 Board
Objective Find equal amounts, write equations, and draw models
Common Core Standards CC.K.OA.1, CC.K–12.MP.2

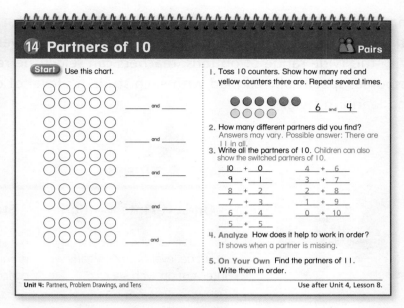

14 Partners of 10 — Pairs

Start Use this chart.

○○○○○○○○○○ _____ and _____
○○○○○○○○○○ _____ and _____
○○○○○○○○○○ _____ and _____
○○○○○○○○○○ _____ and _____
○○○○○○○○○○ _____ and _____

1. Toss 10 counters. Show how many red and yellow counters there are. Repeat several times.

   ⬤⬤⬤⬤⬤⬤◯◯◯◯   6 and 4

2. How many different partners did you find? Answers may vary. Possible answer: There are 11 in all.
3. Write all the partners of 10. Children can also show the switched partners of 10.

10 + 0	4 + 6
9 + 1	3 + 7
8 + 2	2 + 8
7 + 3	1 + 9
6 + 4	0 + 10
5 + 5	

4. **Analyze** How does it help to work in order? It shows when a partner is missing.
5. **On Your Own** Find the partners of 11. Write them in order.

Unit 4: Partners, Problem Drawings, and Tens   Use after Unit 4, Lesson 8.

Grouping Pairs
Materials 10 two-color counters
Objective Identify partners of 10
Common Core Standards CC.K.OA.3, CC.K.OA.4, CC.K–12.MP.2, CC.K–12.MP.7

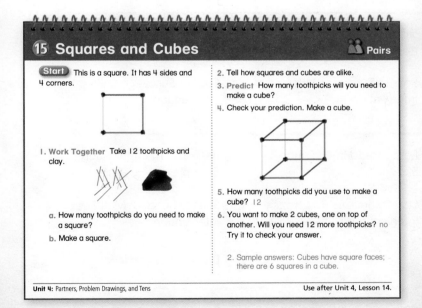

15 Squares and Cubes — Pairs

Start This is a square. It has 4 sides and 4 corners.

1. **Work Together** Take 12 toothpicks and clay.

   a. How many toothpicks do you need to make a square?
   b. Make a square.

2. Tell how squares and cubes are alike.
3. **Predict** How many toothpicks will you need to make a cube?
4. Check your prediction. Make a cube.

5. How many toothpicks did you use to make a cube? 12
6. You want to make 2 cubes, one on top of another. Will you need 12 more toothpicks? no Try it to check your answer.

   2. Sample answers: Cubes have square faces; there are 6 squares in a cube.

Unit 4: Partners, Problem Drawings, and Tens   Use after Unit 4, Lesson 14.

Grouping Pairs
Materials 24 toothpicks, clay
Objective Build and analyze models of cubes
Common Core Standards CC.K.G.4, CC.K.G.5, CC.K.G.6, CC.K–12.MP.1, CC.K–12.MP.7

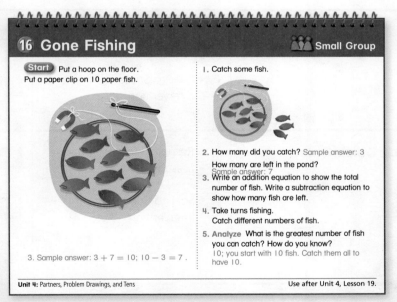

16 Gone Fishing — Small Group

Start Put a hoop on the floor. Put a paper clip on 10 paper fish.

1. Catch some fish.
2. How many did you catch? Sample answer: 3 How many are left in the pond? Sample answer: 7
3. Write an addition equation to show the total number of fish. Write a subtraction equation to show how many fish are left.
4. Take turns fishing. Catch different numbers of fish.
5. **Analyze** What is the greatest number of fish you can catch? How do you know? 10; you start with 10 fish. Catch them all to have 10.

3. Sample answer: 3 + 7 = 10; 10 − 3 = 7 .

Unit 4: Partners, Problem Drawings, and Tens   Use after Unit 4, Lesson 19.

Grouping Small Group
Materials Magnet, string, pencil, hoop, metal paper clips, 10 identical size paper fish
Objective Model and write addition and subtraction story problems
Common Core Standards CC.K.OA.1, CC.K.OA.3, CC.K.OA.4, CC.K–12.MP.1, CC.K–12.MP.2

Response to Intervention

Throughout *Math Expressions*, activities and materials for all levels of RtI engage learners with focused print and online intervention options. With this wide range of options, teachers can select the resource or resources specifically aligned with each student's level of understanding and learning style.

RtI	**TIER 1** On-Level Intervention	**TIER 2** Strategic Intervention	**TIER 3** Intensive Intervention
	For students who are generally at grade level but need early intervention with specific concepts.	For students who need small group instruction to review concepts and skills.	For students who need one-on-one instruction to build foundational skills.
Beginning of Each Unit		Response to Intervention Skill Soar to Success: Math Intervention	Response to Intervention Example Soar to Success: Math Intervention
Each Lesson	Differentiated Instruction Cards – On Level Soar to Success: Math Intervention	Differentiated Instruction Cards – Intervention Soar to Success: Math Intervention	Response to Intervention Example Soar to Success: Math Intervention
Each Quick Quiz	Response to Intervention Lesson Soar to Success: Math Intervention	Response to Intervention Skill Soar to Success: Math Intervention	Response to Intervention Example Soar to Success: Math Intervention Diagnostic Interview
Each Unit Test	Response to Intervention Lesson Soar to Success: Math Intervention	Response to Intervention Skill Soar to Success: Math Intervention	Response to Intervention Example Soar to Success: Math Intervention Diagnostic Interview

Cross-Curricular Connections

Cross-curricular connections are included at the end of each lesson with a Home or School Activity.

Connections

LITERATURE LINKS

Math Literature Library

One Less Fish

One Less Fish
Prepare to explore the deep blue sea where fish will dazzle your eyes as they swim across the pages of this unique book by Kim Michelle Toft and Allan Sheather. Illustrations will inspire children to think up addition and subtraction story problems, which could then be written and illustrated using bold colors.

You may wish to share this selection from the *Math Expressions* Literature Library with children as you begin Unit 4, or you may decide to read the book at another time during the unit. The Teacher's Guide that accompanies the Math Literature Library provides sample discussion questions to use with this selection.

Literature Connections

The Very Hungry Caterpillar by Eric Carle (Philomel Books, 1981)

RESEARCH—BEST PRACTICES

Putting Research into Practice

Dr. Karen C. Fuson,
Math Expressions Author

Developing the Prerequisites for Level 2 and Level 3 Methods of Adding and Subtracting

Kindergarten children are learning general level 1 numerical solution methods that they can extend to larger numbers. They are also working on all the prerequisites for the level 3 derived fact methods, such as make-a-ten $(8 + 6 = 8 + 2 + 4 = 10 + 4 = 14)$.

- Seeing the tens in teen numbers $(10 + 3 = 13)$.

- Knowing all the partners of 10 (e.g., $8 + 2 = 10$).

- Knowing all the partners of numbers below 10 (e.g., know that 6 breaks into 2 and 4).

National Council of Teachers of Mathematics (NCTM). *Focus in Kindergarten.* Reston, Va.: NCTM, 2010, p. 54.

Learning Paths

In Unit 4, children continue to see the tens in teen numbers by making all of the teen numbers on the 1–20 Board with a 10-stick of 10 ones and extra ones cubes. This enables them to begin to see the pattern across all of the written teen numbers of the ones number in the right-hand place. Continued experience with the Number Tiles in which the ones number is placed on top of the 0 in the 10 tile, helps children see the teen number as 10 and 4; in this way the 1 in the tens place is understood as 10 (ten) instead of as 1. Work with equation cards that show $14 = 10 + 4$ and with flashing fingers as ten fingers and 4 fingers relates the written numerals and objects and number words in meaningful ways.

Children work more intensively with partners of 10 in Unit 4 to build the second prerequisite listed above, and they continue to make partners of numbers 5 through 8 to build the third prerequisite.

Children also continue to build their understanding of adding and subtracting by telling and solving such problems with larger numbers in the class grocery store and by solving addition equations without a given scenario. They write the partner numbers within unknown boxes in an equation (e.g., $6 = \square + \square$) and as an addition expression (e.g., $6 = \underline{\hspace{1cm}}$ answered as $6 = 5 + 1$).

In the English language, teen and 2-digit number words are complex and difficult to learn. By contrast, in some Asian languages the word for 13, for example, translates into "ten three." In the English system, teen and 2-digit numbers look like two single-digit numbers written beside each other; nothing shows the ten value for the digit on the left. Young children need verbal and visual supports for understanding these number words and written numbers.

In this program, we provide this scaffolding by using *tens* and *ones* words, as well as standard number words, when working with teen and 2-digit numbers. We say 13 is *thirteen* and is *1 ten 3 ones*. These words are used interchangeably and help reinforce the embedded ten-based thinking and place-value understanding. The words relate to the quantities children make or count that show the ten ones and some further ones. They also relate to the base-ten numerals in an equation such as $14 = 10 + 4$ using Number Tiles.

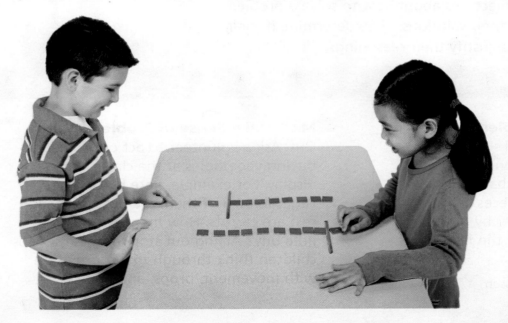

Other Useful References: Place Value

Cross, C. T., Woods, T. A, Schweingruber, H. (Eds.) (2009). *Mathematics learning in early childhood: Paths toward excellence and equity*. Center for Education, Division of Behavioral and Social Sciences and Education. Washington, DC: National Academy Press.

National Council of Teachers of Mathematics (NCTM). *Focus in Kindergarten*. Reston, Va.: NCTM, 2010.

Getting Ready to Teach Unit 4

Using the Common Core Standards for Mathematical Practice

The Common Core State Standards for Mathematical Content indicate what concepts, skills, and types of problem solving children should learn. The Common Core State Standards for Mathematical Practice indicate how children should demonstrate understanding. These *Mathematical Practices* are embedded directly into the Student and Teacher Editions for each unit in *Math Expressions*. As you use the teaching suggestions, you will automatically implement a teaching style that encourages children to demonstrate a thorough understanding of concepts, skills, and problems. In this program, Math Talk suggestions are a vehicle used to encourage discussion that supports all eight Mathematical Practices. See examples in Mathematical Practice 6.

COMMON CORE
Mathematical Practice 1
Make sense of problems and persevere in solving them.

Children analyze and make conjectures about how to solve a problem. They plan, monitor, and check their solutions. They determine if their answers are reasonable and can justify their reasoning.

TEACHER EDITION: Examples from Unit 4

MP.1 Make Sense of Problems Check Answers Elicit addition and subtraction story problems from children about the grocery store display. Then have the class find the total number of pieces of fruit. Have them check the answer by having the whole class count all of the fruit in the problem.

Lesson **4** ACTIVITY 1

MP.1 Make Sense of Problems Act It Out Ask a volunteer to act out someone buying vegetables at the classroom display. For example, Pete buys some vegetables. 6 of them are potatoes. The rest are carrots. How many carrots does Pete buy? Acting out story problems helps children think through the information with movement, props, and visuals.

Lesson **10** ACTIVITY 1

Mathematical Practice 1 is integrated into Unit 4 in the following ways:

Act It Out
Analyze the Problem

Make Sense of Problems
Persevere in Solving Problems

Mathematical Practice 2
Reason abstractly and quantitatively.

Children make sense of quantities and their relationships in problem situations. They can connect models and expressions to a given situation. Quantitative reasoning entails attending to the meaning of quantities. In this unit, this involves identifying a group with a given number of objects, counting out a group with a specified number of objects, connecting the addition and subtraction symbols with the addition and subtraction of quantities/numbers, recognizing the equality or inequality of amounts and correctly using the equal/not equal symbols, and determining the unknown quantity when the total and one partner are known.

TEACHER EDITION: Examples from Unit 4

MP.2 Reason Abstractly Have children practice identifying partners for 6 and 7, for example by playing the *Unknown Partner Game*. In this game children work in pairs and use centimeter cubes and Break-Apart Sticks to separate 6 or 7 into partners. Each set of partners is named.

Lesson **2** ACTIVITY 1

MP.2 Reason Abstractly and Quantitatively Connect Symbols and Models The addition symbol is shown by having children hold one arm vertically and one arm horizontally. Tell children that for the addition symbol things are put together, so they show it by putting arms together. The subtraction symbol is shown by having children hold one arm horizontally (like the subtraction symbol). Children then open and close their hand as if they were grasping things and move their arm to the side to pull away the things they are taking. Altogether, this action links the visual appearance of the subtraction symbol with a meaning of subtraction as "taking away."

Lesson **12** ACTIVITY 3

Mathematical Practice 2 is integrated into Unit 4 in the following ways:

Connect Symbols and Models
Connect Symbols and Words
Reason Abstractly

Reason Abstractly and Quantitatively
Reason Quantitatively

UNIT 4 RESEARCH

Mathematical Practice 3

Construct viable arguments and critique the reasoning of others.

Children use stated assumptions, definitions, and previously established results in constructing arguments. They are able to analyze situations and can recognize and use counterexamples. They justify their conclusions, communicate them to others, and respond to the arguments of others.

Children are also able to distinguish correct logic or reasoning from that which is flawed, and—if there is a flaw in an argument—explain what it is. Children can listen to the arguments of others, decide whether they make sense, and ask useful questions to clarify or improve the arguments.

Math Talk is a conversation tool by which children formulate ideas and analyze responses and engage in discourse. See also MP.6 Attend to Precision.

TEACHER EDITION: Examples from Unit 4

▶ **What's the Error** `WHOLE CLASS`

MP.3 Construct Viable Arguments and Critique the Reasoning of Others Explain that Puzzled Penguin was asked to show partners of 10. Write the following equations on the board.

> $10 = 8 + 2$
> $10 = 6 + 5$
> $10 = 1 + 9$
> $10 = 3 + 6$

- Puzzled Penguin is not sure that all the equations were solved correctly. We'll help Puzzled Penguin find any mistakes.

- Let's look at the first equation. If you think that the equation is solved correctly, raise your hand.

Lesson **8** `ACTIVITY 2`

MP.3 Construct a Viable Argument

 How can we make sure that we find all of the partners of ten?

Jill: We can use Square-Inch Tiles to show the partners.

Eduardo: We have to remember to turn over one more tile each time.

Bonnie: We make the first partner one more each time.

Jill: We can check the partners we find. We can see if all of the numbers are there.

Eduardo: The numbers should be 1, 2, 3, 4, 5, 6, 7, 8, and 9.

Bonnie: If we have all of those numbers, we have found all of the partners of ten.

You are correct.

Lesson **11** `ACTIVITY 3`

Mathematical Practice 3 is integrated into Unit 4 in the following ways:

Compare Methods   **Justify Conclusions**

Compare Representations   **Puzzled Penguin**

Construct a Viable Argument

Mathematical Practice 4
Model with mathematics.

Children can apply the mathematics they know to solve problems that arise in everyday life. This might be as simple as writing an equation to solve a problem. Children might draw pictures to lead them to a solution for a problem.

Children apply what they know and are comfortable making assumptions and approximations to simplify a complicated situation. They are able to identify important quantities in a practical situation and represent their relationships using such tools as sketches and tables.

TEACHER EDITION: Examples from Unit 4

MP.4 Model with Mathematics Ask children to count out 10 Square-Inch Tiles of the same color. Direct children to arrange their Square-Inch Tiles in a horizontal row of 10.

- Now make your bugs go to sleep by placing all of them dot side down, so you can't see them. How many are sleeping? all 10 of them

Have children wake one bug.

- One bug wants to get up and play. Let's turn one over. How many bugs are sleeping now? 9
- How many bugs are awake? 1
- How many bugs in total? 10
- Put your Break-Apart Stick between the sleeping bugs and the bug that is awake, so you can see them clearly.

Lesson 2 ACTIVITY 2

MP.4 Model with Mathematics Write an Expression The emphasis in this unit is on addition and subtraction problems within 10. Keep encouraging children to make up problems with these numbers. Use the grocery store display you made from the fruit that children colored during Unit 4, Lesson 1. Ask for a volunteer to go to the grocery store and buy two kinds of fruit to make a fruit salad. The child will decide how many pieces of each kind of fruit to buy.

- Maria, what two kinds of fruit do you want to buy? I want to buy oranges and bananas.
- How many oranges and how many bananas will you buy? 3 oranges and 4 bananas

Have Maria take the fruit from the store while the whole class counts with you, the storekeeper, to check that the correct amount of fruit is being bought. Record Maria's fruit salad equation on the board: $3 + 4 = $ _____ .

Lesson 4 ACTIVITY 1

Mathematical Practice 4 is integrated into Unit 4 in the following ways:

Model with Mathematics
Write an Expression

COMMON CORE
Mathematical Practice 5
Use appropriate tools strategically.

Children consider the available tools and models when solving mathematical problems. Children make sound decisions about when each of these tools might be helpful. These tools might include paper and pencil for drawings and computation, manipulatives, or even their fingers. They recognize both the insight to be gained from using the tool and the tool's limitations. When making mathematical models, they are able to identify quantities in a practical situation and represent relationships using modeling tools, such as tables, expressions, and equations.

Modeling numbers in problems and in computations is a central focus in *Math Expressions* lessons. Children learn and develop models to solve numerical problems and to model problem situations. Children continually use both kinds of modeling throughout the program.

TEACHER EDITION: Examples from Unit 4

MP.5 Use Appropriate Tools Use a Concrete Model Children make a Teen Number Book in Unit 4 to help them visualize teen numbers as a group of ten ones and some extra ones. It also helps to reinforce this concept as children show and write teen numbers. After the book has been assembled, allow children to explore various ways to use it. Show children how to turn the pages to say the numbers in order from 11 to 20. Ask questions such as the following.

• Point to the page that shows the partners for 13.

• What is an equation for 17?

• Find the number that shows ten ones and 5 ones.

Lesson **20** ACTIVITY 1

MP.5 Use Appropriate Tools Model the Math Children make numbers 11 to 20 using 10-sticks and centimeter cubes on the 1–20 Board. They make 11 with one 10-stick and one centimeter cube. They learn how to make 12 with one 10-stick and 2 centimeter cubes. They continue to model the numbers 13–19 on their 1–20 Boards.

• What are three different ways you can make 20? use 20 centimeter cubes, one 10-stick and 10 centimeter cubes, or two 10-sticks

Lesson **5** ACTIVITY 1

Mathematical Practice 5 is integrated into Unit 4 in the following ways:

Use Appropriate Tools	Use a Concrete Model	Model the Math

Mathematical Practice 6
Attend to precision.

Children try to communicate precisely to others. They try to use clear definitions in discussion with others and in their own reasoning. They state the meaning of the symbols they choose. When restating story problems, they are careful about specifying units to clarify the correspondence with quantities in the problem. They calculate accurately and efficiently, and express numerical answers with a degree of precision appropriate for the problem context. Children give carefully formulated explanations to each other.

TEACHER EDITION: Examples from Unit 4

MP.6 Attend to Precision Explain a Representation Give each group of children a variety of cylinders, including different sized cylinder-shaped objects.

- Who knows the name of these shapes? cylinders

- What do you see that is the same about all of the cylinders? They can roll. They have a circle on both ends. They all look the same but the sizes are different.

- What have you seen that is shaped like a cylinder? a roll of paper towels, a can, a roll of wrapping, a glass

- Are cylinders solid shapes? How do you know? They are solid shapes because they they go across, backward and forward, and up and down.

Lesson 21 ACTIVITY 2

MP.6 Attend to Precision Describe a Method Ask two children to describe how they remember the addition sign.

- How many parts, or lines, does the addition sign have? The addition sign has two parts.

- What does the addition sign show you to do? It shows putting together two partners.

- How do the two parts of the addition sign help you remember to add two things? The addition sign is made up of two things, and we add two things.

- What do you do when you see an addition sign with two partners and an equal sign? You see the partners and find the number those partners make.

Lesson 17 ACTIVITY 1

Mathematical Practice 6 is integrated into Unit 4 in the following ways:

Attend to Precision
Describe
Describe a Method

Explain a Representation
Explain a Solution

COMMON CORE
Mathematical Practice 7
Look for structure.

Children analyze problems to discern the structure. They draw conclusions about the structure or the relationships they have identified.

TEACHER EDITION: Examples from Unit 4

MP.7 Look for Structure Talk about the partners in each Math Mountain. Continue working with those who need support. When children finish, ask them to draw a big Math Mountain on a sheet of paper. Let children draw Tiny Tumblers the way they picture them rolling and playing on the mountains. You can extend the discussion by asking the class what they think the Tiny Tumblers play, how they have fun, what their cozy living places look like, and so on. Stimulate children's thinking by asking questions.

Lesson **11** ACTIVITY 3

MP.7 Look for Structure Identify Relationships Have the class decide what they want the Square-Inch Tiles to be. In this example, the dot side of the tile is a

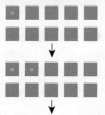

little bug. Sometimes the bugs are awake and turned up so that they can be seen, and sometimes they are sleeping under the tile and turned over so that they are hidden. There are always 10 bugs in total. Continue in this manner, having children turn over the bugs one at a time. Record the partners on the board. Help children notice that they can quickly see how many bugs are asleep and awake when they are arranged in two rows of 5. Remind children that using two rows of 5 will help them count faster. Have children discuss the numbers and sequences they see in the chart on the board.

Lesson **11** ACTIVITY 1

Mathematical Practice 7 is integrated into Unit 4 in the following ways:

Look for Structure | **Identify Relationships**

Mathematical Practice 8

Look for and express regularity in repeated reasoning.

Children use repeated reasoning as they analyze patterns, relationships, and calculations to generalize methods, rules, and shortcuts. As they work to solve a problem, children maintain oversight of the process while attending to the details. They continually evaluate the reasonableness of their intermediate results.

TEACHER EDITION: Examples from Unit 4

MP.8 Use Repeated Reasoning

Generalize Review making teen numbers with 10-sticks and centimeter cubes and have children make observations. For example, children may notice that each of the teen numbers has one 10-stick. They may see that each number has one more cube than the number before it. Children might also discern that the number in the right column matches the number of centimeter cubes and the number in the left column matches the number of 10-sticks.

Lesson **4** ACTIVITY 2

MP.8 Use Repeated Reasoning

Generalize Distribute the Teen Equation Cards. You may want to have some children work only with Set A of the cards. Children will place the cards on the corresponding teen numbers on the 1–20 Board. Cards can be placed below the teen numbers at the top of the 1–20 Board or at the bottom, covering the matching teen equations.

Lesson **5** ACTIVITY 2

Mathematical Practice 8 is integrated into Unit 4 in the following ways:

Draw Conclusions	**Generalize**	**Use Repeated Reasoning**

FOCUS on Mathematical Practices
Unit 4 includes a special lesson that involves solving real world problems and incorporates all 8 Mathematical Practices. In this lesson children use what they know about the attributes of three-dimensional shapes to compare the shapes.

STUDENT EDITION: LESSON 22, PAGES 199–200

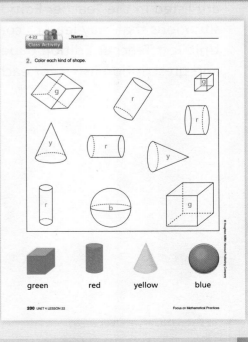

Getting Ready to Teach Unit 4

Learning Path in the Common Core Standards

In this unit, children continue the study of the teen numbers and their structure as ten ones and more ones. The focus on working with and learning the partners of numbers from 2–10 helps children prepare to write and use equations to represent partner situations. They work within the context of a grocery store scene to make up and solve story problems and to sort and compare objects. In geometry, they learn to use attributes to identify three-dimensional shapes.

Help Students Avoid Common Errors

Math Expressions gives students opportunities to analyze and correct errors, explaining why the reasoning was flawed.

In this unit, we use Puzzled Penguin to show typical errors that children make. They enjoy teaching Puzzled Penguin the correct way, telling why this way is correct, and explaining why the error is wrong. The common errors are presented as letters from Puzzled Penguin to the children:

▸ **Lesson 1:** counting 14 instead of 15 cherries

▸ **Lesson 8:** incorrectly identifies partners for 10, writing $10 = 6 + 5$ and $10 = 3 + 6$

▸ **Lesson 17:** after subtracting, finds 3 as the answer for $4 + 1$ instead of finding $4 + 1 = 5$

▸ **Lesson 19:** incorrectly writing an equation for the partners of 6 as $6 = 4 - 2$ instead of $6 = 4 + 2$

In addition to Puzzled Penguin, other suggestions are listed in the Teacher Edition to help you watch for situations that may lead to common errors. As a part of the Unit Test Teacher Edition pages, you will find a common error and prescription listed for each test item.

> ### Math Expressions
> ### VOCABULARY
>
> As you teach this unit, emphasize understanding of these terms.
>
> - addition
> - subtraction
> - partner
> - equation
> - match
>
> *See the Teacher Glossary.*

Solve Story Problems

Lessons

1 **4** **6** **10** **15**

Story Problems Children make up addition and subtraction story problems about buying and selling fruits and vegetables in a grocery store. These story problems should involve totals from 6–10. In Lesson 15, children make up stories for a context of their choice.

Represent the Situation Beginning in Lesson 6, children make simple math drawings to show an addition or subtraction situation and write the expression (or equation) represented by the drawing. As noted in the lessons, emphasize that drawings should be of simple objects that are easy to draw, such as circles, lines, or boxes.

As you record work with addition and subtraction situations, be sure that you write the equation (for example, $6 + 2 = 8$ or $7 - 3 = 4$), but do not expect that many children will be able to do this. During the research phase of this program, it was observed that writing a full equation is difficult for most kindergarteners when they begin using addition or subtraction to solve a problem, something that you have also probably observed. However, most children will be able to write the expression that describes the drawing and/or situation (for example, $6 + 2$ or $7 - 3$).

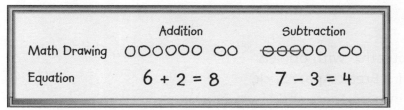

Support Subtraction Understanding Call attention to the connections between the partners of a number and the known and unknown addends in subtraction. For example, in $7 - 3 = 4$, the partners of 7 are 3 and 4.

Model subtraction in your drawings by drawing a long line through the objects taken away and point out that the line looks like a big subtraction sign. Children may use other methods that make sense to them, such as drawing a shorter line or an X through each object. Making a point of drawing the line through the first objects in the drawing prepares children for subtracting by counting on in Grade 1.

---

from **THE PROGRESSIONS FOR THE COMMON CORE STATE STANDARDS ON OPERATIONS AND ALGEBRAIC THINKING**

Kindergarten Students learn and use mathematical and non-mathematical language, especially when they make up problems and explain their representation and solution. The teacher can write expressions (e.g., $3 - 1$) to represent operations, as well as writing equations that represent the whole situation before the solution (e.g., $3 - 1 = \square$) or after (e.g., $3 - 1 = 2$). Expressions like $3 - 1$ or $2 + 1$ show the operation, and it is helpful for students to have experience just with the expression so they can conceptually chunk this part of an equation.

Partners of 10

Lessons
2   **4**   **8**   **11**   **13**

With a Break-Apart Stick Finding partners of 10 prepares children for the Make a Ten subtraction strategy they will learn in Grade 1. Children use the Break-Apart Stick to find partners of 10. In a fun context of sleeping and waking bugs, children use the stick to break apart a 10 they have made with Square-Inch Tiles, either in 1 row of 10 or in 2 rows of 5. This activity helps children solidify subitizing skills. You record results on the board. Notice that the equation form you will use emphasizes that a number is broken apart into partners.

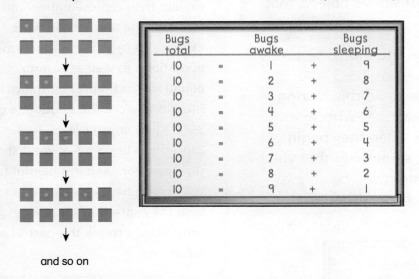

Bugs total		Bugs awake		Bugs sleeping
10	=	1	+	9
10	=	2	+	8
10	=	3	+	7
10	=	4	+	6
10	=	5	+	5
10	=	6	+	4
10	=	7	+	3
10	=	8	+	2
10	=	9	+	1

and so on

With a Line Children move from using the manipulative with objects to finding partners of pictured objects. Instead of a Break-Apart Stick, they draw a line to separate a row of 10 objects into partners and then complete a partner equation for the partners they made.

Draw a line to show the **partners**. Write the partners.

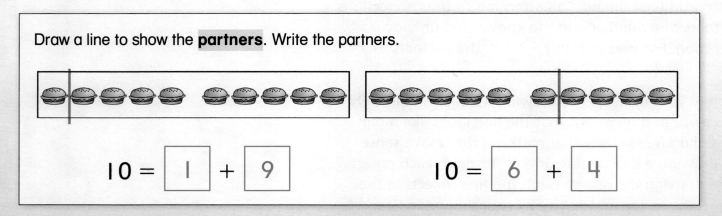

$$10 = \boxed{1} + \boxed{9} \qquad\qquad 10 = \boxed{6} + \boxed{4}$$

Teen Numbers as 10 Ones and Extra Ones

Lessons

Model Ten Ones and Extra Ones The models for this unit's activities with teen numbers are 10-sticks and centimeter cubes. Children model the teen numbers using the 10-stick to represent the 10 ones part of the teen number and the cubes to represent the extra ones. As they model numbers on the 1–20 Board, they see how the numbers change as another one is added. This model helps children build the concept that the 1 in a teen number is not one, but is 10 ones. This fundamental concept gives the children a strong foundation on which they can build their place value concepts in later grades.

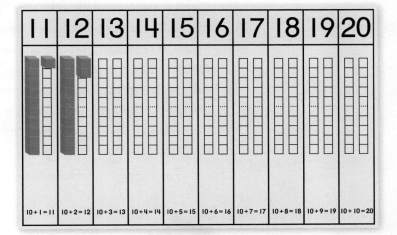

Teen Equation Cards Children also use the 1–20 Board with the Teen Equation Cards. They match the cards to the columns on the board. The two sets of cards reinforce visually the relationship between the partners of a number and the addends that make that number as a total. So, for example, the children begin to see that $11 = 10 + 1$ and $10 + 1 = 11$.

$11 = 10 + 1$ Set A

$10 + 1 = 11$ Set B

from **THE PROGRESSIONS FOR THE COMMON CORE STATE STANDARDS ON OPERATIONS AND ALGEBRAIC THINKING**

Work with numbers from 11 to 19 to gain foundations for place value Children use objects, math drawings, and equations to describe, explore, and explain how the "teen numbers," the counting numbers from 11 through 19, are ten ones and some more ones. Children can count out a given teen number of objects, e.g., 12, and group the objects to see the ten ones and the two ones. It is also helpful to structure the ten ones into patterns that can be seen as ten objects, such as two fives.

The idea that the total can be on either the right or the left side of an equation supports a concept of equality that is important for children's understanding of algebra.

Teen Number Book As a summarizing activity for the work with teen numbers, children will draw models for the teen numbers on separate pages in the Teen Number Book. After children complete pages for all the teen numbers, they will make covers for the books and assemble them. You can then staple the pages together for each child. Think of ways to use the Teen Number Book in activities for a few days so children know that their work produced something useful. Then have children take the books home to share with their families.

> *from* **THE PROGRESSIONS FOR THE COMMON CORE STATE STANDARDS ON OPERATIONS AND ALGEBRAIC THINKING**
>
> **Work with numbers from 11 to 19 to gain foundations for place value** The numerals 11, 12, 13, ..., 19 need special attention for children to understand them. The first nine numerals 1, 2, 3, ..., 9 and 0 are essentially arbitrary marks. These same marks are used again to represent larger numbers. Children need to learn the differences in the ways these marks are used. For example, initially, a numeral such as 16 looks like "one, six," not "1 ten and 6 ones ."

Partners of Numbers 2–10 and Equations

Lessons

2 – 7 8

11 – 13 15 – 19

Knowing partners of numbers through 5 helps children learn to add and subtract within 5. Working with partners of teen numbers and numbers through 10 helps children build subitizing skills and begin to represent addition and subtraction situations with expressions and equations. In this unit, children continue activities from earlier units and build on what they know to carry out new activities.

Math Mountains A new model for addition and subtraction situations is introduced in Lesson 8. The Math Mountain is a powerful visual representation that relates addition and subtraction and will be used in later grades as well as in kindergarten.

For kindergarten children, the model begins with an imaginative context, Tiny Tumblers who live on Math Mountains. The number of Tiny Tumblers who live on a Math Mountain is the same as the number at the top of the Math Mountain. The numbers of Tiny Tumblers who play on the two sides of a Math Mountain must add to the number at the top of the mountain, but different numbers of tumblers may be on the sides.

Children will draw the Tiny Tumblers as circles on the sides of Math Mountains on their Student Activity Book pages. The Tiny Tumblers on each side of a Math Mountain represent the partners of the number at the top of the Math Mountain.

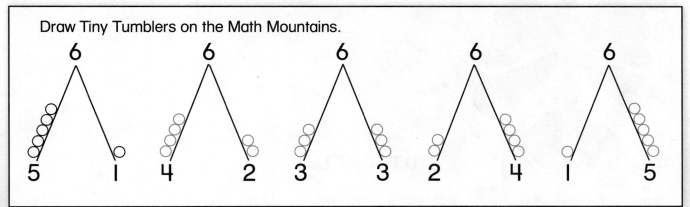

Draw Tiny Tumblers on the Math Mountains.

Equations Children build algebraic concepts as they work with partners, both of numbers 2–10 and teen numbers. They complete equations for break-apart activities, first by writing the partners in answer boxes, next by writing the total in an answer box, and finally by writing a full equation for a partner situation.

---

from **THE PROGRESSIONS FOR THE COMMON CORE STATE STANDARDS ON OPERATIONS AND ALGEBRAIC THINKING**

Kindergarten Put Together/Take Apart situations with Both Addends Unknown play an important role in Kindergarten because they allow students to explore various compositions that make each number. … Students can find patterns in all of the decompositions of a given number and eventually summarize these patterns for several numbers.

Sorting, Comparing, and Ordering

Lessons **1** **6** **9** **12** **13**

Sorting and Comparing Objects Children sort the fruits and vegetables from the Grocery Store scenario by attributes. They first compare by counting two groups of objects to determine which group is greater or less. They also learn to compare amounts by drawing lines to match objects. They then record the results of the matching with a G for "greater than" or an L for "less than."

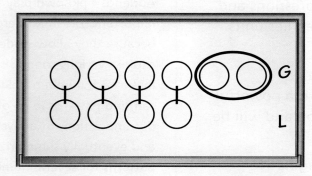

Dot-to-Dot Picture Finding numbers in order to complete a dot-to-dot picture can be an enjoyable way for children to demonstrate their proficiency with the count sequence and for you to informally assess this skill. You may want to write the name of the object on the board when most children have finished so that children who can print may label their pictures.

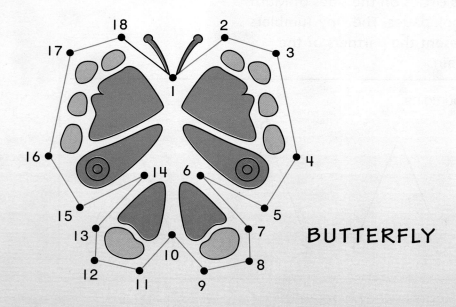

BUTTERFLY

> *from* **THE PROGRESSIONS FOR THE COMMON CORE STATE STANDARDS ON COUNTING AND CARDINALITY**
>
> **From comparison by matching to comparison by numbers to comparison involving adding and subtracting** The standards about comparing numbers focus on students identifying which of two groups has more than (or fewer than, or the same amount as) the other. Students first learn to match the objects in the two groups to see if there are any extra and then to count the objects in each group and use their knowledge of the count sequence to decide which number is greater than the other (the number farther along in the count sequence).

Attributes of Three-Dimensional Shapes

Lessons 9 14 21 22

Among the Geometry skills in the Kindergarten Common Core State Standards are identifying and describing shapes, correctly naming shapes, and describing relative positions of objects. The lessons in this unit focus on these skills as they relate to three-dimensional objects, including cubes, cylinders, and cones.

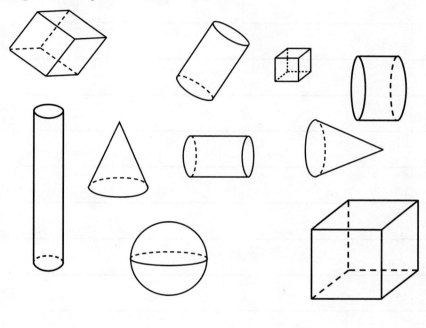

Path to Fluency

Lessons 3 12 15 17

The Common Core State Standards require that kindergarten children fluently add and subtract within 5. One way to acquire this fluency is with persistent practice. The *Path to Fluency* exercise sets on Student Activity Book pages in these lessons provide practice with addition and subtraction within 5 to help children achieve this goal.

$$3 - 2 = \boxed{1} \quad 5 - 5 = \boxed{0} \quad 2 - 2 = \boxed{0}$$

$$4 - 1 = \boxed{3} \quad 4 - 3 = \boxed{1} \quad 3 - 1 = \boxed{2}$$

from **THE PROGRESSIONS FOR THE COMMON CORE STATE STANDARDS ON OPERATIONS AND ALGEBRAIC THINKING**

Working within 10 Later in the year, students solve addition and subtraction equations for numbers within 5, for example, $2 + 1 = \square$ or $3 - 1 = \square$, while still connecting these equations to situations verbally or with drawings. Experience with decompositions of numbers and with Add To and Take From situations enables students to begin to fluently add and subtract within 5.

NOTES:

Numbers 1–10 and Math Stories: Grocery Store Scenario

LESSON FOCUS
- Experience adding and subtracting situations in the real world.
- Define ways to sort objects.

VOCABULARY
story problem

COMMON CORE

Mathematical Practice
CC.K–12.MP.2, CC.K–12.MP.3, CC.K–12.MP.6, CC.K–12.MP.7
Mathematical Content
CC.K.CC.4a, CC.K.CC.4b, CC.K.OA.1, CC.K.MD.3, CC.K.G.1

The Day at a Glance

USE MATH TALK TODAY!

Teaching the Lesson

MATH BACKGROUND for this lesson is included on pp. 329GG and 329LL.

ACTIVITY FOCUS

Activity 1 Create math story problems in a grocery store setting.

Activity 2 Discuss attributes of sorting and classifying as fruits and vegetables are colored for buying and selling.

Activity 3 Define ways to sort objects and count the objects in each group.

MATERIALS

- Student Activity Book pp. 149–156 (includes Family Letter and Fruit and Vegetables) • Crayons or markers • Scissors

- *i*Tools: Counters • Whiteboard

Differentiated Instruction

MATERIALS

- Activity Cards 4-1 • Grocery ads • Glue • Construction paper • Scissors • Math Journals

- Soar to Success Math Intervention • MegaMath • Destination Math®

- **RtI** Tier 1 • Tier 2 • Tier 3

Home and School Connection

MATERIALS

- Family Letter (Student Activity Book pp. 149–150)

QUICK PRACTICE 5 MINUTES

Repeated Quick Practice Use these Quick Practices from previous lessons.

Practice +1 Orally Tell several +1 addition problems with totals through 10: 4 + 1, 6 + 1, 3 + 1, and so on. Children solve these using fingers and discuss if they see any pattern in how they find the total. (See Unit 3, Lesson 17.)

Fast Fingers for 10–19 Two **Student Leaders** show Giant Number Cards for 10 and 1. Then they show 11 by putting the 1 on top of the 0 in the 10. Children say: "10 and 1 is 11." They flash 10 and 1 fingers. At the same time, a third Student Leader points to the corresponding teen drawing in the Teen Display. Continue with numbers 12–19. (See Unit 3, Lesson 16.)

DAILY ROUTINES
Counting Tens and Ones
(See pp. xxxi–xxxii.)

DIGITAL RESOURCES
Use these digital resources along with your eSAB and eTE to support your students' learning experiences.

Professional Development

Whiteboard Lesson

*i*Tools

Soar to Success Math Intervention

MegaMath

Destination Math®

COMMON CORE

Mathematical Practice
CC.K–12.MP.2

Mathematical Content
CC.K.CC.4a, CC.K.CC.4b,
CC.K.OA.1

15 MINUTES

FOCUS Create math story problems in a grocery store setting.

MATERIALS Student Activity Book page 151

 Whiteboard Lesson

Teaching Note

Math Background The mathematical goal of the grocery store enactments is for children to experience adding and subtracting situations in the real world. You will be creating a children's math grocery store in your classroom. This grocery store will link to children's lives, stimulate children's imaginations, help children learn mathematical operations and language, and provide practice in sorting, counting, and categorizing fruits and vegetables.

 MATH TALK in ACTION **Let's make up a grocery store story problem.**

Amy: I bought 4 apples.

John: I bought 1 banana.

Marta: How many pieces of fruit did John and Amy buy?

What are other questions to ask using this same story?

Pam: How many more pieces of fruit did Amy buy than John?

Pablo: How many fewer pieces of fruit did John buy than Amy?

Great. Work with a partner to make up different stories and solve them.

ACTIVITY 1 Social Studies Connection

Buy Things at the Grocery Store

▶ **Tell Grocery Store Story Problems** WHOLE CLASS MATH TALK

MP.2 Reason Quantitatively Have children look at Student Activity Book page 151 and discuss their experiences buying things at a grocery store. In this unit, the class will use the grocery store as a context for addition and subtraction story problems. As children look at the grocery store scene on Student Activity Book page 151, have them find the objects listed below, count them, and then color them.

- 10 potatoes
- 9 apples
- 8 bagels
- 7 carrots
- 6 loaves of bread

- 5 melons
- 4 bananas, 4 wheels on the cart
- 3 boxes of cereal, 3 signs
- 2 heads of lettuce
- 1 child, 1 shopping cart, 1 parent

Ask volunteers to make up some grocery store story problems. For example, they might tell about buying two kinds of fruit and finding how many pieces of fruit they bought in all.

Student Activity Book page 151

Color Fruits and Vegetables to Buy and Sell

▶ Prepare Fruits and Vegetables for Sorting and Classifying WHOLE CLASS

Ask for Ideas Have children look at the Fruit and Vegetables pages (Student Activity Book pages 153 and 155) and discuss the fruits and vegetables that are pictured.

• What is this fruit called? What color is it?

• Have you ever eaten it? How does it taste?

MP.2 Reason Abstractly Ask questions to help children discuss attributes that they will use later on when sorting and classifying.

• How are the carrots and oranges alike?

• How are the apples different than the bananas?

• Which fruits and vegetables will you color orange?

• Which fruits and vegetables will you color green? (Children may color apples green.)

• Count the fruits colored red. How many are in that group?

• Count the vegetables colored green. How many are in that group?

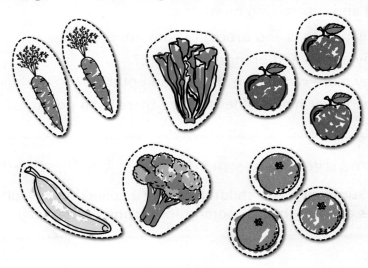

Fruits and Vegetables
(from Student Activity Book pages 153–156)

Then have children color and cut out the fruits and vegetables needed for the grocery store. Since you will only need 10 of each kind of fruit and vegetable, organize children in whatever way makes sense to color and cut out what you need. Throughout the unit, you may want to have children color and cut out additional fruits and vegetables to make other displays.

COMMON CORE

Mathematical Practice
CC.K–12.MP.2
Mathematical Content
CC.K.CC.4a, CC.K.CC.4b,
CC.K.MD.3

15 MINUTES

FOCUS Discuss attributes of sorting and classifying as fruits and vegetables are colored for buying and selling.

MATERIALS Fruit and Vegetables (Student Activity Book pages 153–156), crayons or markers, scissors

 Whiteboard Lesson

English Language Learners

Write *fruits* and *vegetables*. Say: **Fruits and vegetables are plants that we eat. Fruits are sweet and grow on trees or bushes. Vegetables are the roots, stems, or leaves of a plant. Draw a banana under** *fruits* **and a carrot under** *vegetables*.

BEGINNING

Say: **Raise your hand when I point to a** *fruit*. **Say with me:** *fruit*. **Now raise your hand when I point to a** *vegetable*. **Say with me:** *vegetable*.

INTERMEDIATE

Ask: **Is an orange a** *fruit* **or a** *vegetable*? fruit Ask: **Is a potato a** *fruit* **or a** *vegetable*? vegetable

ADVANCED

Say: **Name some fruits that you like.** Then have them name vegetables they like.

COMMON CORE

Mathematical Practice
CC.K–12.MP.3, CC.K–12.MP.6,
CC.K–12.MP.7

Mathematical Content
CC.K.MD.3, CC.K.G.1

20 MINUTES

FOCUS Define ways to sort objects and count the objects in each group.

MATERIALS Fruits and vegetables from the grocery store display

 *i*Tools: Counters

Whiteboard Lesson

Digital Resource

***i*Tools** Choose 'Counters' on the Menu. Use Activity 7 'Explore' with the tab for 'Activities'. Children can use the explore option to sort with counters.

ACTIVITY 3

Define Ways to Sort

▶ Attributes: Sorting and Counting Fruit WHOLE CLASS

MP.7 Look for Structure Identify Relationships Place the collection of fruits and vegetables from the grocery store display randomly in a space where all children can see and touch them. Have children tell how the objects are the same and how they are different. Tell children that sorting is looking for a way that some objects are the same and then grouping them together. Suggest a way that the class can sort the objects in the collection, for example, by color.

- Let's find all the objects that are green and put them together. Then we can say that these are the green objects and the others are not green.

Then put all the objects back in one group, and ask a volunteer to tell another way that the objects can be sorted. Have the class sort the objects again. Continue the activity until the objects have been sorted several ways. Point out that a group of objects can usually be sorted in different ways.

Have children count the number of objects in each group. Ask questions about the sorting such as, "How many vegetables are orange? How many are not? How many pieces of fruit are yellow?"

Ask adding and subtracting questions.

- How many potatoes and broccoli heads are there?
- How many apples and oranges are there?
- How many more carrots are there than potatoes?
- How many fewer heads of lettuce are there than potatoes?

 Formative Assessment: Check Understanding

Student Summary Ask children to sort a collection of fruits or vegetables and tell their reasoning for sorting in that way.

▶ What's the Error? | INDIVIDUALS |

MP.3, MP.6 Construct Viable Arguments/Critique the Reasoning of Others Direct children's attention to Student Activity Book page 152. Tell children that Puzzled Penguin needs help counting.

• Puzzled Penguin counted the cherries and says there are 14 cherries. Is Puzzled Penguin correct? No. There are 15 cherries.

• What did Puzzled Penguin do wrong? Responses should include that Puzzled Penguin counted wrong.

Encourage children to discuss how Puzzled Penguin could have counted wrong. Let several children respond to the question. Their responses should show that Puzzled Penguin may have omitted counting one of the cherries or said a counting number without pointing to one of the cherries.

• How can you help Puzzled Penguin count?

Children may discover that placing a mark on each cherry as they count helps them to see which cherry has been counted. Children may choose to count ten cherries and circle them, and then count on from ten. Challenge children to come up with other ways to count with precision, such as putting a counter on each cherry and then counting the counters.

Student Activity Book page 152

Class Management

Looking Ahead Sometime before Unit 4, Lesson 4, arrange the fruits and vegetables to make a grocery store in the room. The fruits and vegetables need to be accessible to children for buying and selling and for combining into fruit or vegetable salads when enacting story problems. You may want to put the fruits and vegetables in pocket charts. Alternatively, you may want to use a sticky board if you have one.

In addition, for Unit 4, Lesson 4, you will need to make a grocery store fruit display. There should be a different number (6–10) of each kind of fruit. Make sure you have 8 oranges.

For Unit 4, Lesson 10, you will need to make a grocery store vegetable display. Use a different number (6–10) of each kind of vegetable.

Extra copying masters for fruits and vegetables are available in TRB pages M47–M48.

▲ On Level  Tier 1

for students having success

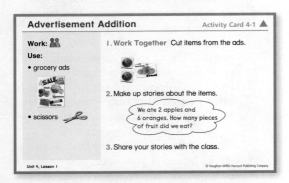

Activity Notes Guide children in finding grocery ads and making up stories. Invite them to share their stories.

 Math Writing Prompt

Write Equations Have children write one addition and one subtraction equation using the numbers 3 and 1.

 MegaMath

Software Support
Numberopolis: Carnival Stories, Level D

■ Challenge

for students seeking a challenge

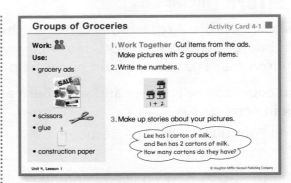

Activity Notes Explain to children that they need to create stories using two different items. Have them share their stories with the class.

 Math Writing Prompt

Write Addition Equations Have children write an addition equation in different ways using the partners 3 and 2.

 Destination Math®

Software Support
Course I: Module 2: Unit 2:
Session 1: Differences Within 10

Family Letter Remind children to take home the Family Letter on Student Activity Book page 149. This letter explains how the concept of story problems is developed in *Math Expressions*. It gives parents and guardians a better understanding of the learning that goes on in math class and creates a bridge between school and home. A Spanish translation of this letter is on the following page in the Student Activity Book.

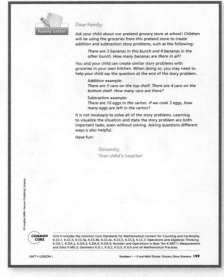

Student Activity Book page 149

Find Partners of 10

LESSON FOCUS
• Identify partners of 6, 7, and 10.

VOCABULARY
partners

COMMON CORE

Mathematical Practice
CC.K–12.MP.1, CC.K–12.MP.2, CC.K–12.MP.4, CC.K–12.MP.7
Mathematical Content
CC.K.OA.1, CC.K.OA.2, CC.K.OA.3, CC.K.OA.4

The Day at a Glance

Teaching the Lesson

MATH BACKGROUND for this lesson is included on pp. 329HH and 329KK.

ACTIVITY FOCUS

Activity 1 Practice identifying partners of 6 and 7 by playing games.

Activity 2 Show and record partners of 10.

MATERIALS

Student Activity Book pp. 157–158 • Counting Mats • Number Tiles 1–7 • +/– Tiles • Centimeter cubes • Break-Apart Sticks • Chart paper • Crayons or markers (optional)

iTools: Counters • Whiteboard

Differentiated Instruction

MATERIALS

Activity Cards 4-2 • Game Cards 1–9 • Math Journals

Soar to Success Math Intervention • MegaMath • Destination Math®

RtI Tier 1 • Tier 2 • Tier 3

Homework

MATERIALS

Homework and Remembering pp. 67–68

QUICK PRACTICE ⏱ **5 MINUTES**

Goal See patterns in 60–100; count by ones from 60–100.

Materials 120 Poster, pointer

Patterns in 60 Through 100 Point out numbers 60 through 100 on the 120 Poster. Discuss patterns children see in those columns.

Count by Ones from 60 Through 100 Have a **Student Leader** point to each number from 60 to 100 on the 120 Poster while children say each number. Children start by flashing ten fingers 6 times saying, "61, 62, 63, … 98, 99, 100." They flash ten fingers again as they come to 70, 80, 90, and 100.

DAILY ROUTINES
Counting Tens and Ones
(See pp. xxxi–xxxii.)

DIGITAL RESOURCES

Use these digital resources along with your eSAB and eTE to support your students' learning experiences.

 Professional Development

 Whiteboard Lesson

 iTools

 Soar to Success Math Intervention

 MegaMath

 Destination Math®

Mathematical Practice
CC.K–12.MP.1, CC.K–12.MP.2,
CC.K–12.MP.7

Mathematical Content
CC.K.OA.1, CC.K.OA.2

15 MINUTES

FOCUS Practice identifying partners of 6 and 7 by playing games.

MATERIALS Counting Mats (1 per pair), Number Tiles 1–7 (1 set per pair), +/– Tiles (1 per pair), centimeter cubes (14 per pair), Break-Apart Sticks (1 per pair)

 Whiteboard Lesson

Differentiated Instruction

Extra Help Some children may have trouble wiggling their fingers. They can just bend their fingers instead.

ACTIVITY 1

Play *The Unknown Partner Game* for 6 and 7

▶ Do Finger Wiggle Partner Practice WHOLE CLASS

Review partners by doing finger wiggles. For each set of partners, do finger wiggles at least four times. Even though initially some combinations (for example, 6 as 3 and 3) may be physically difficult, children enjoy this activity, and they get better at it.

Ask a **Student Leader** to write an expression (such as 2 + 3) on the board for each set of partners named. Begin with the partners of 5.

• Hold up 5 fingers.
• What are some partners of 5? Possible answer: 2 and 3
• Wiggle 2 fingers. Now wiggle the other 3 fingers.
• Let's really feel these partners.
• Wiggle 2; now wiggle 3. Oh, we're getting better.
• Wiggle 2 again; now wiggle 3. It's getting easier!
• Again, wiggle 2; then wiggle 3.

MP.7 Look for Structure Continue with different sets of partners for 5, including 5 + 0. You may want to switch the partners as you work through these sets. Then do the partners for 6 and 7.

▶ Play *The Unknown Partner Game* for 6 and 7 PAIRS MATH TALK

MP.2 Reason Abstractly Use the **Student Pairs** structure for this Activity.

The *Unknown Partner Game* was introduced in Unit 3, Lesson 16, and is repeated here. Have pairs of children sit beside each other facing the workspace on which they have placed a Counting Mat, centimeter cubes, and +/– Tiles. For each turn, children take out only the number of centimeter cubes needed.

• Look at your Counting Mat. Pull down Number Tile 7.
• Now show 7 centimeter cubes below the 7.

Have one child in the Student Pair take a Break-Apart Stick while the other child covers his or her eyes, turning away so as not to peek. The first child places the Break-Apart Stick to make a set of partners for 7 (for example, 5 and 2). That child then removes and hides the centimeter cubes for one partner, leaving the Break-Apart Stick and the other centimeter cubes in place.

MP.1 Persevere in Solving Problems The second child uncovers his or her eyes and determines the unknown partner. Children can count the centimeter cubes they see and count on to 7. They may also visualize 7 centimeter cubes and see how many are missing. As a last resort, they can place 7 centimeter cubes below the ones that are there and see how many are missing. The second child puts the Number Tiles and the +/− Tile in place as shown below and names the partners.

The first child replaces the centimeter cubes that were taken to confirm the unknown partner. The second child says:

• 5 and 2 are partners of 7.

Children then reverse roles. They play the game using various partners for 6 and 7.

English Language Learners

Show 7 centimeter cubes.

BEGINNING

Say: **This is 7 cubes.** Remove 1 cube. Say: **Now, 1 cube is gone.** Have children repeat.

INTERMEDIATE

Ask: **How many cubes is this?** 7 cubes Remove 1 cube. Ask: **How many cubes are gone?** 1 cube

ADVANCED

Model the game with a volunteer. Have children repeat with 6 cubes.

Class Management

Looking Ahead In the next lesson, children will use the back of the 1–20 Board. The back of the 1–20 Board, which has numbers 11 through 20, can be found on TRB M38–M39. These pages will need to be taped together (or photocopied side by side on 11" × 17" paper) so that numbers 11 through 20 are in order across the top.

If you have access to the *Math Expressions* materials kits, the 1–20 Boards are included, so you will not have to prepare these materials.

Children will also need the Teen Equation Cards. They will use these cards on the 1–20 Board. The Teen Equation Cards are on Student Activity Book page 159 and on TRB M49. You may want to set aside time before you begin the lesson for children to cut out their cards, or it may be easier to use a paper cutter or ask an aide or parents to help.

COMMON CORE

Mathematical Practice
CC.K–12.MP.4, CC.K–12.MP.7
Mathematical Content
CC.K.OA.3, CC.K.OA.4

20 MINUTES

FOCUS Show and record partners of 10.

MATERIALS Square-Inch Tiles (10 per child), Break-Apart sticks (1 per child), chart paper, Student Activity Book page 157, crayons or markers (optional)

 *i*Tools: Counters

Whiteboard Lesson

Digital Resource

*i*Tools Choose 'Counters' on the Menu. Use Activity 3 'Add' with the tab for 'Activities'. Children can use counters to help them add 2 numbers. Then they enter the total.

Class Management

Record the partners of 10 on a sheet of chart paper, rather than on the board, so that you can continue to display the chart paper in your classroom once the activity is completed. This will help to reinforce the concepts. It is important for children to discuss how they see the changes in numbers in the partners of 10.

Bugs total		Bugs sleeping		Bugs awake
10	=	9	+	1
10	=	8	+	2
10	=	7	+	3
10	=	6	+	4
10	=	5	+	5
10	=	4	+	6
10	=	3	+	7
10	=	2	+	8
10	=	1	+	9

ACTIVITY 2

Discover Partners of 10 in a Row

▶ Show the "Bug Partners" of 10 [WHOLE CLASS]

Ask children to count out 10 Square-Inch Tiles of the same color. Tell them that they will pretend that the dot side of the tile is a little bug.

- Sometimes the bugs are awake and turned up so that we can see them. Sometimes they are sleeping under the tile and turned over, so we can't see them. But there are always 10 bugs in total.

MP.4 Model with Mathematics Direct children to arrange their Square-Inch Tiles in a horizontal row of 10.

- Now make your bugs go to sleep by placing all of them dot side down, so you can't see them. How many are sleeping? all 10 of them

Have children wake one bug.

- One bug wants to get up and play. Let's turn one over. How many bugs are sleeping now? 9
- How many bugs are awake? 1
- How many bugs in total? 10
- Put your Break-Apart Stick between the sleeping bugs and the bug that is awake, so you can see them clearly.

Record this set of partners for 10 on chart paper.
Bugs total = Bugs sleeping + Bugs awake
        10   =   9   +   1

MP.7 Look for Structure Continue by having children wake up (turn over) another bug.

- Now where does the Break-Apart Stick go? Move it one tile to the left.

Record 10 = 8 + 2 on the partner chart as follows:

Bugs total = Bugs sleeping + Bugs awake
     10   =   9   +   1
     10   =   8   +   2

Continue by having children wake one more bug at a time (moving the stick from right to left.) Record all sets of partners of 10. Invite children to discuss the number sequence for the partners.

▶ **Record Partners of 10** [WHOLE CLASS]

Introduce Student Activity Book page 157.

- Each row has 10 bugs. The bugs with dots on their wings are awake. The bugs without dots are asleep.

Instruct children to draw a Break-Apart Stick (a line) to separate the bugs that are awake from the bugs that are asleep. Then have children write how many there are of each (the partners of 10). If children need more support, have them first do the activity using their Square-Inch Tiles.

Teaching Note

Watch For! A short Break-Apart Stick drawn on Student Activity Book page 157 may look like a 1 to some children. You may want to instruct children to draw long Break-Apart Sticks that extend above and below the rectangle. You might also suggest they draw the Break-Apart Sticks with a crayon or marker.

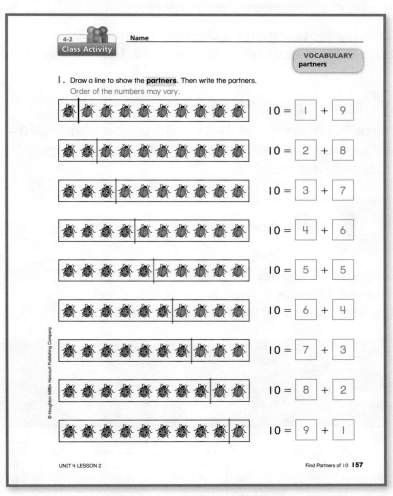

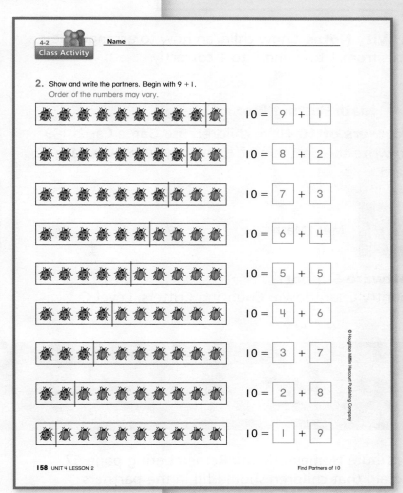

Student Activity Book pages 157–158

MP.7 Look for Structure On Student Activity Book page 158, have children write the 10-partners again, this time beginning with 9 + 1. Have children discuss the partners they see within each list and across the lists.

> ## ✓ Formative Assessment: Check Understanding
>
> **Student Summary** Write the number 7 on the board. Draw 2 squares below. Ask children to suggest ways to show the partners.

▲ On Level  Tier 1
for students having success

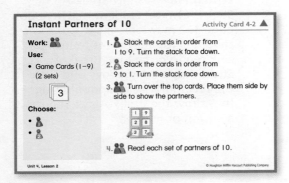

Activity Notes Show children how to arrange their cards from 1 to 9 and 9 to 1 correctly.

 Math Writing Prompt

Partners of 10 Have children use Game Cards 1–9 to write the partners of 10 as they turn over each card.

 MegaMath

Software Support
Country Countdown: Counting Critters, Level C

■ Challenge
for students seeking a challenge

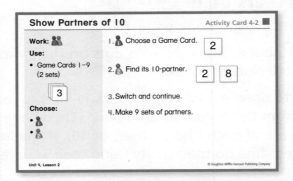

Activity Notes Remind children to choose one partner from each set of Game Cards 1–9.

 Math Writing Prompt

Write Partners of 10 Have children use Game Cards 1–9 to choose a card, write the number, and then write the partner of 10.

 Destination Math®

Software Support
Course I: Module 1: Unit 2: Session 3: Creating Representations of the Numbers from 5 to 10

Distribute Homework and Remembering page 67. Explain that children should fill in the partners shown by the pictures. On the back, have children draw a picture for the equation 7 = 6 + 1.

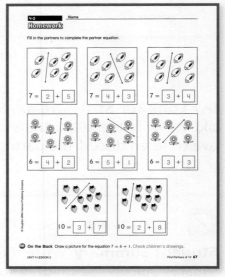

Homework and Remembering page 67

Teen Numbers and Equations

LESSON FOCUS
- Show teen numbers as a group of ten ones and extra ones and as 10 + a 1-digit number.

VOCABULARY
equal sign (=)
addition sign (+)
equation

COMMON CORE

Mathematical Practice
CC.K–12.MP.1, CC.K–12.MP.6
Mathematical Content
CC.K.CC.3, CC.K.CC.4a, CC.K.CC.4b, CC.K.CC.4c, CC.K.OA.1, CC.K.OA.5, CC.K.NBT.1

The Day at a Glance

USE MATH TALK TODAY!

Teaching the Lesson

MATH BACKGROUND for this lesson is included on pp. 329II–329JJ, 329KK, and 329MM.

ACTIVITY FOCUS

Activity 1   Make numbers 11–20 using 10-sticks and centimeter cubes.

Activity 2   Model equations by placing Teen Equation Cards on the 1–20 Board.

Activity 3   Practice with teen numbers, equations, and subtraction fluency.

MATERIALS

- Student Activity Book pp. 159–162 (includes Teen Equation Cards)
  - Fluency Check 1 (Assessment Guide) • 1–20 Boards (back)
  - 10-sticks • Centimeter cubes • Scissors
- iTools: Counters • Whiteboard

Differentiated Instruction

MATERIALS

- Activity Cards 4-3 • Teen Equation Cards • 10-sticks
  - Centimeter cubes • 1–20 Boards • MCC 1 • Math Journals
- Soar to Success Math Intervention • MegaMath • Destination Math®
- RtI   Tier 1 • Tier 2 • Tier 3

Homework

MATERIALS

- Homework and Remembering pp. 69–70

QUICK PRACTICE   5 MINUTES

Partners of 6 Display 6 classroom objects. Ask:

- 4 and what partner make 6? Show me with your fingers.

Children show fingers and say:

- 4 and 2 makes 6. 6 has partners 4 and 2.

Use a Break-Apart Stick to show partners 4 and 2 with classroom objects. Have children close their eyes and visualize. Then ask them to show and say the partners again. Repeat with different partners of 6.

Repeated Quick Practice Use these Quick Practices from previous lessons.

Practice +1 Orally Tell several +1 addition problems with totals through 10; 4 + 1, 6 + 1, 3 + 1, and so on. Children solve these using fingers and discuss what they do every time they find the total. (See Unit 3, Lesson 17.)

DAILY ROUTINES
Counting Tens and Ones
(See pp. xxxi–xxxii.)

DIGITAL RESOURCES

Use these digital resources along with your eSAB and eTE to support your students' learning experiences.

Professional Development

Whiteboard Lesson

iTools

Soar to Success Math Intervention

MegaMath

Destination Math®

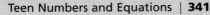

COMMON CORE

Mathematical Practice
CC.K–12.MP.6

Mathematical Content
CC.K.CC.4a, CC.K.CC.4b,
CC.K.CC.4c, CC.K.NBT.1

20 MINUTES

FOCUS Make numbers 11–20 using
10-sticks and centimeter cubes.

MATERIALS 1–20 Boards (back, TRB
M38–M39, 1 per child), 10-sticks (11 per
child), centimeter cubes (45 per child)

 *i*Tools: Counters

Whiteboard Lesson

Digital Resource

*i*Tools Choose 'Counters' on the Menu.
Use Activity 1 'Count' with the tab for
'Activities'. Children can use counters
to count.

Teaching Note

Math Background This activity
develops fine-motor skills, organization,
and an understanding of numbers.

ACTIVITY 1

Make Teen Numbers on the 1–20 Board

▶ **Make Teen Numbers** WHOLE CLASS

MP.6 Attend to Precision Discuss how to make 11 with one 10-stick
and one centimeter cube. Have children put one 10-stick and one
centimeter cube under the 11 on the 1–20 Board.

Discuss how to make 12. Children should put one 10-stick and two
centimeter cubes under the 12.

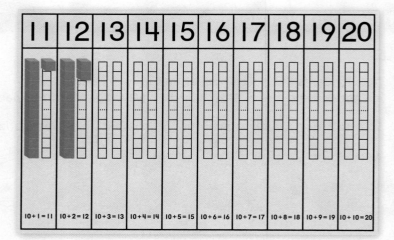

Continue class discussion in this manner as children make the numbers
13–19. Point out that each of the teen numbers is made up of ten ones
and some more ones.

Discuss how to make the number 20. Children should realize that they can use 20 centimeter cubes, or one 10-stick and ten centimeter cubes, or two 10-sticks.

- **Which is the fastest?** two 10-sticks
- **How would the Ten Bug make 20? Why?** with two 10-sticks; Using groups of 10 is easier and faster.

Invite children to discuss the changes in numbers they see when they have placed 10-sticks and centimeter cubes under all of their numbers. There are many changes they can describe.

ACTIVITY 2

Place Teen Equation Cards on the 1–20 Board

▶ Explore Teen Equation Cards   WHOLE CLASS

Distribute and discuss Student Activity Book page 159.

- **What is different about the Cards at the top (Set A) and the Cards at the bottom (Set B)?** In Set A the teen number is first (or on the left). In Set B the teen number is last (or on the right).

Set A	Set B

$$11 = 10 + 1$$

$$10 + 1 = 11$$

Teen Equation Cards
(from Student Activity Book page 159)

MP.6 Attend to Precision Discuss and review the meaning of the equal sign and the addition sign. Then discuss how you have been writing equations.

- For showing partners, we have been writing the total first and then the equal sign. After the equal sign, we have been writing the partners.
- But for addition, we have been writing the partners first with an addition sign in between to show that they are put together (or added to). Then, we have been writing the equal sign and the total on the right.

Activity continued ▶

English Language Learners

Point to the equations on the 1–20 Board. Say: **These are** *equations.* Have children repeat.

BEGINNING

Write and say: **10 + 1 = 11.** Have children repeat the equation.

INTERMEDIATE AND ADVANCED

Have children work in **Student Pairs.** One points to each part of an equation, the other reads it aloud.

COMMON CORE

Mathematical Practice
CC.K–12.MP.6
Mathematical Content
CC.K.OA.1, CC.K.OA.5, CC.K.NBT.1

20 MINUTES

FOCUS Model equations by placing Teen Equation Cards on the 1–20 Board.

MATERIALS 1–20 Boards (back, TRB M38–M39; 1 per child), Teen Equation Cards (Student Activity Book page 159; 1 set per child), scissors (1 per child)

 Whiteboard Lesson

Differentiated Instruction

More advanced learners can manage working with both sets of Teen Equation Cards. Initially, these advanced learners are likely to intermix the sets. Gradually, however, they will notice the difference and separate them. This is a complex task, and children may do it in different ways. That is fine. Sorting the cards differently and arranging both sets will be useful experiences for children.

Teaching Note

Research Understanding that the "answer" does not always go on the right in an equation is central to algebraic understanding. Research indicates that most elementary children only see equations with the answers on the right, making it difficult for them to build a new, more accurate concept of an equation. Kindergarten children can understand equations written in many ways. If you decide to have children use only one set of Teen Equation Cards, you may want them to use the top set, Set A, because children will see such equations less often.

Class Management

Looking Ahead Keep the Teen Equation Cards that children cut out in Activity 2. They will be used again in future lessons.

• We can write the equation either way. They are both correct.

Be sure children understand that both ways are correct because in an equation, the numbers or operations on both sides have the same value, are the same amount, or are equal. This can be true no matter which side the numbers or operations are on.

Have children cut out the Teen Equation Cards from Student Activity Book page 159. Then have them place the Cards on their 1–20 Boards, matching each Teen Equation Card to the corresponding teen number on the 1–20 Board. Cards can be placed below the teen numbers, at the top of the 1–20 Board, or at the bottom, covering the existing teen equation.

11	12	13	14	15	16	17	18	19	20
11 = 10 + 1	12 = 10 + 2	13 = 10 + 3	14 = 10 + 4	15 = 10 + 5	16 = 10 + 6	17 = 10 + 7	18 = 10 + 8	19 = 10 + 9	20 = 10 + 10

10 + 1 = 11	10 + 2 = 12	10 + 3 = 13	10 + 4 = 14	10 + 5 = 15	10 + 6 = 16	10 + 7 = 17	10 + 8 = 18	10 + 9 = 19	10 + 10 = 20

▶ Use Finger Freeze Reinforcement [WHOLE CLASS]

MP.6 Attend to Precision Have children model each set of partners using fingers, while saying the equation aloud. Children should say the entire equation, starting with the total, while showing 10 and the other partner with their fingers. Then children should say and show the same equation, this time starting with the partners.

Say and show with fingers:

• 11 equals 10 and 1.
• 12 equals 10 and 2.
• 13 equals 10 and 3…

Say and show with fingers:

• 10 and 1 make 11.
• 10 and 2 make 12.
• 10 and 3 make 13…

Practice with Teen Numbers and Equations

▶ **Teen Numbers and Equations** | WHOLE CLASS |

On Student Activity Book page 161, have children say the partners and then show the partners with fingers, such as 10 and 1 make 11; and 10 and 2 make 12. Then have them write the numbers from 1 to 20 in order.

PATH to FLUENCY **MP.1 Make Sense of Problems** Use a Different Method On Student Activity Book page 162, connect subtraction situations to children's experiences and ask how they might find the answer. Discuss different ways, such as using fingers, drawing, and knowing partners. Have them choose one equation and draw a subtraction picture to represent the equation. Have them write the equation in the picture.

COMMON CORE

Mathematical Practice
CC.K–12.MP.1

Mathematical Content
CC.K.CC.3, CC.K.OA.1, CC.K.OA.5, CC.K.NBT.1

20 MINUTES

FOCUS Practice with teen numbers, equations, and subtraction fluency.

MATERIALS Student Activity Book pages 161–162

Whiteboard Lesson

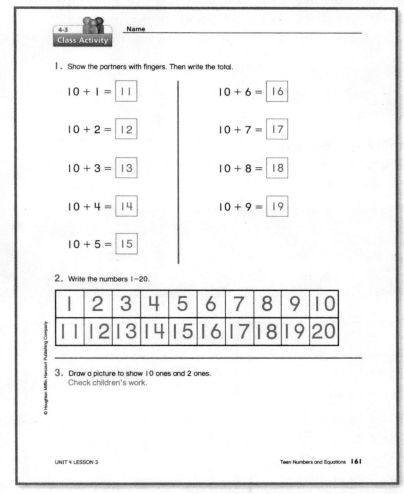

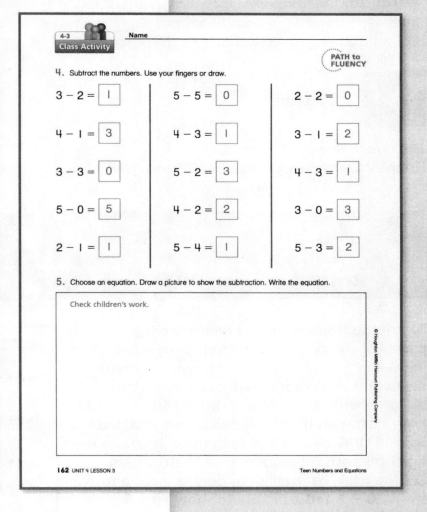

Student Activity Book pages 161–162

✓ Formative Assessment: Check Understanding

Student Summary Write the number 17 on the board. Ask children to suggest ways to show that number. Have them tell an equation for 17.

▲On Level ▲RtI Tier 1

for students having success

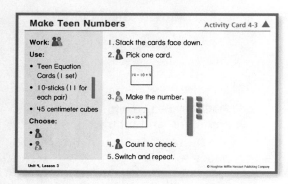

Make Teen Numbers — Activity Card 4-3 ▲

Work: 👥

Use:
- Teen Equation Cards (1 set)
- 10-sticks (11 for each pair)
- 45 centimeter cubes

Choose:
- 👤
- 👤

1. Stack the cards face down.
2. Pick one card.
3. Make the number.
4. Count to check.
5. Switch and repeat.

Unit 4, Lesson 3

Activity Notes Remind children that one 10-stick shows 10 ones.

✏ Math Writing Prompt

Write the Partners Have children write the partners of the Teen Equation Cards using the Commutative Property and then check totals.

 MegaMath

Software Support
Country Countdown: Counting Critters, Level P

■ Challenge

for students seeking a challenge

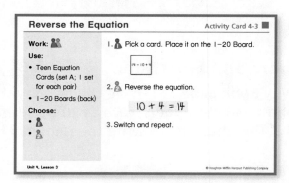

Reverse the Equation — Activity Card 4-3 ■

Work: 👥

Use:
- Teen Equation Cards (set A; 1 set for each pair)
- 1–20 Boards (back)

Choose:
- 👤
- 👤

1. Pick a card. Place it on the 1–20 Board.
2. Reverse the equation.

$$10 + 4 = 14$$

3. Switch and repeat.

Unit 4, Lesson 3

Activity Notes Show children where to correctly place the Teen Equation Card on the 1–20 Board.

✏ Math Writing Prompt

Draw the Partners Have children use Teen Equation Cards (Set A) to reverse the equation and write it. Then have them draw the partners to check.

 Destination Math®

Software Support
Course I: Module 2: Unit 1: Session 3: Sums within 20, with 10 as One Addend

Distribute Homework and Remembering page 69. On this page, children draw a line to show the partners of 10 for strawberries with seeds and strawberries without seeds. Then children write the partners shown. Suggest that they start with the line between the first and second strawberries and then move it one to the right for each subsequent row of strawberries. On the back, have children draw a picture to show 10 + 2 and a picture to show 10 + 5.

✓ Include children's homework pages as part of their portfolios.

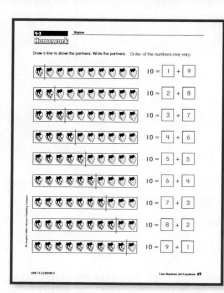

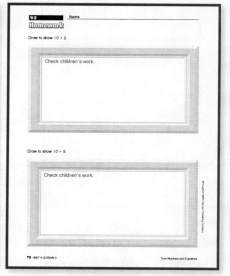

Homework and Remembering pages 69–70

Addition and Subtraction Stories: Grocery Store Scenario

LESSON FOCUS

• Explore and express addition and subtraction story problems in buying and selling experiences.

VOCABULARY

addition
total
subtraction
addition sign (+)
subtraction sign (−)

COMMON CORE

Mathematical Practice
CC.K–12.MP.1, CC.K–12.MP.4, CC.K–12.MP.6, CC.K–12.MP.7
Mathematical Content
CC.K.OA.1, CC.K.OA.2, CC.K.OA.3, CC.K.OA.4

The Day at a Glance

USE
MATH TALK
TODAY!

Teaching the Lesson

MATH BACKGROUND for this lesson is included on pp. 329GG, 329HH, and 329KK.

ACTIVITY FOCUS

Activity 1   Tell and solve grocery store story problems.

Activity 2   Show and record partners of 10.

MATERIALS

Grocery store fruit display • Square-Inch Tiles • Break-Apart Sticks

*i*Tools: Counters • Whiteboard

Differentiated Instruction

MATERIALS

Activity Cards 4-4 • Grocery store fruit display • Number Tiles 1–10 • +/− Tiles • = Tile • Math Journals

Soar to Success Math Intervention • MegaMath • Destination Math®

RtI   Tier 1 • Tier 2 • Tier 3

Homework

MATERIALS

Homework and Remembering pp. 71–72

QUICK PRACTICE   5 MINUTES

Repeated Quick Practice Use these Quick Practices from previous lessons.

Partners of 5 Display 5 classroom objects. Ask, "1 and which partner make 5?" Children show the numbers with their fingers as they say, "1 and 4 make 5. 5 has the partners 1 and 4." Then show the partners using a Break-Apart Stick and the displayed classroom objects. Children close their eyes and visualize. Then they show and say the partners again. Repeat the routine with other partners of 5.

Count by Ones from 60 Through 100 (See Unit 4, Lesson 2.)

DAILY ROUTINES

Counting Tens and Ones (See pp. xxxi–xxxii.)

DIGITAL RESOURCES

Use these digital resources along with your eSAB and eTE to support your students' learning experiences.

Professional Development

Whiteboard Lesson

*i*Tools

Soar to Success Math Intervention

MegaMath

Destination Math®

COMMON CORE

Mathematical Practice
CC.K–12.MP.1, CC.K–12.MP.4,
CC.K–12.MP.6

Mathematical Content
CC.K.OA.1, CC.K.OA.2

20 MINUTES

FOCUS Tell and solve grocery store story problems.

MATERIALS Grocery store fruit display (See the Class Management: Looking Ahead note from Unit 4, Lesson 1.)

 *i*Tools: Counters

Whiteboard Lesson

Digital Resource

*i***Tools** Choose 'Counters' on the Menu. Use Activity 3 'Add' with the tab for 'Activities'. Children can use counters to help them add 2 numbers. Then they enter the total.

*i***Tools** Choose 'Counters' on the Menu. Use Activity 4 'Subtract' with the tab for 'Activities'. Children can use counters to help them subtract. Then they enter the partner.

Teaching Note

Language and Vocabulary Be sure to use a variety of vocabulary when children are buying fruit and when you are discussing the addition equation.

▶ Maria buys 3 oranges and 4 bananas at the grocery store.

▶ Maria has 3 oranges and 4 bananas in a fruit bowl.

▶ Maria has a total of 7 pieces of fruit: 3 oranges and 4 bananas.

▶ Maria puts together 3 oranges and 4 bananas to make a fruit salad.

Have children try to describe adding in many different ways. Children need to learn to express the story problems using different words or phrases and know what they mean.

ACTIVITY 1 🌐 Social Studies Connection

Add and Subtract Fruits

▶ Model Addition by Buying Fruit [WHOLE CLASS]

MP.4 Model with Mathematics Use the **Scenario** structure for this activity.

The emphasis in this unit is on addition and subtraction problems with the totals between 6 and 10. Keep encouraging children to make up problems with these greater numbers. The physical layout of your classroom is important when you do story problems with your class. Everyone needs to be able to see you and the drawings on the board. They also need to be close enough to feel engaged in the activity. Ideally, have children sit on a rug, in rows, directly in front of the board area with a hard surface to write on, and with paper, and pencils. This setup keeps distractions to a minimum.

Use the grocery store display you made from the fruit that children colored during Unit 4, Lesson 1. There should be a different number (6–10) of each kind of fruit. Make sure you have 8 oranges for the subtraction problem on the next page.

Ask for a volunteer to go to the grocery store and buy two kinds of fruit to make a fruit salad. The child will decide how many pieces of each kind of fruit to buy.

• Maria, what two kinds of fruit do you want to buy? I want to buy oranges and bananas.

• How many oranges and how many bananas do you want to buy? 3 oranges and 4 bananas

Have Maria take the fruit from the store while the whole class counts with you, the storekeeper, to check that the correct number of pieces of fruit is being bought. Record Maria's number of pieces of fruit as an equation on the board.

$$3 + 4 = \underline{\hspace{1cm}}$$

▶ Find the Total [WHOLE CLASS]

MP.1 Make Sense of Problems Check Answers Then have the class find the total number of pieces of fruit Maria bought for her fruit salad. Children can use their fingers to solve the problem. Have two children show how they found the answer. Check the answer by having the whole class count all of Maria's fruit together. Show this fruit near the addition equation so that children can see the pieces of fruit, for this example it is 3 oranges and 4 bananas. Write the total, which for this example is 7, in the equation.

▶ Model Subtraction by Buying Fruit [WHOLE CLASS]

MP.4 Model with Mathematics Invite a volunteer to count the number of oranges in the grocery store, 8. Then ask the class to help you use subtraction to show how many oranges are in the store after Maria buys 3 of them for a fruit salad. Elicit from the class that someone buying 3 oranges can be represented by the subtraction expression 8 − 3. Have children solve the subtraction problem and discuss the methods they used. Then discuss how the subtraction problem 8 − 3 is related to partners of 8.

• 3 and what partner make 8? 5; 3 and 5 are partners of 8.

• What happens when you put 3 and 5 together? They make 8.

• What happens when you subtract, or take away, one partner? Sometimes when you subtract, you take away one partner and the other is left.

Repeat the above activity for the bananas. Relate the two partner numbers to the subtraction expression. One partner is the number bought and put into the fruit salad, and the other partner is the number left in the grocery store for other people to buy.

▶ Model the + and − Signs [WHOLE CLASS]   MATH TALK

MP.6 Attend to Precision Repeat these addition and subtraction activities, but this time have children tell you what equations to write. Then have them model the addition and subtraction signs by showing the operation signs with their arms.

The addition sign is shown by having children hold one arm vertically and one arm horizontally. Tell children that for addition, they put together things, so they show it by putting arms together.

The subtraction sign is shown by having children hold one arm horizontally (like the subtraction sign). Children then open and close their hand as if they were grasping things and move their arm to the side to pull away the things they are taking. Altogether, this action links the visual appearance of the minus subtraction with a meaning of subtraction as "taking away."

Activity continued ▶

English Language Learners

Say: **I** *buy* fruit at the market. When I pay for it, I am *buying* it. Yesterday I *bought* oranges.

BEGINNING

Invite children to pretend to buy things. Say: **I** *buy* fruit. **What do you** *buy*? Prompt children to answer with, I buy _____.

INTERMEDIATE

Say: **I** *bought* fruit. **What have you** *bought*? Answer: I *bought* _____. Then repeat with **I am** *buying* _____. **What are you** *buying*?

ADVANCED

Encourage children to repeat after you. **I** *buy* fruit at the market. **When I pay for it, I am** *buying* **it. Yesterday I** *bought* **oranges.** Then omit the italicized word for them to fill in.

Teaching Note

Language and Vocabulary Be sure to use a variety of vocabulary when you are discussing the buying process and the subtraction equation.

▶ The grocery store has 8 oranges. Maria buys 3 oranges. How many oranges does the grocery store have now?

▶ Maria buys 3 oranges at the grocery store. Now the grocery store has 5 oranges. How many oranges did the grocery store have before?

Learning Community— Best Practices

Building Concepts Using partner language when describing subtraction can help children visualize subtraction. It can also help them learn to relate subtraction to addition and to the visualization they are doing with partners on the Counting Mat. Children will learn to visualize the lesser number additions and subtractions, and they will not even need to do them on their fingers.

▶ Tell the Story Problem WHOLE CLASS

Present the following Take From Result Unknown story problem.

• The fruit bowl has 7 bananas. Jeff takes out 3 bananas to peel. How many bananas are in the fruit bowl now?

Ask children how they might solve this problem and what tools, if any, they would use to help them.

▶ Act Out the Story Problem WHOLE CLASS

After discussing the story problem above, guide children in thinking through the details of the problem.

Ask questions such as, "What is the problem asking us to find? How many total bananas are in the fruit bowl? What does Jeff do? Will you be adding or subtracting?"

MP.1 Make Sense of Problems Act It Out Have children suggest ways to act out the problem. Children may say to use fingers, use pieces of fruit from the grocery store display, or draw a picture to represent the problem.

Encourage children to think of other ways to solve a subtraction problem. For example, have them think about the partners that make 7. Say, "3 and what partner makes 7?" Guiding children to think of more than one way to solve a story problem will provide them with tools for solving a variety of situations.

 How can we solve this story problem? (See problem above.)

Julia: We need to find out how many bananas are in the fruit bowl.

Ed: The fruit bowl has 7 bananas. The answer is 7 bananas.

Tom: 7 bananas tells how many we start with.

Beth: Remember, 3 bananas are taken out of the bowl.

Tom: There are still some bananas left in the bowl.

Julia: Count the ones left in the bowl.

Beth: Hold up 7 fingers. Close 3 fingers. 4 fingers are up.

Ed: Then the fruit bowl has 4 bananas. The answer is 4 bananas.

Does everyone agree?

Class: Yes!

Discover Partners of 10 in a Row

▶ Show the "Bug Partners" of 10 [WHOLE CLASS]

This activity is repeated from Unit 4, Lesson 2. However, this time children turn over squares from left to right, starting with $1 + 9$. Have children count out 10 Square-Inch Tiles of the same color and arrange them in a horizontal row, dot side down. Tell children that they will pretend that the dot side of the tile is a little bug. Alternatively, your class can decide that the Square-Inch Tiles represent something else that wakes and sleeps.

• We will pretend that the dot side of the tile is a little bug. Sometimes the bugs are awake and turned up so that we can see them. Sometimes they are asleep under the tile and turned over so we can't see them. But there are always 10 bugs in total.

During this activity, wake up bugs from left to right so that the equations you record will look like those below. Children put the Break-Apart Stick between the bugs that are awake and the bugs that are asleep to show the sets of partners for 10.

• Let's put the Break-Apart Stick between the bugs that are asleep and the bugs that are awake so we can see them clearly. Wake up the first bug. Where does our Break-Apart Stick go? after the first tile, or between the first and second tiles

On chart paper, write the heading and the equation.

Bugs Total	=	Bugs Awake	+	Bugs Asleep
10	=	1	+	9

• Now 1 more bug wakes up. Let's turn this next bug over so we can see it. Where does our Break-Apart Stick go? It needs to move 1 tile to the right.

Record "$10 = 2 + 8$" on your partner chart.

Bugs Total	=	Bugs Awake	+	Bugs Asleep
10	=	1	+	9
10	=	2	+	8

MP.7 Look for Structure Continue waking up one bug at a time (from the left to the right) and writing the sets of partners for 10. Have children discuss the changes in numbers they see in the chart.

✓ Formative Assessment: Check Understanding

Student Summary Give children an addition or subtraction story problem to check for fluency within 5. For example: Four children are sorting fruit for the grocery display. One child leaves. How many children are still sorting fruit?

COMMON CORE

Mathematical Practice
CC.K–12.MP.7

Mathematical Content
CC.K.OA.3, CC.K.OA.4

15 MINUTES

FOCUS Show and record partners of 10.

MATERIALS Square-Inch Tiles (10 of the same color per child), Break-Apart Sticks (1 per child)

 Whiteboard Lesson

Class Management

You may wish to record the partners of 10 on chart paper. You can display this partner chart in your classroom next to the one created in Unit 4, Lesson 2. Together, they will provide a visual display of partners and their partner switches.

▲ On Level  Tier 1

for students having success

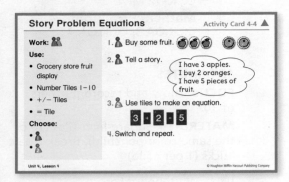

Activity Notes Model how children should buy fruit and use Number Tiles to show the story.

✏️ Math Writing Prompt

Write Equations Provide an equation such as $6 + 2 = 8$. Have children rewrite the equation by putting the total first.

 MegaMath

Software Support
Numberopolis: Carnival Stories, Level D

■ Challenge

for students seeking a challenge

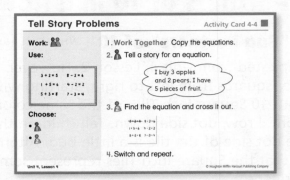

Activity Notes Write several addition and subtraction equations on the board for children.

✏️ Math Writing Prompt

Draw a Picture Provide an equation such as $4 + 2 = 6$. Have children draw a story problem for the equation.

 Destination Math®

Software Support
Course I: Module 2: Unit 1: Session 1: Combining and Joining Within 10

Distribute Homework and Remembering page 71. This page provides children with more practice identifying sets of partners for 4 to 6. Work through the first exercise with your class. Then have children finish the page for homework. On the back page, have children draw a picture for the equation $6 = 2 + 4$.

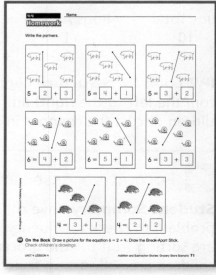

Homework and Remembering page 71

Practice with Teen Numbers and Partners

LESSON FOCUS

- Show teen numbers as a group of ten ones and extra ones and as 10 + a 1-digit number.
- Decompose numbers up to 7 into pairs in more than one way and record the pairs.

VOCABULARY

teen equation
partner

COMMON CORE

Mathematical Practice
CC.K–12.MP.1, CC.K–12.MP.2, CC.K–12.MP.5,
CC.K–12.MP.6, CC.K–12.MP.7, CC.K–12.MP.8
Mathematical Content
CC.K.CC.4, CC.K.CC.4c, CC.K.CC.5, CC.K.OA.1,
CC.K.OA.2, CC.K.OA.3, CC.K.NBT.1

The Day at a Glance

Teaching the Lesson

MATH BACKGROUND for this lesson is included on pp. 329II–329KK.

ACTIVITY FOCUS

Activity 1 Make numbers 11–20 using 10-sticks and centimeter cubes.

Activity 2 Model equations by placing Teen Equation Cards on the 1–20 Board.

Activity 3 Practice finding partners for 6 and 7 with a game.

MATERIALS

Student Activity Book pp. 163–164 (Family Letter) • 1–20 Boards (back) • 10-sticks • Centimeter cubes • Teen Equation Cards • Counting Mats • Number Tiles 1–7 • +/– Tiles • Break-Apart Sticks

*i*Tools: Counters • Whiteboard

Differentiated Instruction

MATERIALS

Activity Cards 4-5 • Teen Equation Cards (TRB M49) • Math Journals

Soar to Success Math Intervention • MegaMath • Destination Math®

RtI   Tier 1 • Tier 2 • Tier 3

Home and School Connection

MATERIALS

Family Letter (Student Activity Book pp. 163–164)

USE MATH TALK TODAY!

QUICK PRACTICE 5 MINUTES

Repeated Quick Practice Use these Quick Practices from previous lessons.

Partners of 4 Display 4 classroom objects. Ask, "1 and what partner make 4?" Children show the numbers with their fingers as they say, "1 and 3 make 4. 4 has the partners 1 and 3." Then show the partners using a Break-Apart Stick and the displayed classroom objects. Children close their eyes and visualize. Then they show and say the partners again. Repeat the routine with other partners of 4.

Count by Ones from 60 Through 100 (See Unit 4, Lesson 2.)

DAILY ROUTINES

Counting Tens and Ones (See pp. xxxi–xxxii.)

DIGITAL RESOURCES

Use these digital resources along with your eSAB and eTE to support your students' learning experiences.

 Professional Development

 Whiteboard Lesson

 *i*Tools

 Soar to Success Math Intervention

 MegaMath

 Destination Math®

COMMON CORE

Mathematical Practice
CC.K–12.MP.5, CC.K–12.MP.6,
CC.K–12.MP.7

Mathematical Content
CC.K.CC.4, CC.K.CC.4c, CC.K.CC.5,
CC.K.NBT.1

15 MINUTES

FOCUS Make numbers 11–20 using
10-sticks and centimeter cubes.

MATERIALS 1–20 Boards (back, TRB
M38–M39 taped together; 1 per child),
10-sticks (11 per child), centimeter cubes
(45 per child)

 Whiteboard Lesson

ACTIVITY 1

Model Teen Numbers on the 1–20 Board

▶ Make Teen Numbers and 20 INDIVIDUALS

MP.7 Look for Structure Identify Relationships Review how to make
11 with one 10-stick and one centimeter cube. Remind children that
the 10-stick shows a group of 10 cubes fastened together. Then ask
how to make 12 with one 10-stick and two centimeter cubes.

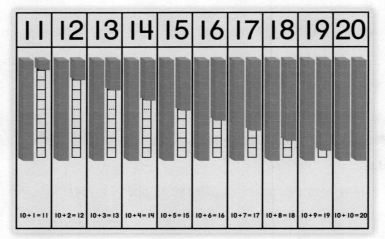

MP.5 Use Appropriate Tools Model the Math Continue in this way,
discussing and having children make the teen numbers 13–19 on their
1–20 Boards. Point out that each of the teen numbers is made up of
ten ones and some more ones. Then discuss how to make 20.

• **What are three different ways you can make 20?** use 20 centimeter
cubes, one 10-stick and 10 centimeter cubes, or two 10-sticks

After children have placed 10-sticks and centimeter cubes under all of
the numbers, ask them to point out different things they notice about
the board.

There are a number of observations children can make. Elicit as many
as you can. Some of the things children may notice are described in the
following Math Talk in Action.

MATH TALK in ACTION **Look over the numbers on your board.**

MP.6 Attend to Precision Explain a Representation **Can you tell me how each number is different from the number next to it?**

Mason: Each number has 1 more cube than the number before it.

Samira: I was going to say that each number has 1 less cube than the number after it.

Mason and Samira noticed that the cubes change by 1. Each number has 1 more cube than the number before it and 1 less cube than the number after it. What else do you see?

Calvin: Each number has one 10-stick.

Thai: Except the 20. It has 2 10-sticks.

Excellent points, Calvin and Thai. What other things do you see?

Disha: The number of 10-sticks matches this number. *She points to the 1 in 12.*

Catherine: And the number on the right matches how many other cubes there are.

....

ACTIVITY 2

Place Teen Equation Cards on the 1–20 Board

▶ Match Equations to Teen Numbers [WHOLE CLASS]

MP.8 Use Repeated Reasoning Generalize Distribute the Teen Equation Cards. You may want to have some children work only with Set A of the cards. Children will place the cards on the corresponding teen numbers on the 1–20 Board. Cards can be placed below the teen numbers at the top of the 1–20 Board or at the bottom, covering the matching teen equations. (See Unit 4, Lesson 3 for a complete description.)

▶ Compare Equations [WHOLE CLASS]

Review that in Set A, the total is on the left, and in Set B, the total is on the right. Stress that both ways to show the equation are correct, because in an equation the partners and the total on either side of the equal sign have the same value.

Discuss the cards with the class.

- Let's look at the cards. Tell me what you notice. For 15 = 10 + 5, for example, there is a 5 on both sides of the equal sign.

English Language Learners

Remove 20 = 10 + 10 and 10 + 10 = 20 from sets of Teen Equation Cards and give the sets to children. Explain that you will be reviewing both **teen numbers** and **teen equations.** Slowly say a few equations from both sets of cards in random order. Ask children to hold up the correct card as you say the equation.

BEGINNING

Say: **These are teen equations. The totals are teen numbers.** Have children repeat.

INTERMEDIATE

Ask: **Are all the totals teen numbers?** yes **Are these teen equations?** yes

ADVANCED

Ask: **What kind of numbers are all the totals?** teen numbers **What kind of equations are these?** teen equations

COMMON CORE

Mathematical Practice
CC.K–12.MP.8
Mathematical Content
CC.K.OA.1, CC.K.NBT.1

25 MINUTES

FOCUS Model equations by placing Teen Equation Cards on the 1–20 Board.

MATERIALS 1–20 Boards (back; TRB M38–M39 taped together; 1 per child), Teen Equation Cards (from Unit 4, Lesson 3 or TRB M49; Sets A and B, cut out and separated for each child)

 Whiteboard Lesson

COMMON CORE

Mathematical Practice
CC.K–12.MP.1, CC.K–12.MP.2,
CC.K–12.MP.5, CC.K–12.MP.8

Mathematical Content
CC.K.OA.1, CC.K.OA.2, CC.K.OA.3

15 MINUTES

FOCUS Practice finding partners for 6 and 7 with a game.

MATERIALS Counting Mats (1 per pair), Number Tiles 1–7 (1 set per pair), +/– Tiles (1 per pair), centimeter cubes (14 per pair), Break-Apart Sticks (1 per pair)

 *i*Tools: Counters

Whiteboard Lesson

Teaching Note

Watch For! If some children have trouble wiggling their fingers, they can bend them instead. Tell children that some combinations are more difficult to do (for example, 6 as 3 and 3). Reassure children that finger wiggles will get easier each time they try.

Digital Resource

*i*Tools Choose 'Counters' on the Menu. Use Activity 3 'Add' with the tab for 'Activities.' Children can use counters to help them add two numbers. Then they enter the total.

Use Activity 4 'Subtract' with the tab for 'Activities.' Children can use counters to help them subtract. Then they enter the partner.

ACTIVITY 3

Play *The Unknown Partner Game* for 6 and 7

▷ Do Finger Wiggle Partner Practice WHOLE CLASS

Do the finger wiggle for each number 2 through 7 at least four times. Select a **Student Leader** to write each expression on the board as it is practiced. Start with the number 6, using 5 + 1, because it will be easy for children to do. Ask children to hold up 5 fingers and name the partner that will make 6. 1 Show them how to say, show, and wiggle with their fingers.

• Wiggle 5 fingers. Now wiggle 1 finger.

Children should wiggle 5 and 1 at least three more times.

• Let's really feel these partners for 6. Wiggle 5; now wiggle 1. Oh, we're getting better.

• Wiggle 5 again; now wiggle 1. Look, it is easier!

• Again, wiggle 5, then wiggle 1.

MP.8 Use Repeated Reasoning Continue with different sets of partners for 6. Demonstrate making a 5-group each time. For 4 + 2, wiggle 4 fingers, then wiggle the remaining 1 finger plus 1 finger on the other hand. Include switching the partners as you work through these sets. Then do the partners for 7, 5, 4, 3, and 2.

▷ Play *The Unknown Partner Game* for 6 and 7 PAIRS MATH TALK

Use the **Student Pairs** structure for this activity.

MP.5 Use Appropriate Tools Use a Concrete Model *The Unknown Partner Game* was introduced in Unit 3, Lesson 16, and was repeated in Unit 4, Lesson 2. It provides auditory and visual practice with the break-apart partners. Ask pairs of children to sit beside each other facing the workspace on which they have placed a Counting Mat, Number Tiles, and +/– Tiles. For each turn, children take out only the number of centimeter cubes needed.

• Look at your Counting Mat. Pull down Number Tile 7.

• Now show 7 centimeter cubes below the 7.

Have the first child in the student pair take a Break-Apart Stick, while the other child covers his or her eyes and turns away so as not to peek. The first child places the Break-Apart Stick to make a set of partners for 7 (for example, 5 and 2). That child then removes and hides the centimeter cubes for one partner, leaving the Break-Apart Stick and the other centimeter cubes in place.

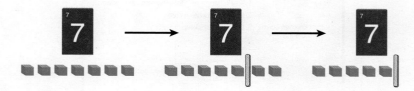

Then the first child asks the second child to identify the partner that was removed.

• What partner of 7 did I take? Look and see how many are gone.

MP.2 Reason Abstractly The second child uncovers his or her eyes and looks to determine the unknown partner. Children can count the centimeter cubes they see and count on to 7. They may also visualize 7 centimeter cubes and see how many are missing. As a last resort, they can place 7 centimeter cubes below the ones that are there and see how many are missing.

The second child then puts the Number Tiles for the partners and the +/− Tile in place, as shown below, and names the partners, 5 and 2.

The first child then replaces the centimeter cubes that were taken to confirm the unknown partner.

Children then reverse roles. They should play the game using various partners for 6 and 7, continuing as time permits.

MP.1 Make Sense of Problems If desired, children may make up simple stories to describe the situation: There are 7 birds sitting in a tree. Five stay in the tree and some fly away. How many fly away?

 Formative Assessment: Check Understanding

Student Summary Sketch squares on the board to represent centimeter cubes for 13, 14, 15, and 16. Ask how 14 is different from 13, how 15 is different from 14, and how 16 is different from 15. Children should indicate that each number is one greater. Then reverse the direction. Ask how 13 is different from 14, and so on. Children should indicate that each number is one less.

Math Background *The Unknown Partner Game* provides auditory and visual numerical practice with break-apart partners. This is particularly helpful for **English Language Learners**. Before playing *The Unknown Partner Game*, children will have reviewed partners by doing finger wiggles.

 **On Level**  Tier 1

for students having success

Equation Game	Activity Card 4-5 ▲

Work: 👥👥

Use:
- Teen Equation Cards (TRB M49, uncut page)
- Teen Equation Cards Sets A and B (2 sets)

Choose:
- a leader 👤

1. Place one set of cards face down. Choose one card. Read it aloud.
2. 👥 Find it on the page. Put your card on it.
3. Repeat until a row is covered.
4. Choose a new leader.
5. Play again.

Unit 4, Lesson 5   © Houghton Mifflin Harcourt Publishing Company

Activity Notes An uncut copy of TRB M49 (Teen Equation Cards) can be used as the game card.

 Math Writing Prompt

Draw Equations After children complete a row, ask them to draw pictures for each equation covered in the winning row.

MegaMath

Software Support
Country Countdown:
Block Busters, Level G

■ **Challenge**

for students seeking a challenge

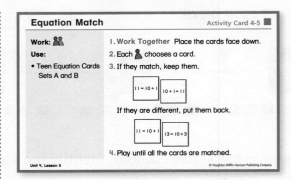

Equation Match	Activity Card 4-5 ■

Work: 👥👥

Use:
- Teen Equation Cards Sets A and B

1. **Work Together** Place the cards face down.
2. Each 👤 chooses a card.
3. If they match, keep them.

If they are different, put them back.

4. Play until all the cards are matched.

Unit 4, Lesson 5   © Houghton Mifflin Harcourt Publishing Company

Activity Notes Review that equations may be written with either the total or the partners first.

 Math Writing Prompt

Write the Equations Provide children with Set B of the Teen Equation Cards. Ask them to write each equation showing the teen number first.

Destination Math®

Software Support
Course I: Module 2: Unit 1: Session 3: Sums within 20, with 10 as One Addend

---

Family Letter Remind children to take home the Family Letter on Student Activity page 163. This letter explains how the concept of partners is developed in *Math Expressions*. It gives parents and guardians a better understanding of the learning that goes on in math class and creates a bridge between school and home. A Spanish translation of this letter is on the following page in the Student Activity Book.

Student Activity Book page 163

Count, Match, and Compare

LESSON FOCUS

- Use drawings and write expressions to solve addition and subtraction story problems.
- Use matching and counting as strategies for comparing the number of objects in groups.

VOCABULARY

addition
subtraction
matching
extra
greater/greater than
less/less than

COMMON CORE

Mathematical Practice
CC.K–12.MP.1, CC.K–12.MP.2, CC.K–12.MP.4, CC.K–12.MP.7, CC.K–12.MP.8
Mathematical Content
CC.K.CC.4, CC.K.CC.5, CC.K.CC.6, CC.K.CC.7, CC.K.OA.1, CC.K.OA.2

The Day at a Glance

Teaching the Lesson

 USE MATH TALK TODAY!

MATH BACKGROUND for this lesson is included on pp. 329GG, 329LL.

ACTIVITY FOCUS

Activity 1 Tell, draw, and solve grocery store story problems.

Activity 2 Compare the number of items in two groups.

MATERIALS

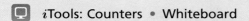 Student Activity Book pp. 165–166 • Grocery store fruit display • Crayons or markers • paper

*i*Tools: Counters • Whiteboard

Differentiated Instruction

MATERIALS

Activity Cards 4-6 • Class grocery store • Large index cards • Crayons or markers • Math Journals

Soar to Success Math Intervention • MegaMath • Destination Math®

 RtI Tier 1 • Tier 2 • Tier 3

Home or School Activity

MATERIALS

Technology Connection p. 364

QUICK PRACTICE 5 MINUTES

Repeated Quick Practice Use these Quick Practices from previous lessons.

Partners of 7 Display 7 classroom objects. Ask "5 and what partner make 7?" Children show the numbers with their fingers as they say, "5 and 2 make 7. 7 has the partners 5 and 2." Then show the partners using a Break-Apart Stick and the displayed classroom objects. Children close their eyes and visualize. Then they show and say the partners again. Repeat the routine with the other partners of 7.

Count by Ones from 60 Through 100 (See Unit 4, Lesson 2.)

DAILY ROUTINES

Counting Tens and Ones (See pp. xxxi–xxxii.)

DIGITAL RESOURCES

Use these digital resources along with your eSAB and eTE to support your students' learning experiences.

 Professional Development

 Whiteboard Lesson

 *i*Tools

 Soar to Success Math Intervention

 MegaMath

Destination Math®

COMMON CORE

Mathematical Practice
CC.K–12.MP.1, CC.K–12.MP.4
Mathematical Content
CC.K.OA.1, CC.K.OA.2

35 MINUTES
FOCUS Tell, draw, and solve grocery store story problems.

MATERIALS Grocery store fruit display, crayons or markers, paper

 *iTools: Counters

 Whiteboard Lesson

Learning Community— Best Practices

MATH TALK When using the **Solve and Discuss** structure, 4 or 5 children solve a problem at the board using any method, while their classmates work at their desks. The teacher then invites 2 or 3 children to explain their methods. Children at their desks are encouraged to ask questions and assist their classmates in understanding. The Solve and Discuss structure includes 4 parts: Solve, Explain, Question, and Justify.

MATH TALK in ACTION **What is the problem we are trying to solve?**

Carolyn: Jun Ming buys 6 pears and 2 bananas. How many pieces of fruit does Jun Ming buy altogether?

Good. Let's think about how to solve this problem.

Roberto: I would add because we need to find how much in all—the pears plus the bananas.

What numbers do we need to add?

Chloe: 6 and 2 because there are 6 pears and 2 bananas.

Digital Resource

iTools Choose 'Counters' on the Menu. Use Activity 3 'Add' with the tab for 'Activities.' Children can use counters to help them add two numbers. Then they enter the total.

Use Activity 4 'Subtract' with the tab for 'Activities.' Children can use counters to help them subtract. Then they enter the partner.

ACTIVITY 1 Social Studies Connection

Add and Subtract at the Class Grocery Store

▶ **Tell Math Grocery Stories** WHOLE CLASS MATH TALK

Use the **Solve and Discuss** structure for this activity.

Similar to Unit 4, Lesson 4, Activity 1, children will add and subtract as they buy items from the grocery store fruit display. (See the Class Management: Looking Ahead note from Unit 4, Lesson 1.) Today, however, children will also make simple math drawings for each problem. Some children can work at the board, while the others draw on paper. The emphasis in this unit is on addition and subtraction problems with the totals between 6 and 10. Keep encouraging children to make up problems with these larger numbers.

First, have children fold a blank sheet of paper into four parts (fold in half vertically and then in half horizontally). This will provide eight spaces for math drawings (four on the front and four on the back).

Describe math drawings and explain why they are helpful.

- Math drawings are very simple. You draw a circle or other shape to show the objects in your story. You should not use a lot of detail for the drawings.
- Math drawings can be used to check your work, share what happened in the story, or help you tell your story again.

MP.1 Make Sense of Problems Analyze the Problem Stress the important steps in solving story problems: listen, draw, solve, and explain. Then work with a volunteer to act out buying fruit at the store (for example, 6 pears + 2 bananas). Urge children to use addition vocabulary to discuss the problem. They may include addition terms such as *altogether, in all, total,* and *put together*.

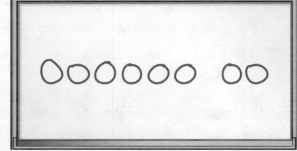

Draw and Solve Ask children to make simple math drawings to show the addition problem. Select two children to explain their drawings.

MP.4 Model with Mathematics Write an Expression Have everyone write the addition expression their drawing shows (in this example, $6 + 2$). See how many children can do this independently. Writing the entire equation ($6 + 2 = 8$) is difficult for many kindergarten children. For now, the goal is to learn to write just the expression. It is fine, however, if advanced children write the entire equation. You may want to write the addition expression ($6 + 2$) on the board and then ask what else you need to write to show an equation. $= 8$ Then complete the equation.

Draw and Solve Repeat the activity for subtraction. Request that a volunteer act out subtracting by buying fruit from the store (for example, 7 pears − 2 pears). Each child should make a simple math drawing and then write the expression or equation.

MP.1 Make Sense of Problems Justify Reasoning Invite two children to explain their math drawings and their subtraction expressions or equations. Write the equation on the board (7 − 2 = 5). Continue with more addition and subtraction problems.

ACTIVITY 2

Match and See the Extra Things

▶ Match to Compare Groups WHOLE CLASS

MP.7 Use Structure Introduce matching as one way to tell whether the number of items in one group is greater than or less than the number of items in another group.

Matching with Drawings	
Draw a row of 6 circles on the board and a row of 4 circles below it. Align the first 4 circles in each row as shown.	
Then draw a line to connect the first two circles in each row, the second two circles, and so on.	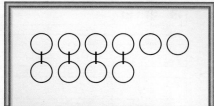
Ask children to identify the circles that are extra (leftover circles that do not have a match). Draw a ring around the circles to show how many more circles that group has.	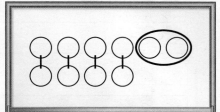

Explain that since the top row has more circles, the number of circles is greater than the number in the bottom row. Write a *G* next to the top row. In the same way, the number of circles in the bottom row is less than the number in the top row. Write an *L* next to the bottom row.

Activity continued ▶

Teaching Note

Language and Vocabulary This activity provides children with the opportunity to use addition and subtraction vocabulary. See the Teaching Note from Unit 4, Lesson 4, Activity 1, for examples of dialogue that use this vocabulary.

 COMMON CORE

Mathematical Practice
CC.K–12.MP.2, CC.K–12.MP.7, CC.K–12.MP.8

Mathematical Content
CC.K.CC.4, CC.K.CC.5, CC.K.CC.6, CC.K.CC.7

25 MINUTES

FOCUS Compare the number of items in two groups.

MATERIALS Student Activity Book pages 165–166

📝 Whiteboard Lesson

English Language Learners

Write *match* on the board. Display a row of 5 individual connecting cubes with another row of 3 cubes aligned below it. Say: **We can match things in two groups.** Have children repeat. Show how to match 3 pairs of cubes by connecting corresponding cubes from each row. Point to the row with 2 extra cubes. Say: **When we match the cubes, we see that this group has more cubes.**

Teaching Note

What to Expect from Students If time allows, you may want to repeat the matching exercise by having children act it out. Ask 10 children to come to the front of the class and make a row of 6 and a row of 4. Matching children may hold hands or put their hands on each others' shoulders.

Learning Community—Best Practices

Helping Community When advanced learners finish their work early, let them help others who may be struggling. Children like to take on this role and enjoy helping one another. Explaining math content helps challenge advanced learners and keeps them engaged as they wait.

▶ **Compare the Groups** INDIVIDUALS

MP.7 Use Structure Direct children's attention to the two rows of snowflakes at the top of Student Activity Book page 165. Point out the lines that connect, or match, the first 3 snowflakes in each row. Explain that the circle around the snowflakes in the top row shows the extras. Then ask children to count the number of snowflakes in each row.

- There are 5 snowflakes in the top row. The number 5 is written in the box to the right of the row.

- There are 3 snowflakes in the next row. The number 3 is written in the box to the right of the row.

- Which row has the greater number of snowflakes? the top row

- Notice the *G* next to the number. *G* means *greater* and shows that 5 is greater than 3.

- Which number is less? 3 The *L* next to the 3 means *less* and shows that 3 is less than 5.

- The 2 extra snowflakes that are circled show how much greater 5 is than 3.

MP.8 Use Repeated Reasoning Generalize Explain that children can use this first exercise as a model to complete the rest of the page.

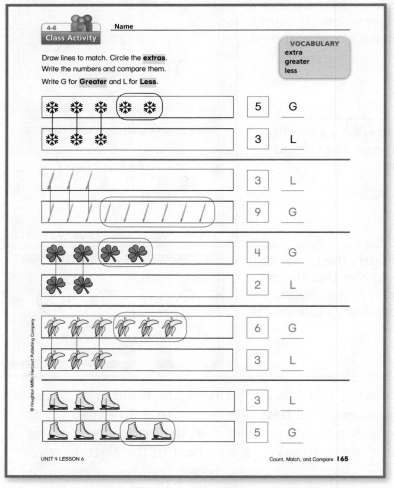

Student Activity Book page 165

▶ Count and Compare INDIVIDUALS

Direct children to look at Student Activity Book page 166. Explain that in the top two rows, they will write the number of circles in each group and circle the number that is greater. In the next two rows, they will write the number of circles in each group and circle the number that is less.

MP.2 Reason Abstractly and Quantitatively Next, children compare two numbers and determine whether the *first* number is greater than or less than the *second* number. Stress the order of the comparison. Children may refer to the Number Parade.

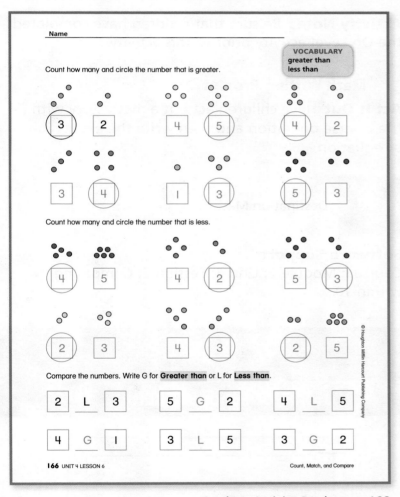

Student Activity Book page 166

Teaching Notes

What to Expect from Students
Some children may need to count the number of circles in each group, while others may recognize the value without counting. Encourage this ability. Subitizing in this way is very useful in the rapid comparison of small groups.

Watch For! This page looks similar to the Student Activity Book pages in Unit 3 in which children were asked to write = or ≠ between the boxes. When completing the last activity, ensure that children write either G or L when comparing the numbers.

✓ Formative Assessment: Check Understanding

Student Summary Draw a row of 3 squares on the board with a row of 5 squares below it. Ask children to name and describe a way to tell which group is greater than the other. Children should indicate matching and describe drawing lines to match pairs and find extras. Then draw groups with 4 squares and 5 squares randomly placed. Ask children to discuss a method for finding which group has less. Children should indicate counting and then comparing.

▲ On Level    **RtI** Tier 1
for students having success

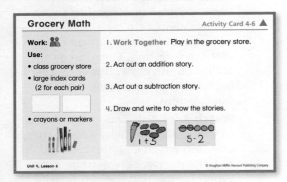

Activity Notes Set up the grocery store as described in Class Management: Looking Ahead on page 333.

 Math Writing Prompt

Write the Expression Challenge each child to draw a new problem about the grocery store. Ask children to exchange papers and write the expressions.

 MegaMath

Software Support
Country Countdown:
Harrison's Comparisons, Level D

■ **Challenge**
for students seeking a challenge

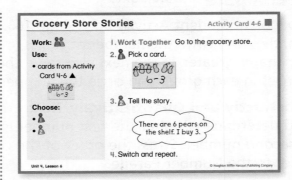

Activity Notes Be sure that children have completed the On Level activity prior to this activity.

 Math Writing Prompt

Act It Out Have children act out a math story with the inverse operation and then write the expression or equation.

 Destination Math®

Software Support
Course I: Module 2: Unit 1: Session 2: Comparing within 10

Technology Connection

Computer Matching Help children use clip art to compare two groups. Assist children as needed to make two rows of the same piece of clip art. For example, a child might make a row of 7 flowers directly below a row of 4 flowers. Then have children use the line tool to draw lines matching items in the two rows. Ask them to print out their drawings and discuss them with their classmates, noting which group has the greater number of objects.

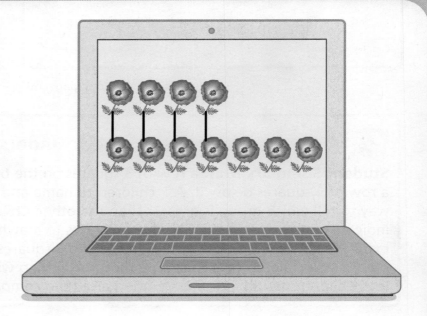

Practice Teen Numbers and Equations

LESSON FOCUS

- Show teen numbers as a group of ten ones and extra ones and as 10 + a 1-digit number.
- Decompose numbers up to 7 into pairs in more than one way and record the pairs.

VOCABULARY

teen equation
partner
unknown partner

COMMON CORE

Mathematical Practice
CC.K–12.MP.2, CC.K–12.MP.5, CC.K–12.MP.6, CC.K–12.MP.7, CC.K–12.MP.8
Mathematical Content
CC.K.CC.4, CC.K.CC.4c, CC.K.CC.5, CC.K.OA.1, CC.K.OA.2, CC.K.OA.3, CC.K.NBT.1

The Day at a Glance

Teaching the Lesson

USE MATH TALK TODAY!

MATH BACKGROUND for this lesson is included on pp. 329II–329KK.

ACTIVITY FOCUS

Activity 1 Make numbers 11–20 using 10-sticks and centimeter cubes.

Activity 2 Model equations by placing Teen Equation Cards on the 1–20 Board.

Activity 3 Practice finding partners for 6 and 7 with a game.

MATERIALS

- 1–20 Boards (back) • 10-sticks • Centimeter cubes • Teen Equation Cards • Counting Mats • Number Tiles 1–7 • Break-Apart Sticks • +/− Tiles

- iTools: Counters • Whiteboard

Differentiated Instruction

MATERIALS

- Activity Cards 4-7 • 10-sticks • Centimeter cubes • Teen Equation Cards • Math Journals

- Soar to Success Math Intervention • MegaMath • Destination Math®

- **RtI** Tier 1 • Tier 2 • Tier 3

Homework

MATERIALS

- Homework and Remembering pp. 73–74

QUICK PRACTICE 5 MINUTES

Repeated Quick Practice Use these Quick Practices from previous lessons.

Count by Ones from 60 Through 100
(See Unit 4, Lesson 2.)

Partners of 4, 5, 6, or 7
(See Unit 4, Lesson 3, 4, 5, or 6.)

DAILY ROUTINES

Counting Tens and Ones
(See pp. xxxi–xxxii.)

DIGITAL RESOURCES

Use these digital resources along with your eSAB and eTE to support your students' learning experiences.

Professional Development

Whiteboard Lesson

iTools

Soar to Success Math Intervention

MegaMath

Destination Math®

COMMON CORE

Mathematical Practice
CC.K–12.MP.7, CC.K–12.MP.8

Mathematical Content
CC.K.CC.4, CC.K.CC.4c, CC.K.CC.5, CC.K.NBT.1

15 MINUTES

FOCUS Make numbers 11–20 using 10-sticks and centimeter cubes.

MATERIALS 1–20 Boards (back, TRB M38–M39 taped together; 1 per child), 10-sticks (11 per child), centimeter cubes (45 per child)

 Whiteboard Lesson

Teaching Note

Watch For! As children work on their 1–20 Boards, circulate around the room. Are children placing the 10-sticks in the correct place? Do they have the correct number of centimeter cubes underneath each teen number?

ACTIVITY 1

Model Teen Numbers on the 1–20 Board

▶ Make Teen Numbers and 20 [INDIVIDUALS]

You may also use the **Student Pairs** structure for this activity.

This activity was also described in Unit 4, Lessons 3 and 5. Please refer to those lessons for additional details.

Discuss with children how to make teen numbers using one 10-stick and some centimeter cubes. Then children may work alone or in helping pairs to make the numbers 11–20 on their 1–20 Boards. You may wish to pair more advanced learners with children who are having difficulty.

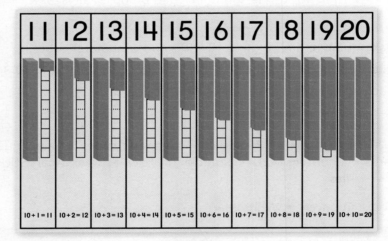

MP.7 Look for Structure Identify Relationships After children have placed 10-sticks and centimeter cubes under all of the numbers, ask them to discuss different things they notice about the board.

MP.8 Use Repeated Reasoning Generalize There are many observations that the class can make. For example, children may notice that each of the teen numbers has one 10-stick. They may see that each number has one more cube than the number before it. Children might also discern that the number in the right column matches the number of centimeter cubes and the number in the left column matches the number of 10-sticks. Elicit as many observations from them as you can.

Place Teen Equations on the 1–20 Board

▶ Compare Equations WHOLE CLASS

This activity was first introduced in Activity 2 of Unit 4, Lesson 3. See that lesson for additional details. Distribute the Teen Equation Cards.

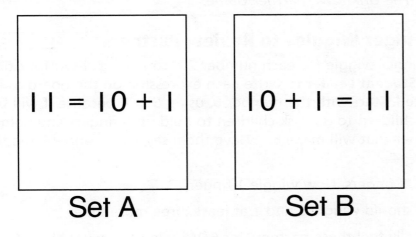

Set A   Set B

Ask:

- What do you see that is different about the equations on the two different sets of cards? *In one set of cards, the teen number is first (or on the left). In the other set, the teen number is last (or on the right).*

MP.2 Reason Abstractly and Quantitatively Connect Symbols and Words Discuss and review the meaning of the = and + signs. Then discuss how you have been writing equations.

- For showing partners, we have been writing the total number first and then the equal sign. After the equal sign, we have been writing the partners.

- For addition problems, however, we have been writing the partners first with a plus sign in between, to show that they are put together or added to each other. Then, we have been writing the equal sign and the total on the right.

- We can write an equation either way. Both ways are correct.

Be sure children understand that both ways are correct because in an equation, the numbers and expressions on both sides of the = sign have the same value, or are equal. This is true no matter which side the numbers and expressions are on.

▶ Match Equations to Teen Numbers WHOLE CLASS

MP.8 Use Repeated Reasoning Generalize Ask children to place the cards on their 1–20 Boards by matching the Teen Equation Cards to the corresponding teen numbers. Cards can be placed below the teen numbers at the top of the 1–20 Board or at the bottom, covering the existing teen equations.

COMMON CORE

Mathematical Practice
CC.K–12.MP.2, CC.K–12.MP.8
Mathematical Content
CC.K.OA.1, CC.K.NBT.1

25 MINUTES

FOCUS Model equations by placing Teen Equation Cards on the 1–20 Board.

MATERIALS 1–20 Boards (back; TRB M38–M39 taped together; 1 per child), Teen Equation Cards (from Unit 4, Lesson 3 or TRB M49; Sets A and B for each child)

Whiteboard Lesson

English Language Learners

Write 10 + 5 = 15, 15 = 10 + 5, and *equation* on the board. Say: **An equation has an equal sign.** Have children repeat. Say: **When we write a teen equation, we add ten and some ones.** Invite a volunteer to circle the equal signs. Ask children to point out other ways the equations are alike. *Both add 10 and 5. The total is 15.* Ask them to say how they are different. *The partners and the total are in a different order.*

Teaching Note

Math Background Visualizing teen numbers as ten ones and some further ones is an important skill. This skill is being developed in a variety of ways. In Unit 3, children "built" teen numbers with real objects and with Teen Displays. In Unit 4, teen numbers are placed in sequential order as they are constructed on the 1–20 Board using 10-sticks and centimeter cubes. Teen Equation Cards reinforce that 10 + 7 = 17 and 17 = 10 + 7. Later in the unit, each child will make a Teen Number Book.

COMMON CORE

Mathematical Practice
CC.K–12.MP.2, CC.K–12.MP.5,
CC.K–12.MP.6, CC.K–12.MP.8

Mathematical Content
CC.K.OA.1, CC.K.OA.2, CC.K.OA.3

15 MINUTES

FOCUS Practice finding partners for 6 and 7 with a game.

MATERIALS Counting Mats (1 per pair), Number Tiles 1–7 (1 set per pair), centimeter cubes (14 per pair), Break-Apart Sticks (1 per pair), +/– Tiles (1 per pair)

 *i*Tools: Counters

Whiteboard Lesson

Teaching Note

What to Expect from Students You may notice that children are becoming increasingly adept at the finger wiggle activity. However, if some children are still having difficulty wiggling their fingers, they can just bend them.

Digital Resource

*i***Tools** Choose 'Counters' on the Menu. Use Activity 3 'Add' with the tab for 'Activities.' Children can use counters to help them add two numbers. Then they enter the total.

Use Activity 4 'Subtract' with the tab for 'Activities.' Children can use counters to help them subtract. Then they enter the partner.

ACTIVITY 3

Play *The Unknown Partner Game* for 6 and 7

This activity is the same as Unit 4, Lesson 5, Activity 3. It provides auditory and visual numerical practice with the break-apart partners. First, children will review partners by doing finger wiggles. Then they will play *The Unknown Partner Game.*

▶ Do Finger Wiggles to Review Partners WHOLE CLASS

Do the finger wiggle for each number 2 through 7 at least four times. Select a **Student Leader** to write each expression on the board as it is practiced. Start with the number 6, using 5 + 1, because it will be easy for children to do. Ask children to hold up 5 fingers and name the partner that will make 6. 1 Have them say, show, and wiggle their fingers.

• Wiggle 5 fingers. Now wiggle 1 finger.

Children should wiggle 5 and 1 at least three more times.

• Let's really feel these partners for 6. Wiggle 5; now wiggle 1. Oh, we're getting better.

• Wiggle 5 again; now wiggle 1. Look, it is easier!

• Again, wiggle 5, then wiggle 1.

MP.8 Use Repeated Reasoning Continue with different sets of partners for 6. Demonstrate making a 5-group each time. For 4 + 2, wiggle 4 fingers, then wiggle the remaining 1 finger plus 1 finger on the other hand. Include switching the partners as you work through these sets. Then do the partners for 7, 5, 4, 3, and 2.

▶ Play *The Unknown Partner Game* for 6 and 7 PAIRS MATH TALK

Use the **Student Pairs** structure for this Activity.

MP.5 Use Appropriate Tools Use a Concrete Model *The Unknown Partner Game* was introduced in Unit 3, Lesson 16, and is repeated here. It provides children with auditory and visual practice with the break-apart partners.

Ask **Student Pairs** to sit beside each other facing the workspace on which they have placed a Counting Mat, Number Tiles, and +/– Tiles. For each turn, children take out only the number of centimeter cubes needed.

Guide children through one round of the game.

• Look at your Counting Mat. Pull down Number Tile 7.

• Now show 7 centimeter cubes below the 7.

Have the first child in the student pair take a Break-Apart Stick, while the other child covers his or her eyes and turns away so as not to peek. The first child places the Break-Apart Stick to make a set of partners for 7 (for example, 5 and 2). That child then removes and hides the centimeter cubes for one partner, leaving the Break-Apart Stick and the other centimeter cubes in place.

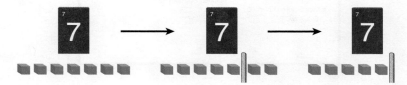

Then the first child asks the second child to identify the partner that was removed.

• What partner of 7 did I take? Look and see how many are gone.

MP.2 Reason Abstractly The second child uncovers his or her eyes and looks to determine the unknown partner. Children can count the centimeter cubes they see and count on to 7. They may also visualize 7 centimeter cubes and see how many are missing. As a last resort, they can place 7 centimeter cubes below the ones that are there and see how many are missing.

MP.6 Attend to Precision Describe a Method Ask several children to describe for the class how they figured out the value of the unknown partner. The second child then puts the Number Tiles for the partners and the +/− Tile in place, as shown below, and names the partners, 5 and 2.

Children then reverse roles.

Children should play the game using different partners for 6 and 7, continuing as time permits. Encourage children to create simple story problems describing the situations.

 Formative Assessment: Check Understanding

Student Summary Write the equations $14 = 10 + 4$ and $10 + 4 = 14$ on the board. Ask children to explain why both ways of writing the equation are correct.

Learning Community— Best Practices

Student Leader The class can practice partners of 6 as children are leaving the classroom. Invite a **Student Leader** to stand at the front of the line. As each child passes by, the Student Leader should show fingers for a different partner of 6. The passerby shows fingers for the other partner.

Building Concepts Ask if any children have had the opportunity to play *The Unknown Partner Game* at home. This game was described in the Family Letter in Unit 4, Lesson 5. Encourage children to play the game at home.

▲ On Level  Tier 1
for students having success

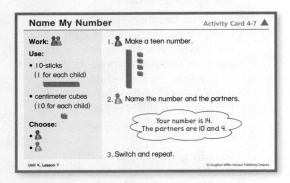

Activity Notes Explain that children first model a teen number with the cubes, and then name the teen number and its partners.

✏ Math Writing Prompt
Write the Partners Ask children to write expressions for each teen number they model.

 MegaMath

Software Support
Country Countdown:
Block Busters, Level G

■ Challenge
for students seeking a challenge

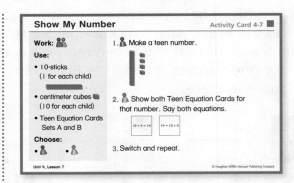

Activity Notes Explain that the first child will model a teen number and the second child will find both Teen Equation Cards showing that number.

✏ Math Writing Prompt
Teen Equations Ask children to write both equations for the teen numbers they make.

 Destination Math®

Software Support
Course I: Module 2: Unit 1: Session 3: Sums within 20, with 10 as One Addend

---

Distribute Homework and Remembering pages 73–74. These pages give children practice both recording and drawing sets of partners for 5, 6, and 7.

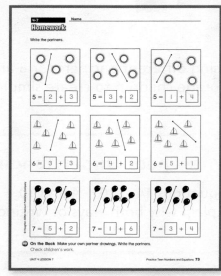

Homework and Remembering page 73

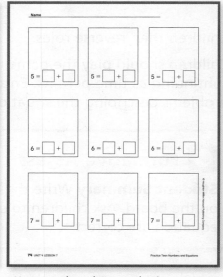

Homework and Remembering page 74

Break-Apart Numbers for 10

LESSON FOCUS
- Find sets of partners for 10.
- Record sets of partners for 5–7 and 10.

VOCABULARY
partner
Tiny Tumbler
Math Mountain

COMMON CORE
Mathematical Practice
CC.K–12.MP.3, CC.K–12.MP.4, CC.K–12.MP.6, CC.K–12.MP.7
Mathematical Content
CC.K.CC.3, CC.K.CC.5, CC.K.OA.3, CC.K.OA.4

The Day at a Glance

USE MATH TALK TODAY!

Teaching the Lesson

MATH BACKGROUND for this lesson is included on pp. 329HH, 329KK.

ACTIVITY FOCUS

Activity 1   Show and record partners of 10.

Activity 2   Draw partners on Math Mountains.

MATERIALS

Student Activity Book pp. 167–170 • Fluency Check 2 (Assessment Guide) • Square-Inch Tiles • Break-Apart Sticks • Crayons or markers • Puzzled Penguin (optional)

iTools: Counters • Whiteboard

Differentiated Instruction

MATERIALS

Activity Cards 4-8 • Number cubes • Real or play money (pennies) • Math Journals

Soar to Success Math Intervention • MegaMath • Destination Math®

RtI   Tier 1 • Tier 2 • Tier 3

Homework

MATERIALS

Homework and Remembering pp. 75–76

QUICK PRACTICE 5 MINUTES

Repeated Quick Practice Use these Quick Practices from previous lessons.

Count by Ones from 60 Through 100
(See Unit 4, Lesson 2.)

Partners of 4, 5, 6, or 7
(See Unit 4, Lesson 3, 4, 5, or 6.)

DAILY ROUTINES
Counting Tens and Ones
(See pp. xxxi–xxxii.)

DIGITAL RESOURCES
Use these digital resources along with your eSAB and eTE to support your students' learning experiences.

Professional Development

Whiteboard Lesson

iTools

Soar to Success Math Intervention

MegaMath

Destination Math®

COMMON CORE

Mathematical Practice
CC.K–12.MP.7

Mathematical Content
CC.K.OA.3, CC.K.OA.4

15 MINUTES

FOCUS Show and record partners of 10.

MATERIALS Student Activity Book page 167, Square-Inch Tiles (10 per child), Break-Apart Sticks (1 per child)

 Whiteboard Lesson

Teaching Note

What to Expect from Students
Children will be working on partners for 10 throughout Unit 4. At this point, it is likely that only some children will know all of the partners for 10. Learning all of these pairs will come gradually. What is important now is that they know how to find correct partners for 10 and that they see the relationships among the different partners and the different partner equations.

ACTIVITY 1

Identify Partners for 10

▶ **Discover Partner Switches for 10**   WHOLE CLASS   MATH TALK

MP.7 Look for Structure Identify Relationships Repeat the activity from Unit 4, Lessons 2 and 4. Wake up "bugs" starting from the right. Write the partners and partner switches next to each other as shown below. Ask children to discuss what they see here and relate these observations to those for the chart papers from Lessons 2 and 4.

Bugs total	=	Bugs sleeping	+	Bugs awake		Bugs total	=	Bugs sleeping	+	Bugs awake
10	=	9	+	1		10	=	1	+	9
10	=	8	+	2		10	=	2	+	8
10	=	7	+	3		10	=	3	+	7
10	=	6	+	4		10	=	4	+	6
10	=	5	+	5						

Instruct children to complete Student Activity Book page 167. Encourage children to record the partners in the same order as on the board.

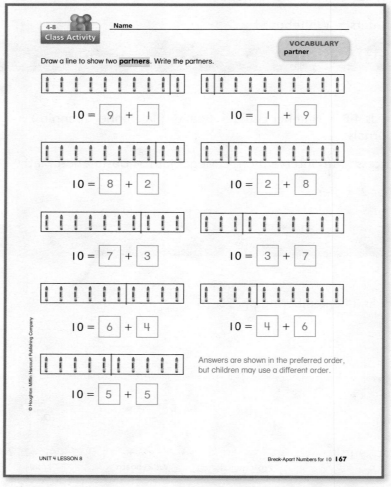

Student Activity Book page 167

Introduce the Math Mountain

▶ The Story of the Tiny Tumblers ⟨WHOLE CLASS⟩

Share the following story with your class:

- In a land far, far away, there are many mountains. At the top of each mountain, in little cozy places, Tiny Tumblers live. Does anyone know what *tumbling* means? It means rolling over and over and over.

- Tiny Tumblers tumble for fun! Each mountain has a different number of Tiny Tumblers on it. Six Tiny Tumblers live on the 6-Math Mountain. Ten Tiny Tumblers live on the 10-Math Mountain.

- Each morning, after eating a good breakfast, the Tiny Tumblers wash, brush their teeth, and do their daily chores. Then the Tiny Tumblers roll down their Math Mountain to play on its sides. Some Tiny Tumblers roll down one side of the mountain, and the rest of the Tiny Tumblers roll down the other side.

▶ Draw Tiny Tumblers on Math Mountains ⟨WHOLE CLASS⟩

MP.7 Look for Structure Identify Relationships Refer to Student Activity Book page 168. Tell children that they will be completing the Math Mountains on that page.

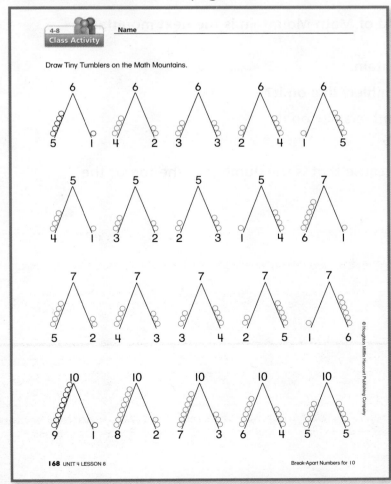

Student Activity Book page 168

Activity continued ▶

COMMON CORE

Mathematical Practice
CC.K–12.MP.3, CC.K–12.MP.4,
CC.K–12.MP.6, CC.K–12.MP.7

Mathematical Content
CC.K.CC.3, CC.K.CC.5,
CC.K.OA.3, CC.K.OA.4

40 MINUTES

FOCUS Draw partners on Math Mountains.

MATERIALS Student Activity Book pages 168–170, paper, crayons or markers, Puzzled Penguin (TRB M95, optional)

 *i*Tools: Counters

📝 Whiteboard Lesson

English Language Learners

Draw Tiny Tumblers on top of a Math Mountain. Use a finger to show how they *tumble* down.

BEGINNING

Say: **Tumble means fall or roll. Tiny Tumblers roll down the sides.** Have children repeat.

INTERMEDIATE

Ask: **Do the Tiny Tumblers walk or roll down the mountain?** roll

ADVANCED

Ask: **How do the Tiny Tumblers get down the mountain?** They tumble or roll down the mountain.

Learning Community— Best Practices

Building Concepts Math Mountains are introduced in a fun, creative way using a story about Tiny Tumblers. Using Math Mountains allows children to work individually on recording sets of partners for different numbers. If you wish, children can make up more things about the lives of the Tiny Tumblers.

Math Mountains and Tiny Tumblers appear again later in Unit 4 and will be continued in Unit 5.

Teaching Note

Research The Math Mountain is a drawing that is used to show the partners of a number. It visually relates the two partners to the total. Children find Math Mountains very helpful when thinking about and discussing how numbers relate to each other. In future lessons, they learn to solve Math Mountains in which any one of the numbers is the unknown number.

Digital Resource

iTools Choose 'Counters' on the Menu. Use Activity 3 'Add' with the tab for 'Activities.' Children can use counters to help them add two numbers. Then they enter the total.

Copy the first Math Mountain onto the board. Explain that children will draw small circles to show the Tiny Tumblers rolling down the Math Mountain.

MP.4 Model with Mathematics Work through the first example together. Draw circles from the bottom up. Explain that the Tiny Tumbler at the bottom of the mountain would be the first one to roll down it and that you want to draw the Tiny Tumblers in order. Draw attention to the numbers on the Math Mountain. Point out that the number at the top shows how many Tiny Tumblers live on the mountain and that the two numbers at the bottom show how many Tiny Tumblers rolled down each side. Point to each number as you discuss it.

- The first Math Mountain is a 6-mountain. How many Tiny Tumblers live on it? 6
- How many Tiny Tumblers tumbled down the left side of the mountain to play? 5 How many Tiny Tumblers tumbled down the right side of the mountain? 1

Explain that these Tiny Tumblers are a way of showing partners for 6 that they are already familiar with. In this example, the partners 5 and 1 on the sides of the mountain equal the 6 at the top.

 What kind of Math Mountain is the next mountain?

Boris: It is a 6-Mountain.

How many Tiny Tumblers live on it?

Suzanne: 6 Tiny Tumblers live on it.

How do you know?

Suzanne: I know because that is the number at the top of the Math Mountain.

What does the 4 at the bottom of the mountain tell you?

Boris: How many Tiny Tumblers rolled down that side of the mountain.

Jhana: 4 Tiny Tumblers rolled down it.

What do you need to do on this side of the Math Mountain?

Jacques: Draw 4 Tiny Tumblers rolling down the mountain.

Where will you start drawing?

Suzanne: I'll start from the bottom of that side.

What will you draw on the other side of the mountain?

Dao: I'll draw 2 Tiny Tumblers rolling down that side of the mountain, because 2 is the other partner.

MP.7 Look for Structure Talk about each Math Mountain on Student Activity Book page 168 until most children can work independently. Continue working with those who need support.

When children finish, ask them to draw a big Math Mountain on a separate sheet of paper. Let children draw Tiny Tumblers the way they picture them rolling and playing on the mountains. You can extend the discussion by asking the class what games they think the Tiny Tumblers play, how they have fun, what their cozy living places look like, and so on. Stimulate children's thinking by asking questions.

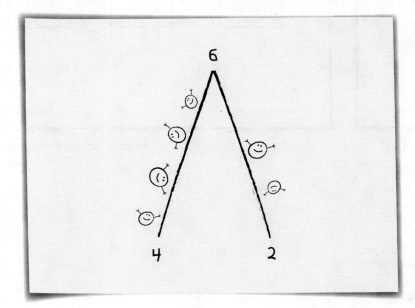

Activity continued ▶

▶ Writing and Counting Practice INDIVIDUALS

Student Activity Book pages 169 and 170 provide children with practice writing numerals and counting. More practice will be provided throughout the unit.

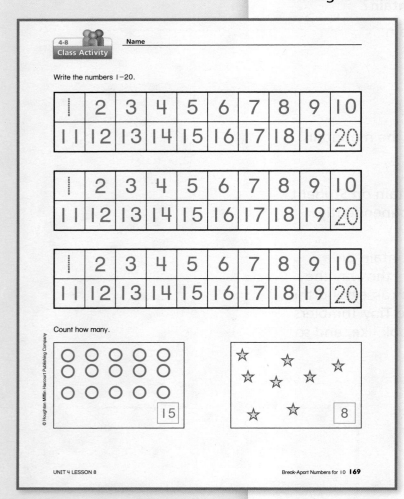

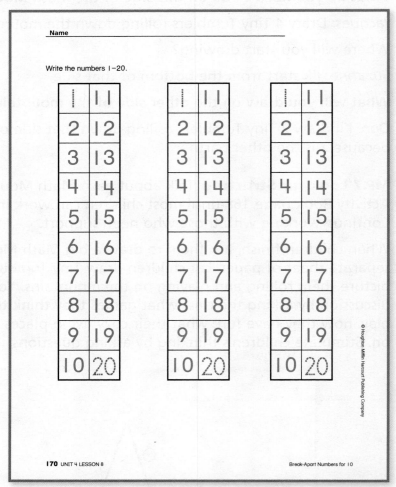

Student Activity Book pages 169–170

▶ What's the Error? WHOLE CLASS

MP.3, MP.6 Construct Viable Arguments/Critique Reasoning of Others Puzzled Penguin If desired, use the Puzzled Penguin puppet for this activity. The Puzzled Penguin activity addresses the error of incorrectly identifying a partner for 10. Write the following 4 equations on the board:

$$10 = 8 + 2$$
$$10 = 6 + 5$$
$$10 = 1 + 9$$
$$10 = 3 + 6$$

Explain that Puzzled Penguin wrote these 4 equations to show different partners for 10.

 Discuss with children whether Puzzled Penguin's work is correct and how they can help. They may refer to the equations on the Unit 4, Lesson 2 chart, if necessary.

- Puzzled Penguin wrote these equations to show partners for 10. Let's look at each equation in turn.
- The first equation shows that 8 and 2 are partners for 10. Is this correct? yes
- The next equation shows that 6 and 5 are partners for 10. Is this correct? no

Underline the 6 in the equation.

- If we want to keep the first partner, 6, what could we do to correct this equation?

Elicit suggestions from the class about how to fix the error. Stress that you want to keep 6 as one of the partners. change the 5 to 4

- That's right! If 6 is one of the partners, the other partner is 4.

Invite a volunteer to cross out the 5 and write 4 beside it.

Continue with the other 2 equations. Children should determine that the last equation should be 10 = 3 + 7.

 Formative Assessment: Check Understanding

Student Summary Draw 10 circles on the board. Shade the first circle. Ask children to name the other partner for 10. 9 Then shade the second circle and ask children to name the other partner for 10. 8 Repeat with the remaining circles.

 Fluency Check

See Assessment Guide for Fluency Check 2 on addition and subtraction within 5.

▲ On Level  Tier 1
for students having success

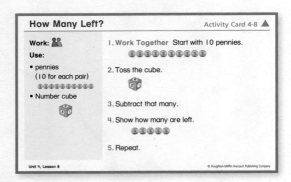

Activity Notes Model how children will begin with 10 pennies and then subtract the number of pennies shown by the number cube.

 Math Writing Prompt

Write the Subtraction Ask children to write the subtraction expression or equation for the pennies.

 MegaMath

Software Support
Country Countdown:
Counting Critters, Level C

■ Challenge
for students seeking a challenge

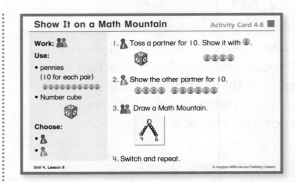

Activity Notes Demonstrate finding the first partner of 10 with the toss of the number cube and showing both partners with pennies.

 Math Writing Prompt

Write the Subtraction Ask children to write a subtraction equation with their Math Mountain numbers.

 Destination Math®

Software Support
Course I: Module 1: Unit 2: Session 3: Creating Representations of the Numbers from 5 to 10

Homework and Remembering page 75 provides children with practice identifying and recording partners for numbers up to 10. Page 76 allows children to make their own partner drawings and record the partners.

Include children's completed homework page as part of their portfolios.

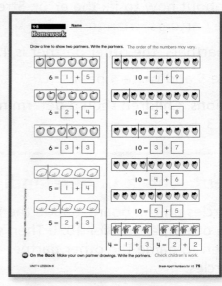

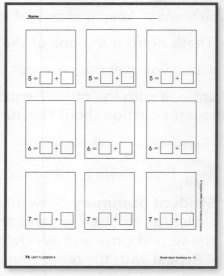

Homework and Remembering page 75   Homework and Remembering page 76

Attributes of 3-Dimensional Shapes

LESSON FOCUS
- Describe and classify three-dimensional shapes.

VOCABULARY
three-dimensional shape
solid shape
sphere
roll
stack

COMMON CORE
Mathematical Practice
CC.K–12.MP.1, CC.K–12.MP.2, C.K–12.MP.3, CC.K–12.MP.5, CC.K–12.MP.6, CC.K–12.MP.7, CC.K–12.MP.8
Mathematical Content
CC.K.MD.3, CC.K.G.1, CC.K.G.2, CC.K.G.3, CC.K.G.4, CC.K.G.5

The Day at a Glance

Teaching the Lesson

USE MATH TALK TODAY!

MATH BACKGROUND for this lesson is included on p. 329MM.

ACTIVITY FOCUS

Activity 1   Use defining attributes to describe three-dimensional shapes.

Activity 2   Classify three-dimensional shapes according to their attributes.

Activity 3   Identify and describe attributes of a sphere.

MATERIALS

Rectangles, squares, triangles, circles, hexagons, spheres, cubes, cones, cylinders • Three-dimensional-shaped objects • School dough (TRB M89) • Comparing Mat • Square-Inch Tiles

*i*Tools: Geometry • Whiteboard

Differentiated Instruction

MATERIALS

Activity Cards 4-9 • Spheres and three-dimensional-shaped objects • Paper bag • Crayons or markers • Math Journals

Soar to Success Math Intervention • MegaMath • Destination Math®

RtI   Tier 1 • Tier 2 • Tier 3

Home or School Activity

MATERIALS

Science Connection p. 384

QUICK PRACTICE 5 MINUTES

Repeated Quick Practice Use these Quick Practices from previous lessons.

Count by Ones from 60 Through 100
(See Unit 4, Lesson 2.)

Partners of 4, 5, 6, or 7
(See Unit 4, Lesson 3, 4, 5, or 6.)

DAILY ROUTINES

Counting Tens and Ones
(See pp. xxxi–xxxii.)

DIGITAL RESOURCES

Use these digital resources along with your eSAB and eTE to support your students' learning experiences.

Professional Development

Whiteboard Lesson

*i*Tools

Soar to Success Math Intervention

MegaMath

Destination Math®

COMMON CORE

Mathematical Practice
CC.K–12.MP.1, CC.K–12.MP.3,
CC.K–12.MP.6, CC.K–12.MP.7
Mathematical Content
CC.K.MD.3, CC.K.G.3, CC.K.G.4

15 MINUTES

FOCUS Use defining attributes to describe three-dimensional shapes.

MATERIALS Rectangles, triangles, circles, hexagons, spheres, cubes, cones, cylinders, three-dimensional-shaped objects

 Whiteboard Lesson

Digital Resource

*i***Tools** Choose 'Geometry' on the Menu. Use Activity 1 'Solid Figures' with the tab for 'Activities.' Children can see and identify three-dimensional shapes.

Class Management

Pacing Provide children with sufficient time to explore the attributes of three-dimensional shapes. It is important for building understanding and visual sense.

ACTIVITY 1

Attributes of Three-Dimensional Shapes

▶ Two-Dimensional Shapes WHOLE CLASS

MP.3, MP.6 Attend to Precision Have children tell about some of the two-dimensional shapes they have learned. Children should name shapes and identify attributes of rectangles, squares, triangles, circles, and hexagons.

▶ roundness or straight sides

▶ number of sides

▶ number of corners

▶ sides being of the same length or not the same length

Remind children that these shapes are called flat shapes, or two-dimensional shapes.

▶ Compare Flat and Solid Shapes SMALL GROUPS

MP.1 Make Sense of Problems Analyze Relationships Provide both two- and three-dimensional shapes to each group and instruct them to compare the same shapes you do. Guide children to take the time to let everyone in the group feel both shapes that you will name before asking questions.

Display a square and a cube. The name "cube" will not be introduced at this time. Children might refer to it as a block.

• Are these shapes the same? no
• What is different? The square is a flat shape, but the block is not flat.

Encourage children to notice that the cube is not flat. Show children that the shape not only has height, but it has depth (or, is deep).

• A shape that goes in all of these directions is called a solid shape, or a three-dimensional shape. Solid shapes take up space.

Display a circle and a sphere.

• Are these shapes the same? no
• What is the same? They are both round.
• What is different? The circle is flat but the ball is not flat.
• Which shape is a flat shape? circle
• Which shape is a solid shape? ball

▶ Compare a Circle and a Ball WHOLE CLASS

MP.6 Attend to Precision Explain a Representation Display two- or three-dimensional shapes one at a time and ask children to identify if each shape is a solid or a flat shape. Discuss what makes it a solid shape or a flat shape. A solid shape takes up more space. A solid shape goes across and back and forward like a flat shape, but it also goes up and down, or is deep. Flat shapes do not have height. They just go across and backward and forward.

MP.1 Make Sense of Problems Describe Relationships Children will compare a circle and a ball. Explain that both a circle and a ball are round. Draw some circles on the board. Discuss how a circle is a flat drawing. Then show a ball.

- A ball is round all over. What can you do with a ball? throw it; roll it
- Look around the room. What are some objects that roll? ball, marble, pencil can
- What are some objects that do not roll? book, box

▶ Find Solid Shapes SMALL GROUPS

MP.7 Look for Structure Identify Relationships Provide spheres, cubes, cones, and cylinders for each group and ask them to find objects in the classroom that are shaped like these solid shapes. Children may discover that a ball and a globe are shaped like a sphere, a block is shaped like a cube, and a pencil can is shaped like a cylinder.

....

ACTIVITY 2

Sort Solid Shapes

▶ Explore Solid Shapes SMALL GROUPS   MATH TALK

Math Talk MP.1 Make Sense of Problems Analyze Relationships Provide groups of children with a Comparing Mat, 2 spheres, 2 cones, 2 cylinders, 2 cubes, and Square-Inch Tiles. Give children time to play with and study the shapes. Tell them to think about what they know about these shapes.

- What is the same about all of these shapes? They are solid shapes.
- How do you know? They are not flat. They take up more space than flat shapes. They go across, backward and forward, and up and down.
- What is different about these shapes? Some have flat parts. Some are round.

Activity continued ▶

COMMON CORE

Mathematical Practice
CC.K–12.MP.1, CC.K–12.MP.2, CC.K–12.MP.5, CC.K–12.MP.8

Mathematical Content
CC.K.MD.3, CC.K.G.4

30 MINUTES

FOCUS Classify three-dimensional shapes according to their attributes.

MATERIALS Comparing Mat, Square-Inch Tiles, spheres, cones, cylinders, cubes

 Whiteboard Lesson

Class Management

Materials If you do not have the *Math Expressions* Kits or if you want to have additional three-dimensional shape models, have common objects shaped like the three-dimensional shapes available in your classroom. To increase manageability, you might set up a center where the shapes are displayed.

Differentiated Instruction

Special Needs Some children have difficulty following a discussion. Use both verbal and visual cues in your teaching or discussions. As often as possible, use concrete objects, drawings, or pictures of real world situations. Describe or ask children to describe the objects, diagrams, or pictures as they relate them to the math.

Teaching Note

Watch for! Children may not recognize a cylinder or a cone as a shape that can roll because it may be standing on a flat side. Tell children that they should try to turn the shapes around to see if they roll when put in a different position.

▶ **Sort Shapes** SMALL GROUPS

MP.2 Reason Abstractly Explain to children that they will be sorting the solid shapes into two groups: shapes that roll and shapes that do not roll. Demonstrate what it means to roll.

• Put all of the shapes that roll in one group.

• Put all of the shapes that do not roll in another group.

Check that children have included spheres, cylinders, and cones in the group that rolls and cubes in the group that does not roll.

MP.5 Use Appropriate Tools Guide children to sort their shapes. Then have them count the shapes. Ask them to record on the Comparing Mat how many shapes they have in each group by placing the Square-Inch Tiles to help them count. Point out that one tile represents one solid shape.

• We can use the Comparing Mat to compare the number of shapes that roll to the number of shapes that do not roll.

• Count how many shapes you have in each category. How many shapes do you have that roll? 6 How many shapes do you have that do not roll? 2

• Which has fewer? the group that does not roll

Have children look for three-dimensional objects in the room and tell which group they would fit into. Examples might include: globe (roll), block (does not roll).

▶ **Sort Shapes Another Way** SMALL GROUPS

MP.8 Use Repeated Reasoning Now children will sort the shapes into the two groups, shapes that stack and shapes that do not stack. Demonstrate what it means to stack. Remind children that some objects may need to be turned to a different position to check if they stack.

• Put all the shapes in one group. Now we are going to sort the same shapes a different way.

• Put all of the shapes that stack in one group.

• Put all of the shapes that do not stack in another group.

Check that children have included cubes and cylinders in the group that stacks and spheres in the group that does not stack. Once again, have children record their results using the Comparing Mat and Square-Inch Tiles as you ask questions similar to those above.

Have children look around the room for three-dimensional objects and tell which group they would belong in. Examples might include: book (stacks), ball (does not stack).

Attributes of Spheres

▶ Explore Roundness [WHOLE CLASS]

MP.7 Look for Structure Draw a circle on the board. Ask children questions to help them describe attributes.

- What shape do you see? a circle
- Describe the shape. It is round.
- Does it take up space? no
- Is it a flat shape or a solid shape? a flat shape

Display a ball.

- What do you see? a ball
- Describe the shape. It is round.
- Does it take up space? yes
- Is it a flat shape or a solid shape? a solid shape

▶ Describe Attributes of a Sphere [SMALL GROUPS]

MP.6 Attend to Precision Explain a Representation Provide each group with a sphere. Children will discover and describe the attributes of a sphere. Display a sphere.

- This shape is called a sphere. It is round all over. It can be any size or any color.

Instruct children to take turns holding and exploring the attributes of the sphere. Make sure all children have had a chance to hold a sphere before questioning.

- Which is a sphere, a circle or a ball? a ball
- How do you know? The ball is round all over. The circle is flat.

Ask children to tell what they know about a sphere. a solid shape, round all over, rolls, does not stack

Encourage children to look around the classroom to find objects that are shaped like a sphere. globe, ball, marble

Provide school dough and have children make spheres of different sizes and colors. Have them sort their models according to attributes. Invite small groups to explain how they sorted.

 Formative Assessment: Check Understanding

Student Summary Show children a circle and a sphere. Have them describe the attributes of each and tell how they are alike and different.

 COMMON CORE

Mathematical Practice
CC.K–12.MP.6, CC.K–12.MP.7
Mathematical Content
CC.K.G.1, CC.K.G.2, CC.K.G.3, CC.K.G.5

15 MINUTES

FOCUS Identify and describe attributes of a sphere.

MATERIALS Spheres and sphere-shaped objects, school dough (TRB M89)

Whiteboard Lesson

Teaching Note

Watch for! Children may name objects such as a coin, a sphere. Explain that although a coin is round and it rolls, it is not a sphere because it is not round all over like a ball. Have them hold the coin to see that parts of it are flat and it is not round all over.

▲ On Level ▲ RtI Tier 1

for students having success

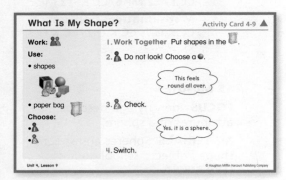

Activity Notes Have children try to determine an object is shaped like a sphere before pulling it out of the bag.

✏ Math Writing Prompt

Name Spheres Have children write about some objects that are shaped like spheres.

 MegaMath

Software Support
Shapes Ahoy: Undersea 3D, Level F

■ Challenge

for students seeking a challenge

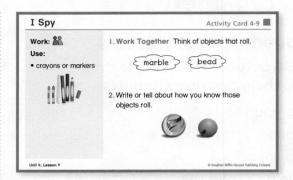

Activity Notes Encourage pairs to describe the shapes and tell how they know they can roll.

✏ Math Writing Prompt

Create Your Own Have children tell or write about a way to sort shapes into two groups.

 Destination Math®

Software Support
Course I: Module 3: Unit 2: Session 2: Three-Dimensional Shapes

Science Connection

Explore Roundness Instruct children to find objects that roll. Have pairs sit on the floor and roll balls back and forth, trying both short and long distances. Then have them experiment with rolling other objects to find things that roll like a ball. Children may discover that many things roll, but not exactly in the same way a ball rolls. They may also discover that some of the objects do not roll.

Addition and Subtraction Drawings: Grocery Store Scenario

LESSON FOCUS

- Tell, draw, and solve addition and subtraction story problems.
- Compare numbers of objects in a group using matching and counting strategies.

VOCABULARY

addition
subtraction
fewer
more
greater than
less than

COMMON CORE

Mathematical Practice
CC.K–12.MP.1, CC.K–12.MP.6
Mathematical Content
CC.K.CC.6, CC.K.CC.7, CC.K.OA.1, CC.K.OA.2

The Day at a Glance

USE MATH TALK TODAY!

Teaching the Lesson

MATH BACKGROUND for this lesson is included on p. 329GG.

ACTIVITY FOCUS

Activity 1 Tell, draw, and solve math story problems in a grocery store setting.

Activity 2 Compare the number of items in two groups, and write the numbers 1–20.

Activity 3 Match two groups of drawings to find greater or less.

MATERIALS

Student Activity Book pp. 171–172 • Grocery store vegetable display • Crayons or markers • Square-Inch Tiles (optional)

*i*Tools: Counters • Whiteboard

Differentiated Instruction

MATERIALS

Activity Cards 4-10 • Game Cards 1–5 • Crayons or markers • Math Journals

Soar to Success Math Intervention • MegaMath • Destination Math®

RtI Tier 1 • Tier 2 • Tier 3

Homework

MATERIALS

Homework and Remembering pp. 77–78

QUICK PRACTICE ⏱ 5 MINUTES

Repeated Quick Practice Use these Quick Practices from previous lessons.

Count by Ones from 60 Through 100
(See Unit 4, Lesson 2.)

Partners of 4, 5, 6 or 7 (See Unit 4, Lesson 3, 4, 5, or 6.)

DAILY ROUTINES

Counting Tens and Ones
(See pp. xxxi–xxxii.)

DIGITAL RESOURCES

Use these digital resources along with your eSAB and eTE to support your students' learning experiences.

Professional Development

Whiteboard Lesson

iTools

Soar to Success Math Intervention

MegaMath

Destination Math®

30 MINUTES

FOCUS Tell, draw, and solve math story problems in a grocery store setting.

MATERIALS Grocery store vegetable display (see the Class Management: Looking Ahead note from Unit 4, Lesson 1), crayons or markers

 Whiteboard Lesson

Teaching Notes

What to Expect from Students
Writing the entire equation is usually difficult for most kindergarten children. Only the more advanced children are likely to be able to write the entire equation. Most children will only be able to write the addition expression (for example, 6 + 3), which is less complex than writing the full equation.

Math Symbols To help children connect the subtraction sign (−) to taking away, have children do any of the following with their math drawings:

1. Draw Xs through each thing they are subtracting and then draw a subtraction sign through all of them.

2. Draw a single long subtraction sign through the objects being taken away.

3. Draw separate little subtraction signs through each object they are taking away.

ACTIVITY 1 Social Studies Connection

Add and Subtract at the Class Grocery Store

▶ Tell Math Grocery Stories   WHOLE CLASS   MATH TALK

Use the **Scenario** and **Solve and Discuss** structures for this activity.

Repeat Activity 1 from Unit 4, Lesson 4. This time, however, children buy vegetables, rather than fruit. They make their purchases from the class grocery store vegetable display.

Have children fold a blank sheet of paper in half vertically and then in half horizontally. You can discuss fraction concepts as you do this. Then review what math drawings are and their purpose. Emphasize that math drawings should be very simple.

• Does anyone remember what math drawings are and why we make them? Math drawings are simple drawings. They let us check our work, share what happened in the story, and help us tell the story again.

Point out the important steps in solving story problems: listen, draw, solve, and explain.

MP.1 Make Sense of Problems Act It Out Acting out story problems helps children think through the information with movement, props, and visuals.

Act Out Addition Ask a volunteer to act out someone buying vegetables at the store (for example, 6 potatoes + 3 carrots). Be sure children use a variety of addition situations. (See Unit 4, Lesson 4, Activity 1 for a sample of addition dialogue.) For example, Pete buys some vegetables. 6 of them are potatoes. The rest are carrots. How many carrots does Pete buy?

Then have children make simple math drawings to show the addition problem. Ask two children to explain their drawings. Then have everyone write the addition expression their drawings show (for example, 6 + 3). See how many children can write this addition expression without help. Then invite a volunteer to write it on the board. Ask children what else they need to write to make an equation (for example, = 9). Write this on the board to complete the equation.

Act Out Subtraction Repeat this activity for subtraction. Ask a volunteer to act out and discuss subtracting using the vegetables in the store (for example, 7 potatoes − 6 potatoes). Be sure children use a variety of subtraction situations. For example, Pete buys 7 potatoes and takes them home. He eats 6 potatoes. How many potatoes does he have now?

Have each child make a simple math drawing and then an expression (for example, 7 − 6) to show this subtraction problem. Have two children explain their math drawings and their subtraction expressions. Elicit the rest of the equation and write it on the board (for example, 7 − 6 = 1).

Continue with more addition and subtraction story problems.

Count and Compare

▶ **Find the Group That Is Greater or Less** | WHOLE CLASS |

MP.6 Attend to Precision Distribute Student Activity Book page 171. Point out and discuss the words *greater* and *less* in the direction line in Exercise 1. Then guide children through the first example by having them count the dots in each group and write the numbers in the boxes below. Explain that they should circle the number that is greater. In Exercise 2, explain that they should circle the number that is less.

In Exercise 3, have children write the numbers 1 through 20. Discuss the teen numbers and how they are like the numbers 1 to 10. Children might notice that each teen number has a group of ten ones and some extra ones, and that the number of extra ones goes up in the same way as the numbers less than 10 go up.

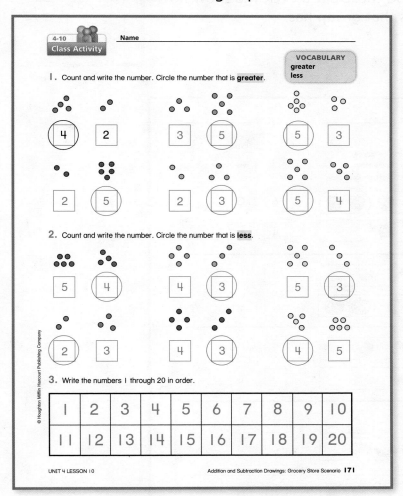

Student Activity Book page 171

COMMON CORE

Mathematical Practice
CC.K–12.MP.6
Mathematical Content
CC.K.CC.6, CC.K.CC.7

15 MINUTES

FOCUS Compare the number of items in two groups, and write the numbers 1–20.

MATERIALS Student Activity Book page 171

 Whiteboard Lesson

English Language Learners

Write **greater** and **less** on the board. Invite 7 volunteers to the front of the room. Form groups of 5 and 2.

BEGINNING

Together count how many in each group. Write 5 and 2 on the board. Ask: **Which number is greater?** 5 Say: **5 is greater.** Have children repeat. Ask: **Which number is less?** 2 Say: **2 is less.** Have children repeat.

INTERMEDIATE

Have the 7 volunteers form groups of 3 and 4. Repeat the questioning.

ADVANCED

Have the group direct the 7 volunteers to show 6 is *greater* than 1.

Differentiated Instruction

Extra Help Encourage children who are struggling to use two different colors of Square-Inch Tiles to compare the two groups. Have them arrange the tiles in a one-to-one correspondence to determine which group has less.

COMMON CORE

Mathematical Practice
CC.K–12.MP.6

Mathematical Content
CC.K.CC.6

15 MINUTES

FOCUS Match two groups of drawings to find greater or less.

MATERIALS Student Activity Book page 172

 Whiteboard Lesson

iT *i*Tools: Counters

Digital Resource

*i*Tools Choose 'Counters' on the Menu. Use Activity 2 'Compare' with the tab for 'Activities'. Children can use counters to compare different numbers of objects.

Teaching Note

What to Expect from Students On Student Activity Book page 172, children are asked to write the letters *G* for *greater* and *L* for *less*. Some children who are learning to read may find it difficult to distinguish between the two letters. You may wish to provide a visual example of *G* and *greater* and *L* and *less* for children to refer to when completing this page.

ACTIVITY 3

Match and See the Extra Things

MP.6 Attend to Precision Draw a row of 6 circles on the board with a row of 4 circles below it, aligned like the first problem on Student Activity Book page 172.

Draw lines to connect the first circles in each row, the second circles, and so on.

Ask children:

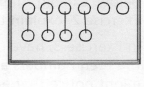

• Which circles are left over that did not make a match? Which circles are extra? the two circles in the top row

Draw a ring around those extra circles to show how many more circles that group has.

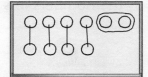

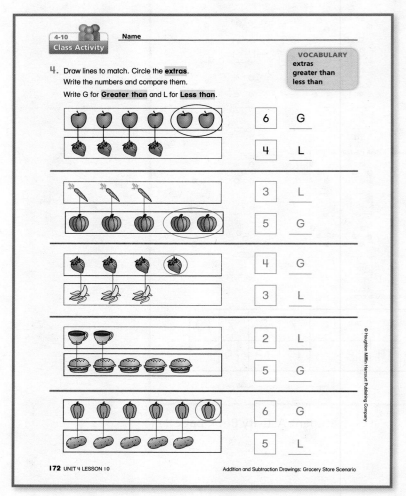

Student Activity Book page 172

▶ Match to See Greater and Less   WHOLE CLASS

Focus children's attention on the top two rows of apples and strawberries on Student Activity Book page 172. Discuss apples and strawberries with children so they can share what they know.

MP.6 Attend to Precision Have children count how many apples are in the top row and trace the number in the box. Then have them count how many strawberries are in the second row and trace that number in the second box.

• Which row has more pieces of fruit? the top row
• Which row has fewer pieces of fruit? the bottom row

Remind them that matching is a useful way to tell which of two groups of things has more and which has fewer.

Have children use the matching procedure to complete Student Activity Book page 172. For the first exercise, they should trace the lines to match the first 4 apples with the 4 strawberries, trace the circle around the extra 2 apples in the top row, trace how many are in each group, and then trace *G* for *greater* and *L* for *less*.

✓ Formative Assessment: Check Understanding

Student Summary Ask children to tell whether 7 apples is greater than or less than 3 oranges. Have them explain the reasoning for their answer. Guide them to demonstrate a matching or counting procedure to support their answer using objects or a drawing.

▲ On Level  Tier 1

for students having success

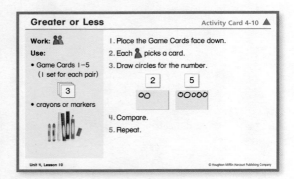

Activity Notes Show children how to overlap the cards to do a direct image comparison.

 Math Writing Prompt

Compare Write the numbers 5 and 4 on the board. Have children write the numbers and use the words *greater* or *less* to compare.

 MegaMath

Software Support
Country Countdown: Counting Critters, Level H

■ Challenge

for students seeking a challenge

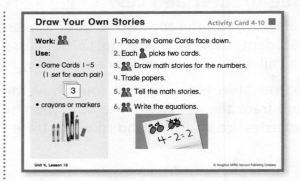

Activity Notes Remind children how to write an expression or an equation.

 Math Writing Prompt

Write an Equation Have children switch the partners in $2 + 3 = 5$ and then write the new equation.

 Destination Math®

Software Support
Course I: Module 2: Unit 1: Session 1: Combining and Joining Within 10

Distribute Homework and Remembering pages 77 and 78. Page 77 provides children with more practice identifying the group that is greater or less and writing numbers. On page 78, children practice counting and writing how many in each group. They write *G* or *L* to show which is greater or less.

✓ Include children's Homework and Remembering page as part of their portfolios.

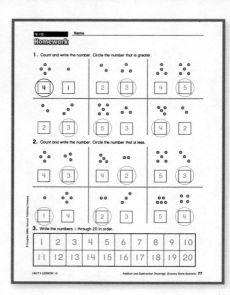

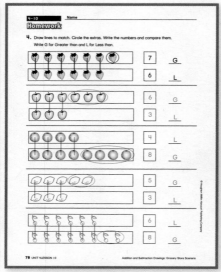

Homework and Remembering pages 77–78

Partners of 10 with 5-Groups

LESSON FOCUS

- Find partners of 10 in 5-groups.
- Record sets of partners for 10, 6, 5, 4, 3, and 2.

VOCABULARY

5-frame
partner
Tiny Tumbler
Math Mountain

COMMON CORE

Mathematical Practice
CC.K–12.MP.3, CC.K–12.MP.6, CC.K–12.MP.7
Mathematical Content
CC.K.OA.3, K.OA.4

The Day at a Glance

Teaching the Lesson

 USE MATH TALK TODAY!

MATH BACKGROUND for this lesson is included on pp. 329HH and 329KK.

ACTIVITY FOCUS

Activity 1   Find partners of 10 in 5-groups using Square-Inch Tiles.

Activity 2   Find partners of 10 in a row of 10.

Activity 3   Draw partners on Math Mountains.

MATERIALS

- Student Activity Book pp. 173–174 • Square-Inch Tiles • Crayons
- iTools: Counters • Whiteboard

Differentiated Instruction

MATERIALS

- Activity Cards 4-11 • Crayons or markers • Jars • Counters • Math Journals
- Soar to Success Math Intervention • MegaMath • Destination Math®
- RtI   Tier 1 • Tier 2 • Tier 3

Homework

MATERIALS

- Homework and Remembering pp. 79–80

QUICK PRACTICE ⏱ 5 MINUTES

Repeated Quick Practice Use this Quick Practice from previous lessons.

Partners of 4, 5, 6, or 7 (See Unit 4, Lesson 3, 4, 5, or 6.)

Count to 100 by Tens

Goal Count by tens and understand how many tens are in each decade number (10, 20, 30, ... to 100).

Materials 120 Poster, pointer, "How Many Tens?" Card

Point to the numbers in the bottom row of the 120 Poster while children count by tens and flash 10 fingers with each count.

- Ready. 10, 20, 30, 40, 50, 60, 70, 80, 90, 100. 100 is ten tens!

Meanwhile, a **Student Leader** wears the "How Many Tens?" Card and raises one finger for each decade number that is counted (starting with one finger for 10 and ending with all ten fingers for 100).

DAILY ROUTINES

Counting Tens and Ones
(See pp. xxxi–xxxii.)

DIGITAL RESOURCES

Use these digital resources along with your eSAB and eTE to support your students' learning experiences.

 Professional Development

 Whiteboard Lesson

 iTools

 Soar to Success Math Intervention

 MegaMath

 Destination Math®

COMMON CORE

Mathematical Practice
CC.CC.K–12.MP.7

Mathematical Content
CC.K.OA.3, K.OA.4

20 MINUTES

FOCUS Find partners of ten in 5-groups using Square-Inch Tiles.

MATERIALS Square-Inch Tiles (10 per child)

 Whiteboard Lesson

Learning Community— Best Practices

Building Concepts This is similar to the activity in Unit 4, Lessons 2 and 8. In the current lesson, children learn to arrange their tiles in a 5-group, rather than a single row.

Discover 10-Partners in 5-Groups

▶ Arrange Tiles in 5-Groups [WHOLE CLASS]

Have the class decide what they want the Square-Inch Tiles to be today. In this example, the dot side of the tile is a little bug. Sometimes the bugs are awake and turned up so that they can be seen, and sometimes they are sleeping under the tile and turned over so that they are hidden. There are always 10 bugs in total. Tell children:

• Today, the bugs are closer together instead of in a long row.

• They are sleeping in 5-groups, or in two rows of 5. Let's put our 10 sleeping bugs in rows of 5.

• Turn your tiles down so we can see all of the bugs sleeping.

• One bug wants to get up and play. Let's turn one bug over.

• How many bugs are sleeping now? 9

• How many bugs are awake? 1

• How many bugs in total? 10

MP.7 Look for Structure Continue in this manner, having children turn over the bugs one at a time. Record the partners on the board:

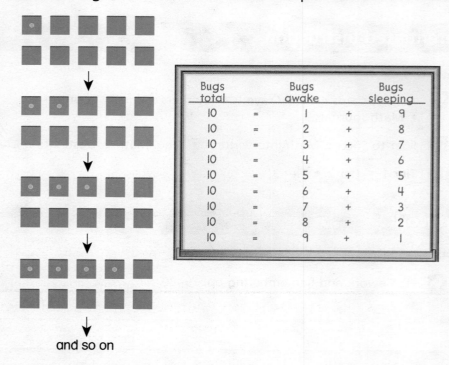

Bugs total		Bugs awake		Bugs sleeping
10	=	1	+	9
10	=	2	+	8
10	=	3	+	7
10	=	4	+	6
10	=	5	+	5
10	=	6	+	4
10	=	7	+	3
10	=	8	+	2
10	=	9	+	1

and so on

MP.7 Use Structure Help children notice that they can quickly see how many bugs are asleep and awake when they are arranged in two rows of 5. Remind children that using 5-groups will help them count faster.

Have children discuss the numbers and number sequences they see in the chart on the board.

Discover 10-Partners in a Row of 10

COMMON CORE
Mathematical Practice
CC.CC.K–12.MP.7
Mathematical Content
CC.K.OA.3, K.OA.4

20 MINUTES
FOCUS Find partners of 10 in a row of 10.
MATERIALS Student Activity Book page 173

Whiteboard Lesson

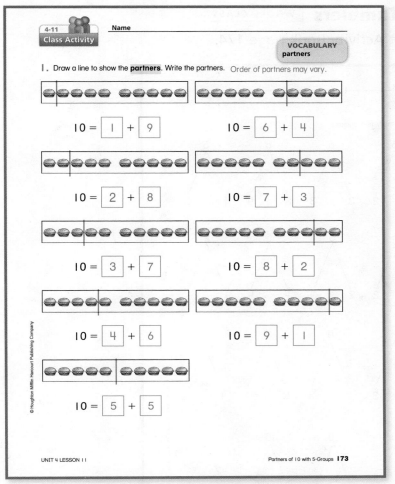

Student Activity Book page 173

▶ Find 10-Partners in a Row of 10 [WHOLE CLASS]

MP.7 Look for Structure On Student Activity Book page 173, children will separate the sandwiches into partners of 10 by drawing Break-Apart Sticks. Emphasize that they will find partner switches again. This time they will start with 1 + 9.

Have children discuss the numbers they see on the completed page.

Ask if anyone has played *The Unknown Partner Game* at home. (The game was described in the Family Letter sent home in Unit 4, Lesson 5.) Encourage children to continue to play the game at home with family members.

English Language Learners

Draw and identify two *rows* of 5 and a *row* of 10 on the board. Have children count the tiles in each.

BEGINNING

Point and say: **This is a *row* of 10. There are 10 tiles in 1 *row*.** Have children repeat. Point to the two *rows* of 5. Say: **There are 2 *rows* of 5.**

INTERMEDIATE

Point to the two *rows* of 5 Say: **This group has 2 *rows*.** Ask: **How many *rows* are in a *row* of 10?** 1 row

ADVANCED

Have children say what is alike and different about the sets of tiles. Make sure they describe the *rows*.

Teaching Note

Math Background As children find and record partners of a number, they are able to see how the partners relate to the total. In addition situations, they develop visual recognition of small addition problems.

COMMON CORE

Mathematical Practice
CC.CC.K–12.MP.3, CC.CC.K–12.MP.6,
CC.CC.K–12.MP.7

Mathematical Content
CC.K.OA.3, K.OA.4

15 MINUTES

FOCUS Draw partners on Math Mountains.

MATERIALS Student Activity Book page 174

Whiteboard Lesson

*i*T *i*Tools: Counters

Digital Resource

*i*Tools Choose 'Counters' on the Menu. Use Activity 3 'Add' with the tab for 'Activities'. Children can use counters to help them add 2 numbers. Then they enter the total.

Learning Community— Best Practices

Building Concepts Throughout the grades, Math Mountains and the Tiny Tumblers work as a visual representation for relating addition and subtraction. Kindergartners begin by drawing partners in this creative context.

Learning Community— Best Practices

MATH TALK What types of questions are you asking your students? Are you asking questions that elicit a short answer, or do you probe to learn more about children's thinking as they tell about their work? If possible, make a video or audio recording of yourself leading a math lesson. Play it back and make notes about the types of questions you ask. Reflect on any changes you would like to make. Write a date in your planning book to do this again and make note of your professional growth.

ACTIVITY 3

Draw Tiny Tumblers on Math Mountains

▶ **Draw Tiny Tumblers** WHOLE CLASS

Distribute Student Activity Book page 174.

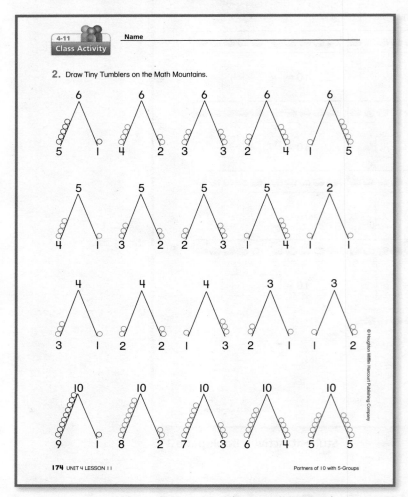

Student Activity Book page 174

Ask children what they remember about the similar page in Unit 4, Lesson 8, and about the Tiny Tumblers. Discuss again what the Tiny Tumblers might be playing on the sides of Math Mountain. Have children complete Student Activity Book page 174 by drawing Tiny Tumblers to show the partners of the number at the top of the Math Mountain.

MP.7 Look for Structure When children have finished, discuss the numbers they see on the page.

• Look at the top row. 6 is at the top of each mountain, and the partners for 6 are below. What do you see in the partners for 6? The left number decreases and the right number increases; the Math Mountains on the outside show partner switches.

▶ What's the Error? [WHOLE CLASS]

MP.3, MP.6 Construct Viable Arguments/Critique the Reasoning of Others Explain that Puzzled Penguin was asked to wake up bugs and then say the partners of 10. Draw the following 5-groups on the board.

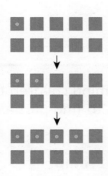

Point to the first two rows of 5.

- Puzzled Penguin woke up one bug and said the partners were 1 and 9.

Point to the second two rows of 5.

- Puzzled Penguin woke up another bug and said the partners were 2 and 8.

Point to the third two rows of 5.

- Then Puzzled Penguin woke up two more bugs and said the partners were 3 and 7. Is Puzzled Penguin correct? No. Puzzled Penguin woke up four bugs and said the partners were 3 and 7.

- What did Puzzled Penguin do wrong? Puzzled Penguin did not say the right partners. Puzzled Penguin turned over 4 bugs and should have said the partners were 4 and 6. The partners should match the number of tiles shown.

Invite a volunteer to correctly say the partners of 10 that match the tiles shown, 4 and 6.

✓ Formative Assessment: Check Understanding

Student Summary Ask children to name as many of the 10-partners that they know. Invite volunteers to record the 10-partners as they are named.

MATH TALK *in ACTION* **How can we make sure that we find all of the partners for ten?**

Jill: We can use Square-Inch Tiles to show the partners.

Eduardo: We have to remember to turn over one more tile each time.

Bonnie: We make the first partner one more each time.

Jill: We can check the partners we find. We can see if all of the numbers are there.

Eduardo: The numbers should be 1, 2, 3, 4, 5, 6, 7, 8, and 9.

Bonnie: If we have all of those numbers, we have found all of the partners for ten.

You are correct.

▲ On Level ▲RtI Tier 1
for students having success

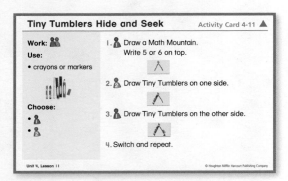

Activity Notes Model how to make a Math Mountain and how the partners work together.

✏️ Math Writing Prompt

Partner Equation Have children draw a Math Mountain for 5 and write a partner equation.

 MegaMath

Software Support
Country Countdown: Counting Critters, Level C

■ Challenge
for students seeking a challenge

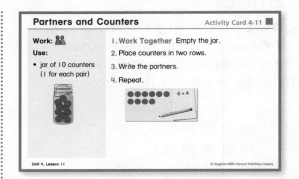

Activity Notes Remind children to sort the counters into heads and tails to find partners for 10.

✏️ Math Writing Prompt

Subtraction Equations Challenge children to write 10-partner subtraction equations using 8 and 2 and 5 and 5.

 Destination Math®

Software Support
Course I: Module 1: Unit 2: Session 3: Creating Representations of the Numbers from 5 to 10

Distribute Homework and Remembering pages 79 and 80. These pages provide practice drawing Tiny Tumblers on the front and making 10-Partners on the back. They are similar to the pages completed in class.

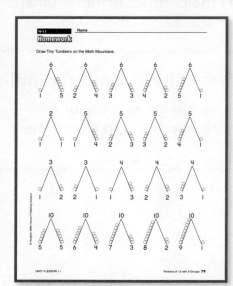
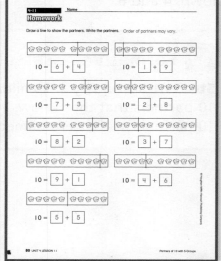

Homework and Remembering pages 79–80

Addition Equations

LESSON FOCUS

- Show teen numbers as a group of ten ones and extra ones and as 10 and a 1-digit number.
- Add within 6 through 10 and practice addition and subtraction fluency within 5.

VOCABULARY

partner
equation
addition
add
equal
equal sign (=)
addition sign (+)

COMMON CORE

Mathematical Practice
CC.K–12.MP.1, CC.K–12.MP.2, CC.K–12.MP.4, CC.K–12.MP.6, CC.K–12.MP.7
Mathematical Content
CC.K.CC.4a, CC.K.CC.4b, CC.K.CC.4c, CC.K.OA.1, CC.K.OA.2, CC.K.OA.5, CC.K.NBT.1

The Day at a Glance

USE MATH TALK TODAY!

Teaching the Lesson

MATH BACKGROUND for this lesson is included on pp. 329II–329JJ, 329KK, 329LL, and 329MM.

ACTIVITY FOCUS

Activity 1 Model numbers 11–20 using 10-sticks and centimeter cubes.

Activity 2 Match and compare teen equations to numbers 1–20 using Teen Equation Cards and the 1–20 Board.

Activity 3 Add within 6 through 10, order numbers 1–18 by completing a dot-to-dot, and practice addition and subtraction fluency within 5.

MATERIALS

- Student Activity Book pp. 175–178 (includes Family Letter) • 1–20 Boards • 10-sticks • Centimeter cubes • Teen Equation Cards
- iTools: Counters • Whiteboard

Differentiated Instruction

MATERIALS

- Activity Cards 4-12 • Large index cards • Scissors • Number Tiles 1–5 • Math Journals
- Soar to Success Math Intervention • MegaMath • Destination Math®
- **RtI** Tier 1 • Tier 2 • Tier 3

Home and School Connection

MATERIALS

- Family Letter (Student Activity Book pp. 175–176)

QUICK PRACTICE ⏱ 5 MINUTES

Repeated Quick Practice Use these Quick Practices from previous lessons.

Count to 100 by Tens Point to the numbers in the bottom row of the 120 Poster while children count and flash 10 fingers with each count. A **Student Leader** wears the "How Many Tens?" Card and raises one finger for each decade number that is counted. (See Unit 4, Lesson 11.)

Partners of 4, 5, 6, or 7 (See Unit 4, Lesson 3, 4, 5, or 6.)

DAILY ROUTINES

Counting Tens and Ones
(See pp. xxxi–xxxii.)

DIGITAL RESOURCES

Use these digital resources along with your eSAB and eTE to support your students' learning experiences.

 Professional Development

 Whiteboard Lesson

 iTools

 Soar to Success Math Intervention

MegaMath

 Destination Math®

COMMON CORE

Mathematical Practice
CC.K–12.MP.6, CC.K–12.MP.7

Mathematical Content
CC.K.CC.4a, CC.K.CC.4b,
CC.K.CC.4c, CC.K.NBT.1

20 MINUTES

FOCUS Model numbers 11–20 using 10-sticks and centimeter cubes.

MATERIALS 1–20 Boards (back; 1 per child), 10-sticks (11 per child), centimeter cubes (45 per child)

 Whiteboard Lesson

*i*T *i*Tools: Counters

Digital Resource

*i*Tools Choose 'Counters' on the Menu. Use Activity 1 'Count' with the tab for 'Activities'. Children can use counters to count.

ACTIVITY 1

Make Teen Numbers on the 1–20 Board

▶ **Make Teen Numbers**

You can use the **Student Pairs** structure for this activity.

This activity is repeated from Unit 4, Lessons 3, 5, and 7. See Lesson 3, where it was introduced, for additional detail.

MP.6 Attend to Precision Discuss with children how to use 10-sticks and centimeter cubes to make teen numbers on the 1–20 Board.

Then have children work alone or in helping Student Pairs to make the teen numbers 11–20. You may wish to pair more advanced learners with children who are having difficulty.

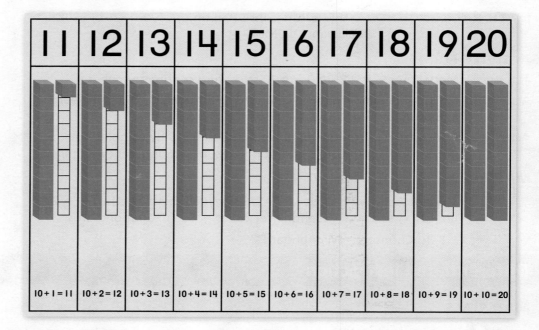

MP.7 Look for Structure When children have placed 10-sticks and centimeter cubes on all of their numbers, have them discuss the numbers they see. There are many ways they can describe the numbers.

• How can you describe the numbers? There is one more cube for each number as I count up; there is one less cube for each number as I count back; the 10-stick is always there, but the centimeter cubes vary; the number of ones matches the number of centimeter cubes, and the groups of ten match the 10-sticks.

Elicit as many ways to describe the numbers as you can from children.

Place Teen Equation Cards on the 1–20 Board

▶ Match Equations to Teen Numbers WHOLE CLASS

MP.6 Attend to Precision This activity also appears in Unit 4, Lessons 3, 5, and 7. Distribute the Teen Equation Cards children cut out in Lesson 3. Children will place the cards on the 1–20 Board, matching the Teen Equation Cards to the teen numbers on the 1–20 Board. Cards can be placed at the top under the teen number or at the bottom.

▶ Write Equations WHOLE CLASS

Ask children to look at the Teen Equation Cards.

• Do you see anything different about the equations on the two sets of cards? The teen number is first and on the left in one set; the teen number is last and on the right in the other set.

MP.7 Look for Structure Discuss and review the meaning of the equal sign and addition sign. Then discuss how you have been writing equations.

• For showing partners, we have been writing the total first and then the equal sign. After the equal sign, we have been writing the partners.

• But for addition, we have been writing the partners first with an addition sign in between to show that they are put together (added). Then we have been writing the equal sign and the total on the right.

• We can write the equation either way. They are both correct.

Be sure children understand that both ways are correct because in an equation, the numbers or operations on both sides have the same value, or are equal. This is true no matter which side the numbers or operations are on.

COMMON CORE

Mathematical Practice
CC.K–12.MP.6, CC.K–12.MP.7
Mathematical Content
CC.K.CC.4a, CC.K.CC.4b, CC.K.NBT.1

15 MINUTES

FOCUS Match and compare teen equations to numbers 1–20 using Teen Equation Cards and the 1–20 Board.

MATERIALS Teen Equation Cards (both sets, A and B, per child; TRB M49), 1–20 Boards (1 per child)

 Whiteboard Lesson

English Language Learners

Write **match** on the board. Say: **When we match things, we put alike things together.** Draw groups of 1, 2, and 3 dots on the board. Invite volunteers to match the number cards with the groups of 1, 2, or 3 dots.

BEGINNING

Say: **We match the number to the group of dots.** Ask children to repeat.

INTERMEDIATE

Ask: **What do you do when you put alike things together?** match them

ADVANCED

Ask: **What do you do when you put each number with the correct group of dots?** match the group of dots and the number

---

Teaching Note

What to Expect from Students By now, most children will be comfortable using both sets of Teen Equation Cards (set A format: 12 = 10 + 2; set B format: 10 + 2 = 12). If some children are still using just one set of cards, you may want to consider introducing the other set to them now.

COMMON CORE
Mathematical Practice
CC.K–12.MP.1, CC.K–12.MP.2,
CC.K–12.MP.4
Mathematical Content
CC.K.OA.1, CC.K.OA.2, CC.K.OA.5

20 MINUTES

FOCUS Add within 6 through 10, order numbers 1–18 by completing a dot-to-dot, and practice addition and subtraction fluency within 5.

MATERIALS Student Activity Book page 177

 Whiteboard Lesson

Teaching Notes

Math Background You have been developing the connections among real world situations, story problems about situations, drawings, finger solutions, and equations. Today, children will work in the opposite direction. They will look at the equations on Student Activity Book page 177, tell story problems, and use fingers (or make simple math drawings) to solve them. It is very important to support all of these connections so that equations remain meaningful to children.

What to Expect from Students In this lesson, children will have practice solving addition equations within 6 to 10 as well as addition and subtraction equations to build fluency within 5. You may want to go over Student Activity Book pages 177 and 178 with the class. Monitor children who are having difficulty and suggest tools and strategies to help them be successful.

ACTIVITY 3

Add Within 6 Through 10

▶ Review Addition Equations and Signs WHOLE CLASS

Distribute Student Activity Book page 177.

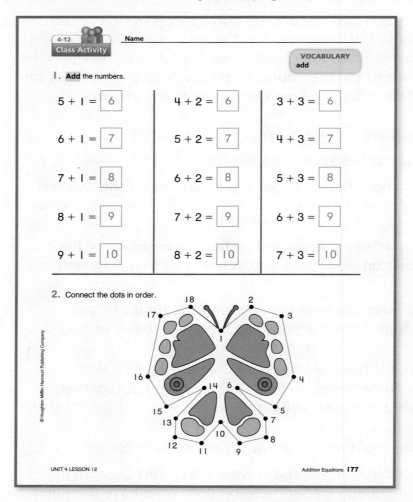

Student Activity Book page 177

MP.2 Reason Abstractly Connect addition equations to children's experiences.

• What do you see on the top of the page? addition equations

• Where else have you written or seen addition equations? in stories at the park (Unit 3); in stories at the grocery store (Unit 4)

• Ask children to give a story problem for each of the first three problems to make sure they are understanding the addition situations.

Remind children of this easy way to remember the addition sign that uses their arms:

• The addition sign is shown by having one arm vertical and one arm horizontal. For addition, we add to, or put together, and we show it with our two arms.

▶ Solve the Addition Equations `WHOLE CLASS`

Focus children on the first problem, 5 + 1, on Student Activity Book page 177, and elicit ways to solve it. Then invite them to share their methods for solving the next problem, 6 + 1.

MP.1 Make Sense of Problems Use a Different Method What other methods could you use for solving this problem? I could use my fingers; I already know that 6 and 1 are partners of 7; I could draw 6 circles and 1 circle, and count them all.

For most children, using fingers is faster than drawing circles, but allow children to draw if this is their preferred method.

Solve as many problems together as necessary for children in your class to feel confident. Ask several children to prove their answers by using fingers, objects, or drawings.

• Can you show with fingers (objects, drawings) that your answer is correct?

• Look at the first column. What do you notice about the partners in each of the problems? The first partner increases by one each time. The second partner is the same number.

When children are ready, have them complete the page independently. You may wish to choose some **Student Leaders** to provide assistance to those who need it.

▶ Drawing a Dot-to-Dot from 1 Through 18 `INDIVIDUALS`

MP.4 Model with Mathematics Direct children's attention to the bottom half of Student Activity Book page 177.

• How would you do this exercise? Start at 1 and draw a line to 2, then 3, and so on, until you get to the last number.

 Fluency Check

On Student Activity Book page 178, encourage children to complete all of the addition and subtraction equations to practice fluency within 5. You may want them to complete the addition equations at one session and the subtraction equations at another session. Remind children of the methods for solving the equations.

 Formative Assessment: Check Understanding

Student Summary Select a number on the 1–20 Board, such as 14. Ask children to choose the Teen Equation Card that matches the number. Then have them tell the meaning of the addition and equal signs.

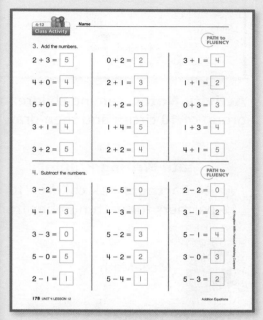

Student Activity Book page 178

▲ On Level ▲ RtI Tier 1

for students having success

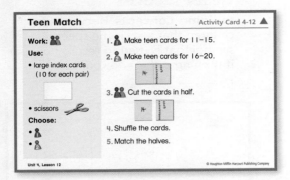

Teen Match Activity Card 4-12 ▲

Work: 👥
Use:
- large index cards (10 for each pair)
- scissors ✂

Choose:
- 🧍
- 🧍

1. 🧍 Make teen cards for 11–15.
2. 🧍 Make teen cards for 16–20.
3. 👥 Cut the cards in half.
4. Shuffle the cards.
5. Match the halves.

Unit 4, Lesson 12 © Houghton Mifflin Harcourt Publishing Company

Activity Notes Remind children to first draw a group of 10 circles and then draw the extras.

✏ **Math Writing Prompt**

Write Partners Ask children to write the 10-partners for each number from 11–20.

 MegaMath

Software Support
Country Countdown: Block Busters, Level G

■ Challenge

for students seeking a challenge

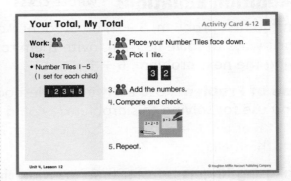

Your Total, My Total Activity Card 4-12 ■

Work: 👥
Use:
- Number Tiles 1–5 (1 set for each child)

1 2 3 4 5

1. Place your Number Tiles face down.
2. Pick 1 tile.

3 2

3. Add the numbers.
4. Compare and check.
5. Repeat.

Unit 4, Lesson 12 © Houghton Mifflin Harcourt Publishing Company

Activity Notes Explain that each child should choose from their own set of tiles.

✏ **Math Writing Prompt**

Write Equations Have children write equations using Number Tiles 1–5 for partners.

 Destination Math®

Software Support
Course I: Module 2: Unit 1: Session 3: Sums Within 20, With 10 as One Addend

Family Letter Remind children to take home the Family Letter on Student Activity Book page 175. This letter explains how the concept of partners is developed in *Math Expressions*. It gives parents and guardians a better understanding of the learning that goes on in math class and creates a bridge between school and home. A Spanish translation of this letter is on the following page in the Student Activity Book.

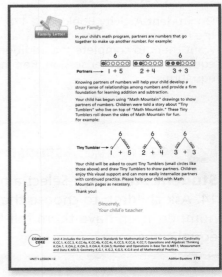

Student Activity Book page 175

More Partners of 10 with 5-Groups

LESSON FOCUS
• Find partners of 10 and review partners of 7, 8, and 9.

VOCABULARY
5-frame
Tiny Tumbler
Math Mountain

COMMON CORE

Mathematical Practice
CC.K–12.MP.3, CC.K–12.MP.6, CC.K–12.MP.7, CC.K–12.MP.8
Mathematical Content
CC.K.OA.1, CC.K.OA.3, CC.K.OA.4

The Day at a Glance

Teaching the Lesson

USE MATH TALK TODAY!

MATH BACKGROUND for this lesson is included on pp. 329HH, 329KK, and 329LL.

ACTIVITY FOCUS
Activity 1   Find 10-Partners in 5-groups using Square-Inch Tiles.
Activity 2   Draw partners of 6, 8, and 10 on Math Mountains.
Activity 3   Read expressions and review partners of 7, 8, and 9.

MATERIALS
📖 Student Activity Book pp. 179–180 • Square-Inch Tiles • Number Tiles • +/− Tiles • Break-Apart Sticks • Counting Mat

💻 iTools: Counters • Whiteboard

Differentiated Instruction

MATERIALS
📖 Activity Cards 4-13 • Number Tiles 1–5 • Math Journals

💻 Soar to Success Math Intervention • MegaMath • Destination Math®

🔺 **RtI** Tier 1 • Tier 2 • Tier 3

Homework

MATERIALS
📖 Homework and Remembering pp. 81–82

QUICK PRACTICE ⏱ 5 MINUTES

Repeated Quick Practice Use these Quick Practices from previous lessons.

Count to 100 by Tens
(See Unit 4, Lesson 11.)

Partners of 4, 5, 6, or 7
(See Unit 4, Lesson 3, 4, 5, or 6.)

DAILY ROUTINES
Counting Tens and Ones
(See pp. xxxi–xxxii.)

DIGITAL RESOURCES
Use these digital resources along with your eSAB and eTE to support your students' learning experiences.

Professional Development

Whiteboard Lesson

iTools

Soar to Success Math Intervention

MegaMath

Destination Math®

COMMON CORE

Mathematical Practice
CC.K–12.MP.7

Mathematical Content
CC.K.OA.1, CC.K.OA.3, CC.K.OA.4

20 MINUTES

FOCUS Find 10-Partners in 5-groups using Square-Inch Tiles.

MATERIALS Square-Inch Tiles (10 per child)

 Whiteboard Lesson

ACTIVITY 1

Discover 10-Partners in 5-Groups

▶ Arrange Tiles in 5-Groups [WHOLE CLASS]

Have the class decide what they want the Square-Inch Tiles to be today. The example provided here is the same as in Unit 4, Lesson 11.

- The dot side of the tile is a little bug. Sometimes the bugs are awake (with tiles turned dot side up so you can see them). Sometimes they are asleep under the tile (with dot side down so they are hidden). There are always 10 bugs in total.

- They are sleeping in 5-groups, or in two rows of 5. Let's put our 10 sleeping bugs in rows of 5.

- Turn your dots down to show the bugs are sleeping.

- One bug wants to get up and play. Let's turn one bug over.

- How many bugs are sleeping now? 9 How many bugs are awake? 1 How many bugs in total? 10

MP.7 Look for Structure Continue in this manner, having children turn over the bugs one at a time. Help children notice that they can easily see how many bugs are asleep and awake when they are arranged in two rows of 5.

Record the partners on the board:

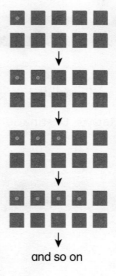

and so on

Bugs total		Bugs awake		Bugs sleeping
10	=	1	+	9
10	=	2	+	8
10	=	3	+	7
10	=	4	+	6
10	=	5	+	5
10	=	6	+	4
10	=	7	+	3
10	=	8	+	2
10	=	9	+	1

Draw Tiny Tumblers on Math Mountains

▶ Draw Tiny Tumblers PAIRS

Direct children's attention to Student Activity Book page 179. This page is similar to those in Unit 4, Lessons 8 and 11.

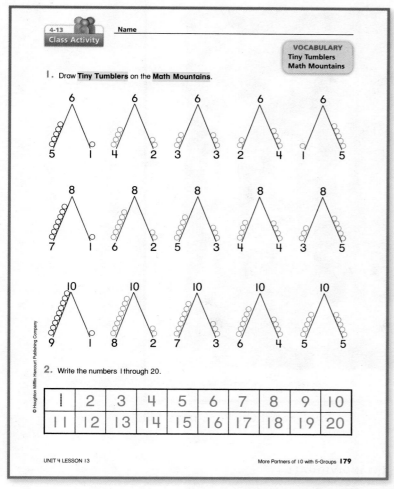

Student Activity Book page 179

MP.3 Critique the Reasoning of Others Encourage children to share what they remember about the similar pages in previous lessons and about the Tiny Tumblers. As children complete the top section of the page by drawing the partners, have pairs of children check each other's pages. At the bottom of the page, children write the numbers 1–20.

▶ Do Finger Wiggles WHOLE CLASS

MP.6 Attend to Precision Lead the class in doing finger wiggles to show the partners of 2–10. You can refer back to Unit 4, Lesson 2, Activity 1, which focuses on finger wiggles for the numbers 2–7. For the current lesson, also include the numbers 8–10.

 COMMON CORE

Mathematical Practice
CC.K–12.MP.3, CC.K–12.MP.6
Mathematical Content
CC.K.OA.1, CC.K.OA.3

15 MINUTES

FOCUS Draw partners of 6, 8, and 10 on Math Mountains.

MATERIALS Student Activity Book page 179

Whiteboard Lesson

English Language Learners

Write *total* on the board. Say: **Total means how many in the whole group.** Ask children to hold up 5 fingers. Then have them hold up 5 more fingers.

BEGINNING

Together count the number of fingers in all. Say: **I am holding up 10 fingers in total.** Ask children to repeat.

INTERMEDIATE

Say: **You are holding up 10 fingers in total.** Ask: **What word tells how many in the whole group?** total

ADVANCED

Have children count to find the total number of fingers. Ask: **What does the total tell you?** The total tells you there are 10 in the whole group.

Teaching Note

What to Expect from Students
Children continue number writing practice on the bottom of Student Activity Book page 179. Some children may be quite proficient, but you may need to continue to work with individual children on particular numbers.

Class Management

Remember to practice each finger wiggle several times so that children can really feel the number and each of its partners. If wiggling fingers for both partners is too difficult, you can have children just bend fingers to show the first partner and wiggle fingers for the other partner.

COMMON CORE

Mathematical Practice
CC.K–12.MP.6, CC.K–12.MP.7,
CC.K–12.MP.8

Mathematical Content
CC.K.OA.1, CC.K.OA.3

15 MINUTES

FOCUS Read expressions and review partners of 7, 8, and 9.

Materials Student Activity Book page 180, Square-Inch Tiles, Number Tiles, +/– Tiles, Break-Apart Sticks, Counting Mat

 Whiteboard Lesson

iT *i*Tools: Counters

Digital Resource

*i***Tools** Choose 'Counters' on the Menu. Use Activity 3 'Add' with the tab for 'Activities'. Children can use counters to help them add 2 numbers. Then they enter the total.

Differentiated Instruction

Extra Help Some children may find it helpful to cross out the expressions that are *not* partners of 8 prior to drawing the line to the gate.

ACTIVITY 3

Read Expressions

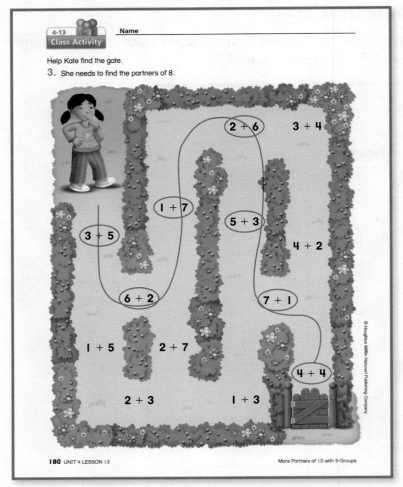

Student Activity Book page 180

▶ Partners of 8 [INDIVIDUALS]

MP.6 Attend to Precision On Student Activity Book page 180 children will be completing a garden maze in which they identify sets of partners for 8. You may wish to begin by reviewing the partners of 8. Draw a Math Mountain for 8 on the board and ask a volunteer to draw the Tiny Tumblers.

Continue with several other Math Mountains that show other partners of 8.

Distribute Student Activity Book page 180. Read the rhyme at the top. Explain that there are several different ways to get to the gate, but Kate needs to follow the partners of 8.

Suggest that children first draw rings around the partners of 8, and then draw a line from Kate to the gate by following the ringed numbers. Some children will need to refer to the board or use their fingers or drawings to determine which sets of numbers are partners of 8.

▶ **Critical Thinking** WHOLE CLASS   MATH TALK

MP.8 Use Repeated Reasoning Draw Conclusions After they have completed the page, ask children to look again carefully at the partners on the page. Ask questions such as these to help them draw conclusions.

- There are many partners of 8 in the garden maze. Are all of the partners here? no

- Which partners of 8 are *not* shown? 0 + 8 or 8 + 0

▶ **Reviewing Partners of 7, 8, and 9** WHOLE CLASS

Children will use Square-Inch Tiles, Number Tiles, +/− Tiles, and Break-Apart Sticks to show partners. You may wish to have children do their work on the Counting Mat. Encourage children to begin by finding partners of 7.

Remind children to practice partner switches. Have them switch the Number Tiles and move the Break-Apart Stick.

MP.7 Look for Structure Identify Relationships Children may suggest finding the partners in any order. However, when you write them and draw them on the board, show them in the order below. Invite children to discuss their observations of the number relationships.

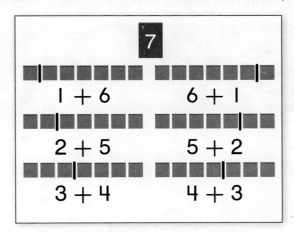

Have children make the target number with their fingers and then separate their fingers to show the partners.

Continue by having children find and show the partners for 8 and 9.

 Formative Assessment: Check Understanding

Student Summary Ask children to name a set of partners for 9 in an addition expression or equation.

▲ On Level  Tier 1
for students having success

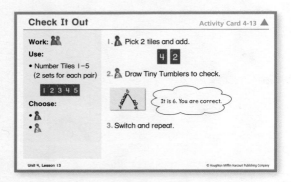

Activity Notes Remind children how to draw Tiny Tumblers on a Math Mountain for the two tiles they pick.

✏ Math Writing Prompt

Make a Drawing Provide children with two Number Tiles. Encourage them to use drawings to help find the partner total.

 MegaMath

Software Support
Country Countdown: Counting Critters, Level C

■ Challenge
for students seeking a challenge

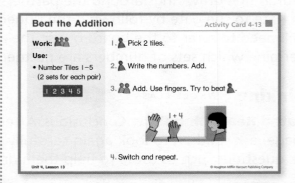

Activity Notes Encourage children to write an expression or an equation for the two tiles.

✏ Math Writing Prompt

Solve It Write partners on the board for children to add. Encourage them to describe the way they found the total.

 Destination Math®

Software Support
Course I: Module 1: Unit 2: Session 3: Creating Representations of the Numbers from 5 to 10

The Homework activity on page 81 provides children with practice drawing the partners of 5, 7, and 10, as well as writing numbers 1–20. On page 82, children draw pictures with squares, circles, triangles, and rectangles.

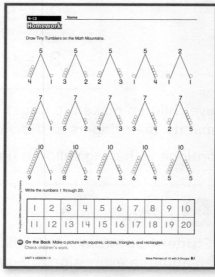

Homework and Remembering page 81

Identify Cubes

LESSON FOCUS

- Describe a cube and identify relative positions of shapes.

VOCABULARY

cube
above
below
in front of
behind

COMMON CORE

Mathematical Practice
CC.K–12.MP.1, CC.K–12.MP3, CC.K–12.MP.4,
CC.K–12.MP.5, CC.K–12.MP.6, CC.K–12.MP.7
Mathematical Content
CC.K.G.1, CC.K.G.2, CC.K.G.3, CC.K.G.4

The Day at a Glance

USE MATH TALK TODAY!

Teaching the Lesson

MATH BACKGROUND for this lesson is included on p. 329MM.

ACTIVITY FOCUS

Activity 1   Use defining attributes to describe a cube.

Activity 2   Describe the relative positions of shapes.

MATERIALS

Cubes • Cube-shaped objects • Math Journals

*i*Tools: Geometry • Whiteboard

Differentiated Instruction

MATERIALS

Activity Cards 4-14 • Connecting cubes • Inch Grid Paper (TRB M76)
• Crayons or markers • School dough (TRB M89)

Soar to Success Math Intervention • MegaMath • Destination Math®

 Tier 1 • Tier 2 • Tier 3

Home or School Activity

MATERIALS

Technology Connection, p. 414

QUICK PRACTICE · 5 MINUTES

Repeated Quick Practice Use these Quick Practices from previous lessons.

Count by Ones from 60 Through 100
(See Unit 4, Lesson 2.)

Partners of 4, 5, 6, or 7
(See Unit 4, Lesson 3, 4, 5, or 6.)

DAILY ROUTINES
Counting Tens and Ones
(See pp. xxxi–xxxii.)

DIGITAL RESOURCES
Use these digital resources along with your eSAB and eTE to support your students' learning experiences.

Professional Development

Whiteboard Lesson

iTools

Soar to Success Math Intervention

MegaMath

Destination Math®

COMMON CORE

Mathematical Practice
CC.K–12.MP.1, CC.K–12.MP.3,
CC.K–12.MP.5, CC.K–12.MP.6,
CC.K–12.MP.7

Mathematical Content
CC.K.G.2, CC.K.G.3, CC.K.G.4

30 MINUTES

FOCUS Use defining attributes to describe a cube.

MATERIALS Cubes and cube-shaped objects

 Whiteboard Lesson

Class Management

Pacing Provide children with sufficient time to explore the attributes of the cube. It is important for building understanding of visual spatial relationships.

ACTIVITY 1

Attributes of Cubes

▶ Describe Squares WHOLE CLASS

MP.3, MP.6 Attend to Precision Invite volunteers to share what they know about a square. Tell children that they will be learning about another shape that is similar to a square in certain ways. Have children list attributes of a square. They should identify the following:

▶ 4 sides

▶ 4 corners

▶ all sides the same length

▶ flat shape

▶ Introduce Cubes SMALL GROUPS

MP.5 Use Appropriate Tools Provide large and small cubes for each group. Allow time to let everyone in the group hold and study the cubes before you begin asking questions. Display a cube.

• This shape is called a cube.

• What can you say about this shape? It is a solid shape. All faces are the same. Every face is shaped like a square. There are 6 faces.

MP.7 Look for Structure Point out the two dimensions of a square by tracing the sides. Contrast this by tracing the two dimensions of the face of a cube and then the third dimension to help children distinguish between two- and three-dimensional figures.

Demonstrate how to count the faces by counting the top and bottom and then working your way around to count all 6 faces. After counting the top and bottom demonstrate how to keep one finger on the first face, then count around to avoid counting the same face again.

▶ See Faces of Cubes as Squares

MP.6 Attend to Precision Explain a Representation Display a small cube.

- What is this shape? a cube
- Look at one face of the cube.
- What flat shape do you see? a square

Repeat with other faces.

- What do you notice about all the faces? They are all squares.
- What do you notice about the size of all the squares on this small cube? They are all the same size.

Repeat with a large cube.

- What flat shapes do you see on the faces? The faces are all squares.
- What do you notice about the size of all the squares on this large cube? They are all the same size.

If using the cubes from the manipulative kit, children may notice the score marks on the larger cube and see that each face is made of four small squares.

MP.1 Make Sense of Problems Analyze Relationships Display both cubes. Discuss with children how the small and large cube compare to each other.

- What are these shapes? cubes
- How are they alike? Both cubes have square faces. Each cube has the same size squares on all faces.
- How are they different? The squares are different sizes. The size of the squares on the larger cube are different from the size of the squares on the smaller cube.
- Even though they are different sizes, are they both cubes? yes That is correct. Size does not change what kind of shape it is.

Discuss with children where they may see cubes in the environment.

- Where do you see cubes outside of class? I see cubes at the grocery store. I have cube blocks at home. We play games with number cubes. My footstool is a giant cube.

English Language Learners

Write *square* and *cube* on the board. Display examples of each shape. Explain that a *square* is flat. Point out that a *cube* is solid.

BEGINNING

Display a *cube* and a *square*. Say: **This is a cube. This is a square.** Ask children to repeat the words as they point to each shape.

INTERMEDIATE

Display a *square*. Ask: **What shape is this?** a square Display a *cube*. Ask: **What shape is this?** a cube

ADVANCED

Ask: **How are a *square* and a *cube* different?** A square is a flat shape. A cube is a solid shape.

Digital Resource

*i*Tools Choose 'Geometry' on the Menu. Use Activity 1 'Solid Figures' with the tab for 'Activities.' Children can see and identify three-dimensional shapes.

COMMON CORE

Mathematical Practice
CC.K–12.MP.1, CC.K–12.MP.4,
CC.K–12.MP.5, CC.K–12.MP.6

Mathematical Content
CC.K.G.1, CC.K.G.2, CC.K.G.3

30 MINUTES

FOCUS Describe the relative positions of shapes.

MATERIALS Spheres, cubes, cones, cylinders

 Whiteboard Lesson

Teaching Note

Watch for! Children may not recognize that they can look at the shapes from a different viewpoint. For example, they can look at where the cube is in relation to the cylinder, not just where the cylinder is in relation to the cube, as was originally stated. Help children understand how to use the position of each shape to provide multiple ways to describe the positions of the shapes.

ACTIVITY 2

Describe Positions of Shapes

▶ **Shapes and Attributes** WHOLE CLASS   MATH TALK

MP.1 Make Sense of Problems Display a sphere, cone, cylinder, and cube. Name a shape and have volunteers pick up that shape. Have them describe the attributes of each shape to justify their reasoning.

MP.6 Attend to Precision Explain a Representation Have children choose a shape and tell what they know about that shape. Children should verbalize the following ideas:

▶ Spheres are round. They have no faces.

▶ Cubes have all faces the same. Each face is a square.

▶ Spheres are round all over. They roll and do not stack.

▶ Cubes and spheres are solid shapes.

▶ **Review Position Words** WHOLE CLASS

MP.1 Make Sense of Problems Display a cube.

• Who knows the name of this shape? a cube

Display a cylinder.

• Who knows the name of this shape? a cylinder

Place the cylinder below the cube.

• The cylinder is *below* the cube. What else can you say about the positions of the shapes? The cube is above the cylinder.

Discuss how there is more than one way to describe the position of shapes. Let children suggest possible answers.

Display a sphere.

• Who knows the name of this shape? a sphere

Display a cone.

• Who knows the name of this shape? a cone

Place the sphere next to the cone.

• The sphere is *next to* the cone. What else can you say about the positions of the shapes? The sphere is beside the cone. The cone is next to the sphere. The cone is beside the sphere.

Remind children that for *next to* and *beside*, the shape can be on either side, right or left.

Display a cylinder and a cone. Have children identify the shapes. Then place the cylinder behind the cone.

• The cylinder is *behind* the cone. What else can you say about the positions of the shapes? The cone is in front of the cylinder.

▶ Show Positions Using Shapes WHOLE CLASS

MP.4, MP.5 Use Appropriate Tools/Model with Mathematics Select children to take turns coming to the front of the classroom and placing two shapes in the positions you describe. Have children hold one shape in each hand to give them more flexibility. Place at least one of each shape out for children to use to show positions. For some shapes, use two different sizes.

• Place a small cube *below* a sphere.

Repeat the directions as needed for the child to be successful. Allow time for him or her to find the shapes and set them in place. Have the class tell if the shapes are in the correct positions.

MP.6 Attend to Precision Explain a Representation Ask children to describe the position of the shapes another way. The sphere is above the small cube.

Continue until all children have had a turn. Use all the shapes, different sizes of shapes, and position words. Concentrate on the words *above, below, in front of,* and *behind.* You may also use *beside* and *next to.*

▶ Practice Positions Using Shapes PAIRS

MP.1 Make Sense of Problems Act It Out Group children into pairs. Give the pairs an assortment of three-dimensional shapes in which no two shapes are exactly alike. Provide different sizes of some of the same shapes. Pairs do not have to have every shape.

Have each child in the pair choose a shape. Then have them stand next to one another holding that shape. Ask them to work together to move and position their shapes as you say:

• The cube is *above* the sphere.

• The sphere is *beside* the cube.

• The cube is *in front of* the sphere.

Invite pairs to take turns making up positions in which to act out and place their shapes.

 Formative Assessment: Check Understanding

Student Summary Challenge children to describe a cube using as many descriptive words as possible.

▲ On Level ▲ RtI Tier 1
for students having success

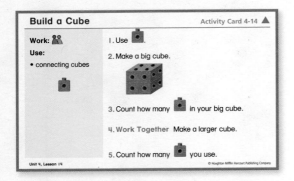

Build a Cube — Activity Card 4-14 ▲

Work: 👥

Use:
- connecting cubes

1. Use ▣.
2. Make a big cube.
3. Count how many ▣ in your big cube.
4. Work Together Make a larger cube.
5. Count how many ▣ you use.

Unit 4, Lesson 14 | © Houghton Mifflin Harcourt Publishing Company

Activity Notes Remind children of the attributes of a cube.

✏️ Math Writing Prompt

Compare Provide two different cubes. Have children write or tell how are the cubes are alike and how they are different.

MegaMath

Software Support
Shapes Ahoy: Undersea 3D, Level C

■ Challenge
for students seeking a challenge

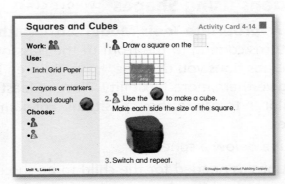

Squares and Cubes — Activity Card 4-14 ■

Work: 👥

Use:
- Inch Grid Paper
- crayons or markers
- school dough

Choose:
- 👤
- 👤

1. Draw a square on the ▦.
2. Use the ● to make a cube. Make each side the size of the square.
3. Switch and repeat.

Unit 4, Lesson 14 | © Houghton Mifflin Harcourt Publishing Company

Activity Notes Model how to draw a square on Inch Grid Paper.

✏️ Math Writing Prompt

Build a Cube Have children tell or write to show how many squares are on the cube model they built.

Destination Math®

Software Support
Course I: Module 3: Unit 2: Session 2: Three-Dimensional Shapes

---

💻 Technology Connection

Square Designs Have children use a computer art program to create interesting designs made entirely from squares. Some possibilities include a big square with small squares inside, a checkerboard design, or a quilt made of squares. Children may enjoy printing and displaying their designs. Discuss the different sizes and colors of the squares in their designs.

Encourage children to describe the positions of the squares in their designs. For example, the red square is *beside* the blue square; the purple square is *below* the green square.

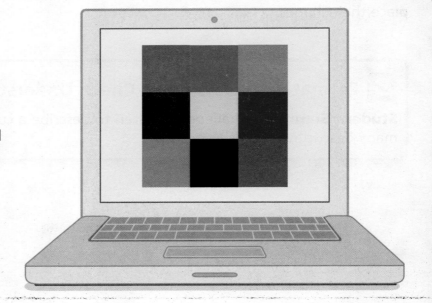

Addition and Subtraction Equations

LESSON FOCUS
- Create and solve addition and subtraction story problems and equations for numbers within 6–10 and for fluency within 5.
- Order numbers 1 through 20.

VOCABULARY
addition sign (+)
subtraction sign (−)
add

COMMON CORE
Mathematical Practice
CC.K–12.MP.1, CC.K–12.MP.6, CC.K–12.MP.7, CC.K–12.MP.8
Mathematical Content
CC.K.CC.2, CC.K.CC.4c, K.OA.1, K.OA.2, K.OA.5

The Day at a Glance

USE **MATH TALK** TODAY!

Teaching the Lesson

MATH BACKGROUND for this lesson is included on pp. 329GG, 329KK, and 329MM.

ACTIVITY FOCUS

Activity 1   Create and solve addition and subtraction story problems.

Activity 2   Solve addition equations within 6–10, complete a dot-to-dot for numbers 1–20, and practice addition and subtraction fluency within 5.

MATERIALS

◻ Student Activity Book pp. 181–182 • Fluency Check 3 (Assessment Guide)

▭ *i*Tools: Counters • Whiteboard

Differentiated Instruction

MATERIALS

◻ Activity Cards 4-15 • Paper clips • Old calendar pages • Math Journals

▭ Soar to Success Math Intervention • MegaMath • Destination Math®

△ **RtI**   Tier 1 • Tier 2 • Tier 3

Home or School Activity

MATERIALS

ABC Language Arts Connection p. 420

QUICK PRACTICE ⏲ 5 MINUTES

Practice −1 Orally

Goal Subtract 1.

Materials Number Parade, pointer
Write on the board several −1 problems, such as 4 − 1, 6 − 1, and 3 − 1. Have children show the first number in each expression with fingers, lower 1 finger, and know or count the remaining fingers. Point to the Number Parade so children can recognize the pattern of −1 as the number "just before."

- What pattern do you see? −1 is the number just before.

Repeated Quick Practice Use this Quick Practice from previous lessons.

Count to 100 by Tens (See Unit 4, Lesson 11.)

DAILY ROUTINES

Counting Tens and Ones
See (pp. xxxi–xxxii.)

DIGITAL RESOURCES

Use these digital resources along with your eSAB and eTE to support your students' learning experiences.

Professional Development

Whiteboard Lesson

*i*Tools

Soar to Success Math Intervention

MegaMath

Destination Math®

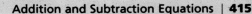

COMMON CORE

Mathematical Practice
CC.K–12.MP.1

Mathematical Content
CC.K.OA.1, CC.K.OA.2

20 MINUTES

FOCUS Create and solve addition and subtraction story problems.

 Whiteboard Lesson

iT *i*Tools: Counters

Digital Resource

*i*Tools Choose 'Counters' on the Menu. Use Activity 3 'Add' with the tab for 'Activities'. Children can use counters to help them add 2 numbers. Then they enter the total.

*i*Tools Choose 'Counters' on the Menu. Use Activity 4 'Subtract' with the tab for 'Activities'. Children can use counters to help them subtract. Then they enter the partner.

Teaching Note

What to Expect from Students
Children should now be connecting story problem situations, finger solutions, drawings, and equations. Their explanations should be improving, and they should be comfortable with the mixing of addition and subtraction stories.

ACTIVITY 1

Solve Addition and Subtraction Story Problems

Use **Solve and Discuss** for this activity.

▶ Tell and Solve Story Problems WHOLE CLASS   MATH TALK

Discuss the addition and subtraction signs and have children show these symbols with their arms, as described in Unit 4, Lesson 4, Activity 1.

- What is the addition sign, and how can you remember it? two crossing lines; it shows two partners put together

- What is the subtraction sign, and how can you remember it? one sideways line; it takes away the second number

Elicit story problems of several kinds of situations from children. Use totals of 6, 7, 8, 9, or 10. Invite several children to the board to make math drawings and write expressions (for example, $4 + 2$ or $10 - 3$) while the other children draw and write at their desks. Encourage children to explain their drawings and expressions.

MP.1 Make Sense of Problems Guide children to draw 5-groups as they show and solve the problems. 5-groups are especially helpful for subtraction because they help children see right away whether they have drawn the correct number of total items.

Below are some examples of addition and subtraction situations for story problems. However, be sure to elicit stories from children as well.

- **Take From Result Unknown:** 8 children are having lunch. 3 children leave. How many children are having lunch now?

- **Add To Result Unknown:** 6 children are riding bikes. Then 3 more children come to ride their bikes. How many children are riding bikes?

- **Put Together Total Unknown:** Lillian has 4 apples. Jenna has 3 apples. How many apples are there?

- **Both Addends Unknown:** John has 6 toy cars. How many cars can he put in his brown box and how many can he put in his green box?

Solve Addition Equations

▶ **Add Numbers** WHOLE CLASS

Distribute Student Activity Book page 181.

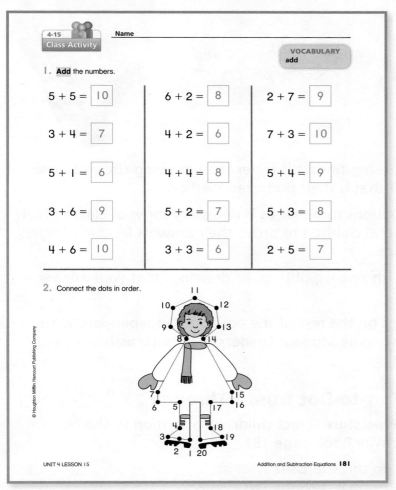

Student Activity Book page 181

COMMON CORE

Mathematical Practice
CC.K–12.MP.6, CC.K–12.MP.7,
CC.K–12.MP.8

Mathematical Content
CC.K.CC.2, CC.K.CC.4c,
CC.K.OA.1, CC.K.OA.2,
CC.K.OA.5

30 MINUTES

FOCUS Solve addition equations within 6–10, complete a dot-to-dot for numbers 1–20, and practice addition and subtraction fluency within 5.

MATERIALS Student Activity Book page 181

Whiteboard Lesson

English Language Learners

Write and identify an *addition* and a *subtraction* equation on the board.

BEGINNING

Point to the *addition* sign. Say: **This sign tells us this is an *addition* equation.** Have children repeat. Continue with the *subtraction* sign.

INTERMEDIATE

Point to the *addition* sign. Ask: **Is this is an *addition* or a *subtraction* sign?** addition sign Say: **Point to the *subtraction* sign.**

ADVANCED

Point to the *addition* and *subtraction* signs and have children identify them.

Connect addition equations to children's experiences.

• **What do you see on the top of the page?** addition equations

• **Where have you written or seen addition equations?** in stories at the park (Unit 3); in stories at the grocery store (Unit 4)

MP.8 Use Repeated Reasoning Generalize Review how to remember the addition sign. (One arm is vertical and one arm is horizontal; we put together two partners, and we show it with our two arms.)

Have children look at the first problem on the page, 5 + 5, and elicit ways to solve it. Have children share their methods.

Activity continued ▶

Differentiated Instruction

Special Needs At the end of a math lesson, summarize the lesson's underlying concept or skill. After this discussion, some children may benefit from writing or drawing a brief summary of the discussion in their Math Journals.

MP.6 Attend to Precision Describe Methods **What methods could you use for solving this problem?** I could use my fingers; I already know that 5 and 5 are partners of 10; I just know the answer; I would draw 5 circles and 5 more circles, and count them all.

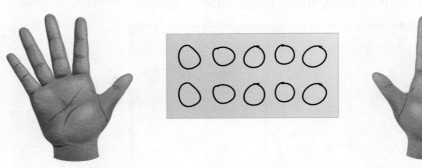

For most children, using fingers is faster than drawing circles, but allow children to draw if that is their preferred method.

Solve as many equations together as is necessary for your class to feel confident. Ask several children to prove their answers by using fingers, objects, or drawings.

• Can you show with fingers, objects, or drawings that your answer is correct?

Have the class work on the rest of the equations independently. You may wish to choose some **Student Leaders** to provide assistance to those who need it.

▶ Drawing a Dot-to-Dot from 1 Through 20   INDIVIDUALS

MP.6 Attend to Precision Direct children's attention to the bottom half of Student Activity Book page 181.

• How would you do this exercise? Start at 1 and draw a line to 2, then 3, and so on, until you get to the last number.

Discuss with children the counting sequence 1–20 and that the value of the next number in the sequence is one greater than the last number. As an extension to the activity, have one child choose any number 1–19 on the dot-to-dot. Then have another child tell the next number and continue to count in the sequence.

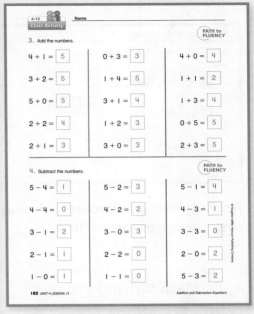

Student Activity Book page 182

▶ PATH to FLUENCY **Fluency Within 5** WHOLE CLASS

MP.7 Use Structure In this activity, children practice addition and subtraction within 5 to gain fluency. Tell children they may use fingers or drawings, if necessary. Distribute Student Activity Book page 182.

Invite children to look at the page and identify addition and subtraction facts they already know. Some children may respond by saying that they know all of the + 0 or + 1 facts. Give each of several children the opportunity to name an equation and the correct sum or difference.

Encourage children to share strategies they use to help them learn the facts. Children may say that they know $0 + 2 = 2$, because zero plus any number is that number. They know $1 + 2 = 3$, because one plus any number is one more. Similarly, $2 - 0 = 2$, because any number minus zero is that number. And $3 - 1 = 2$, because any number minus one is one less.

To help children link equations to everyday life, invite them to think of an addition or subtraction story problem to go with one of the equations.

As children complete the page, you may want to watch for those children who are becoming fluent within 5 and those who are still using aids.

✓ **Formative Assessment: Check Understanding**

Student Summary Provide children with an equation such as $3 + 5 =$ ___. Have them draw a picture to show the equation and the total.

▲ On Level    Tier 1
for students having success

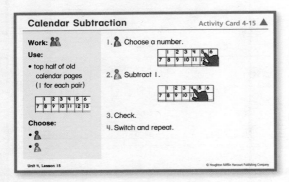

Activity Notes Prepare old calendar pages so that they show numbers 1 to 19.

 Math Writing Prompt

Write Equations Choose two numbers from the top half of a calendar. Have children write an equation for those numbers.

 MegaMath

Software Support
Numberopolis: Carnival Stories, Level D

■ Challenge
for students seeking a challenge

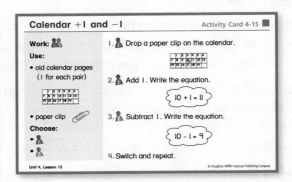

Activity Notes Remind children how to write addition and subtraction equations for the partners of 10.

 Math Writing Prompt

+1 and −1 Equations Choose two numbers from the top half of a calendar. Have children write an addition equation and a subtraction equation.

 Destination Math®

Software Support
Course I: Module 2: Unit 1: Session 1: Combining and Joining Within 10

Language Arts Connection

Counting Letters Display an assortment of books. Invite children to look for the longest word they can find, the shortest word, a word with more than one *t*, a favorite word, and so on. Help children as needed to read each word and name its letters. As children work, have them count the letters in each word and write the number.

Teen Number Book

LESSON FOCUS
- Model teen numbers as a group of ten ones and extra ones and order numbers 1–19.

VOCABULARY
teen numbers
equation

COMMON CORE
Mathematical Practice
CC.K–12.MP.2, CC.K–12.MP.7
Mathematical Content
CC.K.CC.3, CC.K.CC.4a, CC.K.CC.5, CC.K.NBT.1

The Day at a Glance

USE MATH TALK TODAY!

Teaching the Lesson

MATH BACKGROUND for this lesson is included on pp. 329II–329JJ, 329LL.

ACTIVITY FOCUS

Activity 1   Model teen numbers 11–14 using the Teen Number Book.

Activity 2   Match numbers to pictorial quantities, order numbers 1–19 in a dot-to-dot, and practice addition within 10.

MATERIALS

Student Activity Book pp. 183–186 (includes Unit 4 Teen Number Book 11–14) • 1–20 Board

*i*Tools: Counters • Whiteboard

Differentiated Instruction

MATERIALS

Activity Cards 4-16 • *The Very Hungry Caterpillar* by Eric Carle • Counting books • Construction paper • Crayons or markers • Math Journals

Soar to Success Math Intervention • MegaMath • Destination Math®

RtI   Tier 1 • Tier 2 • Tier 3

Homework

MATERIALS

Homework and Remembering pp. 83–84

QUICK PRACTICE 5 MINUTES

Repeated Quick Practice Use these Quick Practices from previous lessons.

Count to 100 by Tens (See Unit 4, Lesson 11.)

Practice −1 Orally (See Unit 4, Lesson 15.)

DAILY ROUTINES
Counting Tens and Ones
(See pp. xxxi–xxxii.)

DIGITAL RESOURCES

Use these digital resources along with your eSAB and eTE to support your students' learning experiences.

Professional Development

Whiteboard Lesson

*i*Tools

Soar to Success Math Intervention

MegaMath

Destination Math®

COMMON CORE

Mathematical Practice
CC.K–12.MP.2

Mathematical Content
CC.K.CC.3, CC.K.NBT.1

15 MINUTES

FOCUS Model teen numbers 11–14 using the Teen Number Book.

MATERIALS Unit 4 Teen Number Book 11–14 (Student Activity Book page 183), 1–20 Board (back)

 iTools: Counters

Whiteboard Lesson

Digital Resource

iTools Choose 'Counters' on the Menu. Use Activity 1 'Count' with the tab for 'Activities'. Children can use counters to count.

Class Management

Looking Ahead Children will continue to work on their Teen Number Books in Lesson 18, and will complete the books in Lesson 20. After today's activity, collect the pages children made, and return them during Lesson 20.

Differentiated Instruction

Extra Help After children complete the dot-to-dot on Student Activity Book page 185, have them say the numbers together, pointing to each number as they say it. Repeat this activity as needed. Also encourage them to say numbers posted in the classroom, including those on the calendar.

ACTIVITY 1

Draw Teen Numbers

▶ **Begin Making the Teen Number Book** WHOLE CLASS

MATH TALK

MP.2 Reason Quantitatively Using the 1–20 Board, have children look at the number 12.

- **What do you see for the number 12 on the 1–20 board?** The number 12; a group of 10 ones and 2 ones; $10 + 2 = 12$; an equation

Distribute Student Activity Book page 183.

- **Now look at the Teen Number Book page for 12. How can you show 12?** Draw 10 circles and then 2 more circles in the boxes; Write the number 12 on the blanks; write the numbers to complete the equation, $10 + 2 = 12$

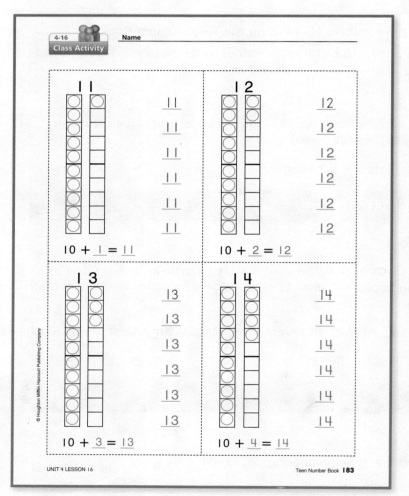

Student Activity Book page 183

Draw Lines to Match

▶ Match and Order Numbers INDIVIDUALS

MP.7 Use Structure At the top of Student Activity Book page 185, children draw lines to match numerals with the appropriate number of circles and fingers. At the bottom of the page, children complete the dot-to-dot for 1–19.

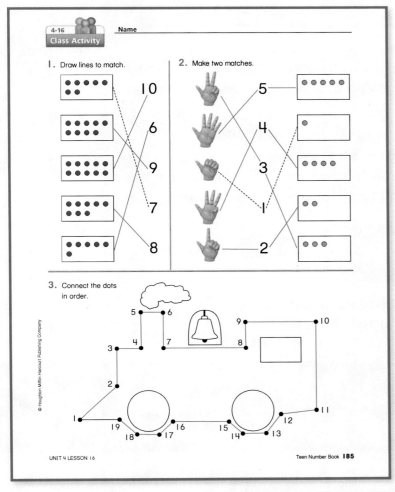

Student Activity Book page 185

▶ Practice Addition Within 10 INDIVIDUALS

MP.2 Reason Abstractly Children practice addition equations to build upon fluency experiences within 5. Direct children's attention to Student Activity Book page 186. Connect addition equations to children's experiences. Ask children to give a story problem for an equation to monitor understanding of addition.

> ✓ **Formative Assessment: Check Understanding**
>
> **Student Summary** Ask children to show the number 13 in different ways. Encourage them to use the 1–20 Board, 10-sticks, an equation, and a group of 10 ones and 3 ones.

COMMON CORE

Mathematical Practice
CC.K–12.MP.2, CC.K–12.MP.7
Mathematical Content
CC.K.CC.4a, CC.K.CC.5

10 MINUTES

FOCUS Match numbers to pictorial quantities, order numbers 1–19 in a dot-to-dot, and practice addition within 10.

MATERIALS Student Activity Book pages 185 and 186

 Whiteboard Lesson

English Language Learners

Write *blanks* on the board. Say: **When we write answers on lines, we fill in the blanks.** Point out the blanks on Student Activity Book page 183.

BEGINNING

Say: **We fill in the *blanks*.** Have children repeat. Ask: **How many *blanks* are in the equation below?** 2 *blanks*

INTERMEDIATE

Ask: **What do you do when you write on the answer lines?** fill in the *blanks* **How many *blanks* are in the equation below?** 2 *blanks*

ADVANCED

Ask: **What is another way to say "Write on the answer lines?"** Fill in the *blanks*. **How many numbers will you write to fill in the *blanks* in the equation?** 2 numbers

Student Activity Book page 186

▲ On Level ▲ RtI Tier 1
for students having success

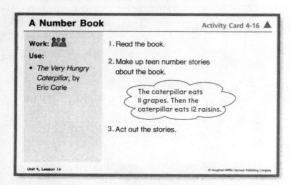

Activity Notes Read *The Very Hungry Caterpillar* by Eric Carle to the class. Have children work together to make up stories with teen numbers.

 Math Writing Prompt

Write Number Stories Have children draw between 11 and 19 items. Then have them write number stories about their drawings.

 MegaMath

Software Support
Country Countdown: Counting Critters, Level P

■ Challenge
for students seeking a challenge

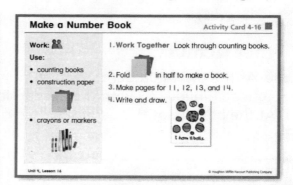

Activity Notes Provide a variety of counting picture books for children. Explain that children will be drawing and writing their own books.

 Math Writing Prompt

Write an Equation Have children look through counting picture books. Then have them write an equation for one of the pictures.

 Destination Math®

Software Support
Course I: Module 2: Unit 1: Session 3: Sums Within 20, with 10 as One Addend

The Homework activity on page 83 gives children practice matching numbers to pictorial quantities and connecting dots in numeric order. On page 84, children write numbers 1 through 20 and practice addition facts within 10.

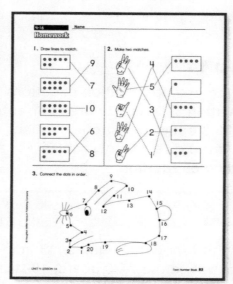

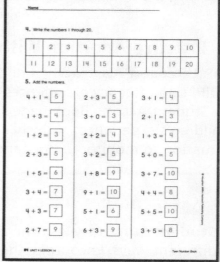

Homework and Remembering page 83   Homework and Remembering page 84

Addition Equations

LESSON FOCUS
- Solve addition equations within 5 and explore addition strategies.

VOCABULARY
equation
add

COMMON CORE
Mathematical Practice
CC.K–12.MP.2, CC.K–12.MP.3, CC.K–12.MP.6
Mathematical Content
CC.K.CC.1, CC.K.OA.1, CC.K.OA.5

The Day at a Glance

USE
MATH TALK
TODAY!

Teaching the Lesson

MATH BACKGROUND for this lesson is included on p. 329KK, 329LL.

ACTIVITY FOCUS
Activity 1   Solve addition equations within 5 and order numbers in a dot-to-dot.
Activity 2   Practice fluency within 5.

MATERIALS

    Student Activity Book pp. 187–188

    *i*Tools: Counters • Whiteboard

Differentiated Instruction

MATERIALS

    Activity Cards 4-17 • Number cubes • Math Journals

    Soar to Success Math Intervention • MegaMath • Destination Math®

    RtI Tier 1 • Tier 2 • Tier 3

Practice

MATERIALS

    Homework and Remembering pp. 85–86

QUICK PRACTICE 5 MINUTES

Repeated Quick Practice Use these Quick Practices from previous lessions.

Count to 100 by Tens (See Unit 4, Lesson 11.)

Practice −1 Orally (See Unit 4, Lesson 15.)

DAILY ROUTINES
Counting Tens and Ones
(See pp. xxxi–xxxii.)

DIGITAL RESOURCES
Use these digital resources along with your eSAB and eTE to support your students' learning experiences.

Professional
Development

Whiteboard
Lesson

*i*Tools

Soar to Success
Math Intervention

MegaMath

Destination
Math®

25 MINUTES

FOCUS Solve addition equations within 5 and order numbers in a dot-to-dot.

MATERIALS Student Activity Book page 187

 *i*Tools: Counters

Whiteboard Lesson

Teaching Note

What to Expect from Students Using fingers is usually faster than drawing circles for most children, but some children may prefer to draw. Focus children on the first exercise, 3 + 1, and elicit ways to solve it. Have children share their methods. Children may use a variety of methods, such as using fingers, drawing circles, or knowing the partners.

Differentiated Instruction

Extra Help You can form a group of children who need additional help and solve as many problems with them as necessary. Alternatively, choose some Student Leaders to help those who need assistance, while the rest of the class works on the problems independently.

ACTIVITY 1

Solve Addition Equations and Complete a Dot-to-Dot Drawing

▶ Review Addition Concepts WHOLE CLASS

MP.6 Attend to Precision Describe a Method Direct children's attention to Student Activity Book page 187. Ask children to describe how they remember the addition sign.

- How many parts, or lines, does the addition sign have? The addition sign has two parts.

- What does the addition sign show you to do? It shows putting together two partners.

Elicit from children how to complete the dot-to-dot on the bottom of the page. Encourage them to see that connecting the numbers in counting order helps them to complete the dot-to-dot correctly. As an extension for this activity, you may ask children to begin counting at the number 8, for example, instead of the number 1.

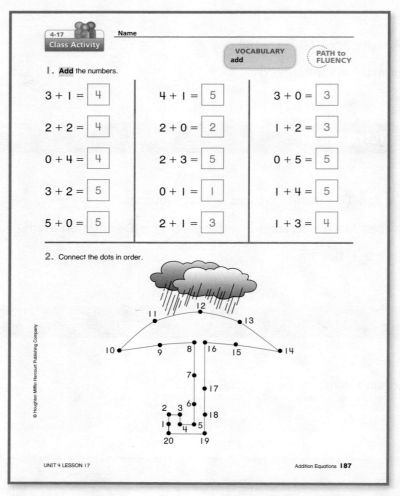

Student Activity Book page 187

Fluency and Equations

▶ **PATH to FLUENCY Subtraction Fluency within 5** INDIVIDUALS

MP.2 Reason Abstractly Direct children's attention to the top of Student Activity Book page 188. Connect subtraction equations to children's experiences. Ask children to give a story problem for each of the first three equations to monitor understanding of subtraction situations.

▶ **What's the Error?** WHOLE CLASS

MP.3, MP.6 Construct Viable Arguments/Critique the Reasoning of Others Direct children's attention to the Puzzled Penguin section. Encourage children to discuss how Puzzled Penguin could have done the equation incorrectly.

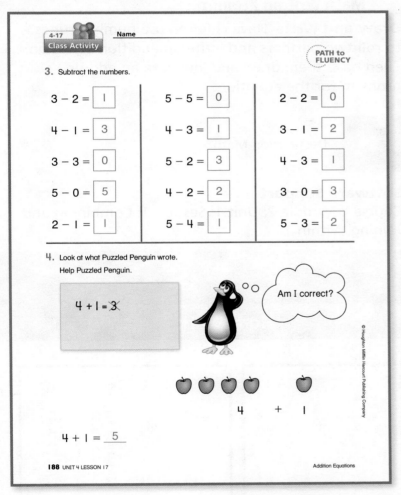

Student Activity Book page 188

✓ **Formative Assessment: Check Understanding**

Student Summary Write $3 + 2 =$ ___ on the board and ask children to explain how they would solve the equation.

COMMON CORE

Mathematical Practice
CC.K–12.MP.2, CC.K–12.MP.3, CC.K–12.MP.6

Mathematical Content
CC.K.OA.1, CC.K.OA.5

15 MINUTES

FOCUS Practice fluency within 5.

MATERIALS Student Activity Book page 188

Whiteboard Lesson

English Language Learners

Display a simple color drawing. Describe the drawing, talking about all of the details.

BEGINNING

Say: **When we *describe* something, we tell about it.** Have children repeat.

INTERMEDIATE

Ask: **How do you *describe* something?** We tell about it.

ADVANCED

Ask: ***Describe* the picture on the board.** Accept children's descriptions. **What word is used to tell about something?** *describe*

MATH TALK in ACTION Puzzled Penguin looked at the equation $4 + 1 =$ ___ and said the answer is 3. **What did Puzzled Penguin do wrong?**

Mark: Puzzled Penguin may have forgotten to count all of the apples.

Jami: Maybe Puzzled Penguin counted 3 apples and wrote the answer.

Sauna: I think Puzzled Penguin added 4 and 1 and got 3.

Joel: Maybe Puzzled Penguin looked at the addition sign and subtracted.

Mark: We should look at the sign.

Sauna: The addition sign has two parts. One part goes up and down. The other part goes across.

Joel: The subtraction sign only has the part that goes across.

▲ On Level △ RtI Tier 1
for students having success

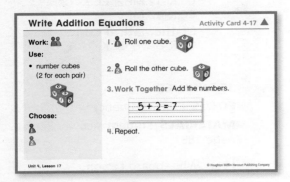

Activity Notes Number the cubes 1, 1, 2, 3, 4, 5 to limit practice to within 10.

✏ Math Writing Prompt

Write Equations Have children use number cubes to roll two partners and write an addition equation. Then have them use those partners to write other addition and subtraction equations.

 MegaMath

Software Support
Country Countdown: Counting Critters, Level G

■ Challenge
for students seeking a challenge

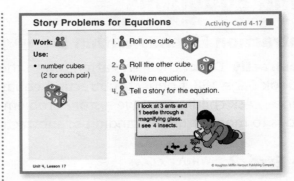

Activity Notes Encourage children to use subtraction equations as well as addition equations.

✏ Math Writing Prompt

Draw and Write Have children use number cubes to roll two partners and write an addition equation. Then have them draw and illustrate an addition story problem for the equation.

 Destination Math®

Software Support
Course I: Module 2: Unit 1: Session 1: Combining and Joining Within 10

The Homework activity on page 85 provides children with more practice finding partners on Math Mountains and writing the numbers 1 through 20. On page 86, children practice addition equations within 10.

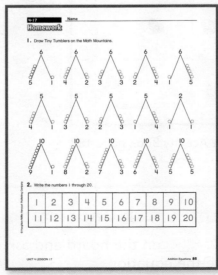

Homework and Remembering page 85

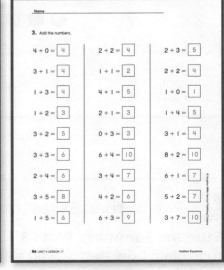

Homework and Remembering page 86

Partners and Equations

LESSON FOCUS

- Write equations for partners.
- Show teen numbers as a group of 10 ones and extra ones.

VOCABULARY

partner equation

COMMON CORE

Mathematical Practice
CC.K–12.MP.2, CC.K–12.MP.6
Mathematical Content
CC.K.CC.3, CC.K.OA.3, CC.K.OA.4, CC.K.NBT.1

The Day at a Glance

Teaching the Lesson

 USE MATH TALK TODAY!

MATH BACKGROUND for this lesson is included on pp. 329II–329KK.

ACTIVITY FOCUS

Activity 1 Write partner equations and practice addition within 10.

Activity 2 Model teen numbers 15–18 using the Teen Number Book.

MATERIALS

Student Activity Book pp. 189–192 (includes Unit 4 Teen Number Book 15–18) • 1–20 Board (back)

*i*Tools: Counters • Whiteboard

Differentiated Instruction

MATERIALS

Activity Cards 4-18 • Counters • Break-Apart Sticks • Math Journals

Soar to Success Math Intervention • MegaMath • Destination Math®

RtI Tier 1 • Tier 2 • Tier 3

Home or School Activity

MATERIALS

Math Connection p. 432

QUICK PRACTICE ⏱ 5 MINUTES

Repeated Quick Practice Use these Quick Practices from previous lessons.

Count to 100 by Tens (See Unit 4, Lesson 11.)

Partners of 4, 5, 6 or 7 (See Unit 4, Lesson 3, 4, 5, or 6.)

Practice −1 Orally Present several −1 problems, such as $4 − 1$, $6 − 1$, and $3 − 1$. Children show the first number on fingers and then lower one finger to subtract 1. Point to the Number Parade to reinforce the pattern that −1 is the number before. (See Unit 4, Lesson 15.)

DAILY ROUTINES

Counting Tens and Ones (See pp. xxxi–xxxii.)

DIGITAL RESOURCES

Use these digital resources along with your eSAB and eTE to support your students' learning experiences.

Professional Development

Whiteboard Lesson

*i*Tools

Soar to Success Math Intervention

MegaMath

Destination Math®

COMMON CORE

Mathematical Practice
CC.K–12.MP.6

Mathematical Content
CC.K.OA.3, CC.K.OA.4

20 MINUTES

FOCUS Write partner equations and practice addition within 10.

MATERIALS Student Activity Book pages 189 and 190

 *i*Tools: Counters

Whiteboard Lesson

Digital Resource

*i*Tools Choose 'Counters' on the Menu. Use Activity 3 'Add' with the tab for 'Activities'. Children can use counters to help them add 2 numbers. Then they enter the total.

Teaching Note

Partner equations are written with the number first, followed by the partners that make the number. This helps children become familiar with this form of an equation, which is very important for their algebraic understanding.

 MATH TALK in ACTION

How do the numbers in the 5-dots equations on Student Activity Book page 189 change from one to the next?

Carlos: The Break-Apart Stick moves over one as you go down.

Tran: The Break-Apart Stick moves over 1 to the left.

Susan: The numbers on the left of the sign go down by 1 as you go down.

Carlos: It shows 4, 3, 2, 1 as you go down.

Kim: The numbers on the right of the addition sign go up by 1 as you go down.

Susan: Those numbers are 1, 2, 3, 4.

You are all correct.

ACTIVITY 1

Write Equations for Partners

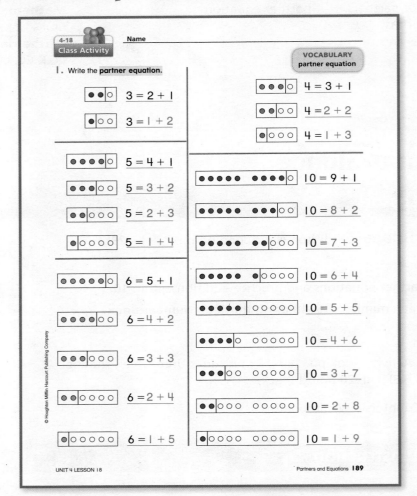

Student Activity Book page 189

▶ Write Partner Equations [WHOLE CLASS]

MP.6 Attend to Precision Distribute Student Activity Book page 189. Discuss the first equation. Have children complete the equations for 4-partners. Then discuss the series of equations on the page.

• Look at the first problem on Student Activity Book page 189. Describe the things you see in the problems. The equation says 3 = 2 + 1; The partners are 2 and 1; There is a picture of 2 circles, a Break-Apart Stick, and then 1 circle; The 2 sets of circles stand for the partners, 2 and 1; The Break-Apart Stick shows the partners; 2 is the first partner because the picture shows 2 circles first.

Have children complete the page, either as a class or independently. Discuss the series of equations again when children have completed the page so that more children have an opportunity to describe the equations and the pictorial representations.

▶ Practice Addition Within 10 [WHOLE CLASS]

MP.2 Reason Abstractly Direct children's attention to Student Activity Book page 190. Children practice addition equations to build fluency within 5. Tell story problems to connect addition equations to children's experiences.

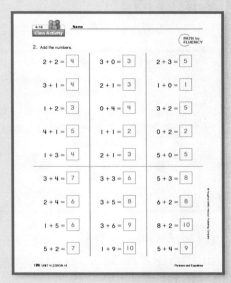

Student Activity Book page 190

ACTIVITY 2

Continue Teen Number Book Pages

▶ Continue Making the Teen Number Book [WHOLE CLASS]

MP.2 Reason Quantitatively Distribute Student Activity Book page 191. Discuss the Teen Number Book, which children began in Unit 4, Lesson 16. You may wish to display a completed page of the book from Lesson 16.

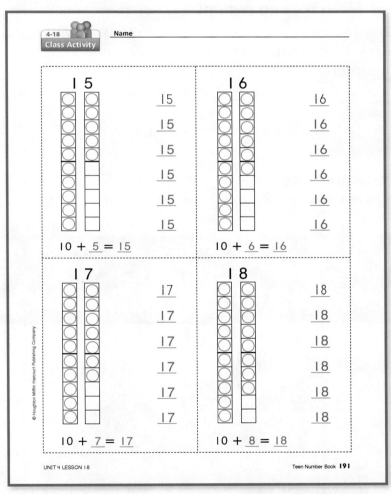

Student Activity Book page 191

COMMON CORE

Mathematical Practice
CC.K–12.MP.2

Mathematical Content
CC.K.CC.3, CC.K.NBT.1

20 MINUTES

FOCUS Model teen numbers 15–18 using the Teen Number Book.

MATERIALS Unit 4 Teen Number Book 15–18 (Student Activity Book page 191), 1–20 Board (back)

🖊 Whiteboard Lesson

English Language Learners

Write *teen number* on the board. Say: *Teen numbers* have **10 ones and extra ones.** Write 15 and draw a group of 10 ones and 5 extra ones.

BEGINNING

Ask: **Is 15 a *teen number*?** yes

INTERMEDIATE

Ask: **How do you know that 15 is a *teen number*?** Fifteen is a teen number because it has 10 ones and 5 extra ones.

ADVANCED

Say: Name a *teen number*. Accept answers 11 to 19.

▲ On Level    Tier 1
for students having success

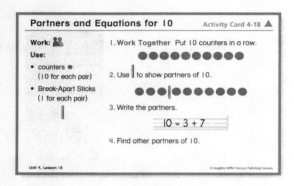

Activity Notes Model how to use the Break-Apart Stick to separate the counters and then make partners.

 Math Writing Prompt

Switched Partners Write 10 = 8 + 2, 10 = 7 + 3, and 10 = 6 + 4 on the board. Have children show the partner switches for each.

 MegaMath

Software Support
Country Countdown: Counting Critters, Level P

■ Challenge
for students seeking a challenge

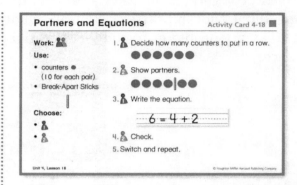

Activity Notes Explain that children can choose any number between 2 and 10 for which to find partners.

 Math Writing Prompt

Three Partners Challenge children to use two Break-Apart Sticks and write an equation with 3 partners.

 Destination Math®

Software Support
Course I: Module 2: Unit 1: Session 3: Sums Within 20, with 10 as One Addend

---

Teaching the Lesson   Differentiated Instruction   **Home or School Activity**

 Math Connection

Provide children with books that have page numbers up to at least page 20. Call out a teen number, such as 13, and have children turn to page 13. Encourage them to point to the number when they see it. Then have them close the book. Call out another teen number in random order. Repeat the activity until children are comfortable finding teen numbers on the pages of a book.

Write Addition Equations

<table>
<tr><td>

LESSON FOCUS
- Find and write equations for partners.
- Solve subtraction equations within 6 to 10.

</td><td>

VOCABULARY
partners

</td><td>

COMMON CORE

Mathematical Practice
CC.K–12.MP.2, CC.K–12.MP.3, CC.K–12.MP.6
Mathematical Content
CC.K.OA.1, CC.K.OA.3, CC.K.OA.4

</td></tr>
</table>

The Day at a Glance

USE MATH TALK TODAY!

Teaching the Lesson

MATH BACKGROUND for this lesson is included on p. 329KK.

ACTIVITY FOCUS

Activity 1   Write equations for partners.

Activity 2   Solve subtraction equations within 6 to 10.

MATERIALS

- Student Activity Book pp. 193–194

- *i*Tools: Counters • Whiteboard

Differentiated Instruction

MATERIALS

- Activity Cards 4-19 • Break-Apart Sticks • Centimeter cubes • Crayons or markers • Math Journals

- Soar to Success Math Intervention • MegaMath • Destination Math®

- **RtI** Tier 1 • Tier 2 • Tier 3

Homework

MATERIALS

- Homework and Remembering pp. 87–88

QUICK PRACTICE 🕐 5 MINUTES

Repeated Quick Practice Use these Quick Practices from previous lessons.

Practice −1 Orally (See Unit 4, Lesson 15.)

Count to 100 by Tens (See Unit 4, Lesson 11.)

DAILY ROUTINES

Counting Tens and Ones
(See pp. xxxi–xxxii.)

DIGITAL RESOURCES

Use these digital resources along with your eSAB and eTE to support your students' learning experiences.

Professional Development

Whiteboard Lesson

*i*Tools

Soar to Success Math Intervention

MegaMath

Destination Math®

COMMON CORE

Mathematical Practice
CC.K–12.MP.2

Mathematical Content
CC.K.OA.3, CC.K.OA.4

10 MINUTES

FOCUS Write equations for partners.

MATERIALS Student Activity Book
page 193

i**T** *i*Tools: Counters

 Whiteboard Lesson

Digital Resource

*i***Tools** Choose 'Counters' on the Menu.
Use Activity 3 'Add' with the tab for
'Activities'. Children can use counters to
help them add 2 numbers. Then they
enter the total.

ACTIVITY 1

Write Partner Equations

▶ Write Partner Equations Within 10 [WHOLE CLASS]

MP.2 Reason Abstractly and Quantitatively Connect Diagrams
and Equations Student Activity Book page 193 shows partners (circles
in boxes) with a Break-Apart Stick. This page is similar to the Student
Activity Book page that was completed in Lesson 18.

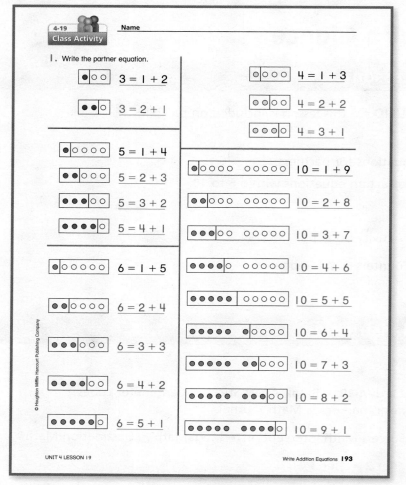

Student Activity Book page 193

Children write the equations for the partners by writing the total first
and then the partners. This helps children understand that equations
can start with the total. Have children complete the page, either as a
class, in **Student Pairs**, or independently.

Discuss the partners for a given total.

• **What do you see for the partners of 5?** The partners on the right of
the equal sign increase by 1 in each row. The partners just after the
addition sign decrease by 1 as you go down. The Break-Apart Stick
moves over to the right as you go up.

Subtraction and Equations

▶ **PATH to FLUENCY** **Subtraction within 6 to 10** [INDIVIDUALS]

MP.2 Reason Abstractly Direct children's attention to Student Activity Book page 194. Connect subtraction equations to children's experiences. Ask children to give a story problem for each of the first three equations to monitor understanding of subtraction.

▶ **What's the Error?** [WHOLE CLASS]

MP.3, MP.6 Construct Viable Arguments/Critique the Reasoning of Others Direct children's attention to the Puzzled Penguin section. Encourage children to discuss how Puzzled Penguin could have written the equation incorrectly.

Student Activity Book page 194

COMMON CORE

Mathematical Practice
CC.K–12.MP.2, CC.K–12.MP.3, CC.K–12.MP.6
Mathematical Content
CC.K.OA.1, CC.K.OA.3

15 MINUTES

FOCUS Solve subtraction equations within 6 to 10.

MATERIALS Student Activity Book page 194

 Whiteboard Lesson

English Language Learners

Write $1 + 2 = 3$ and $3 = 1 + 2$ on the board.

BEGINNING

Say: **These are *addition equations*.** Ask: **Are both totals?** yes **Are both sets of partners 2 and 1?** yes

INTERMEDIATE

Point to each equation. Ask: **Are they both *addition equations*?** yes **What are the partners in both equations?** 1 and 2 **What is the total in both equations?** 3

ADVANCED

Have children identify the partners and totals and then say how the equations are alike and different.

 MATH TALK in ACTION

Puzzled Penguin looked at the picture of 4 green dots and 2 white dots and said the equation is $6 = 4 - 2$. What did Puzzled Penguin do wrong?

Sami: Something is wrong with 6.

Yolanda: 4 minus 2 is 2, not 6.

Jake: Puzzled Penguin may not know the picture shows dots being put together. It should be addition.

Miri:: Puzzled Penguin used a subtraction sign.

Sami: Puzzled Penguin should have used an addition sign.

Jake: The equation is $6 = 4 + 2$.

✅ Formative Assessment: Check Understanding

Student Summary Write $10 = \_\_\_ + \_\_\_$ on the board and ask children to explain how they would solve for the partners in the equation.

▲ On Level    Tier 1
for students having success

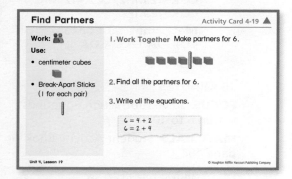

Activity Notes Model how to use the cubes and the Break-Apart Stick to show the partners for 6.

 Math Writing Prompt

Write an Equation Draw a model for the partners of 6. Have children write an equation.

 MegaMath

Software Support
Country Countdown: Counting Critters, Level G

■ Challenge
for students seeking a challenge

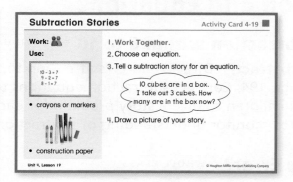

Activity Notes Remind children to write the chosen equation below the picture they drew.

 Math Writing Prompt

Write an Equation Have children write a different equation using the same numbers in $10 - 3 = 7$.

 Destination Math®

Software Support
Course I: Module 2: Unit 1: Session 1: Combining and Joining Within 10

The Homework activity on page 87 provides children with practice solving addition equations for fluency within 5 and connecting dots for numbers 1–17. On page 88, children practice solving addition facts within 10.

✓ Include children's homework pages as part of their portfolios.

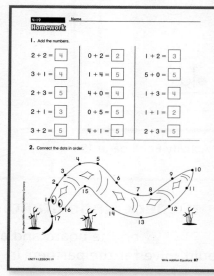

Homework and Remembering page 87

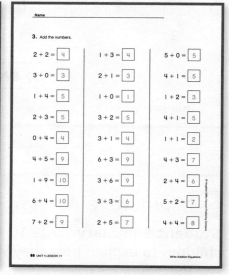

Homework and Remembering page 88

Teen Number Book

LESSON FOCUS

- Model teen numbers as a group of ten ones and extra ones.
- Match pictures to numbers, compare groups, and practice addition within 10.

VOCABULARY

teen number

COMMON CORE

Mathematical Practice
CC.K–12.MP.4, CC.K–12.MP.5, CC.K–12.MP.6, CC.K–12.MP.7
Mathematical Content
CC.K.CC.2, CC.K.CC.3, CC.K.CC.4a, CC.K.CC.4b, CC.K.CC.6, CC.K.CC.7, CC.K.NBT.1

The Day at a Glance

USE MATH TALK TODAY!

Teaching the Lesson

MATH BACKGROUND for this lesson is included on pp. 329II–329JJ, 329LL.

ACTIVITY FOCUS

Activity 1   Model teen numbers 19–20 using the Teen Number Book.

Activity 2   Match pictures to numbers, compare groups, and practice addition within 10.

MATERIALS

Student Activity Book pp. 195–198 (includes Unit 4 Teen Number Book 19–20) • Crayons or markers • Scissors • Stapler

*i*Tools: Counters • Whiteboard

Differentiated Instruction

MATERIALS

Activity Cards 4-20 • Construction paper • Crayons • Counters • 10-Counter Strip • Math Journals

Soar to Success Math Intervention • MegaMath • Destination Math®

RtI   Tier 1 • Tier 2 • Tier 3

Home and School Activity

MATERIALS

Language Arts Connection p. 442

QUICK PRACTICE ⏱ 5 MINUTES

Repeated Quick Practice Use these Quick Practices from previous lessons.

Practice −1 Orally (See Unit 4, Lesson 15.)

Count to 100 by Tens (See Unit 4, Lesson 11.)

DAILY ROUTINES

Counting Tens and Ones
(See pp. xxxi–xxxii.)

DIGITAL RESOURCES

Use these digital resources along with your eSAB and eTE to support your students' learning experiences.

 Professional Development

 Whiteboard Lesson

 iTools

 Soar to Success Math Intervention

 MegaMath

 Destination Math®

COMMON CORE
Mathematical Practice
CC.K–12.MP.5, CC.K–12.MP.6
Mathematical Content
CC.K.CC.3, CC.K.NBT.1

35 MINUTES

FOCUS Model teen numbers 19–20 using the Teen Number Book.

MATERIALS Unit 4 Teen Number Book 19–20 (Student Activity Book page 195), crayons or markers, scissors (1 per child), stapler

 *i*Tools: Counters

Whiteboard Lesson

Digital Resource

*i*Tools Choose 'Counters' on the Menu. Use Activity 1 'Count' with the tab for 'Activities'. Children can use counters to count.

Teaching Note

Math Background An important Unit 4 skill is to visualize teen numbers as a group of 10 ones and some extra ones. The 1–20 Board activities and the Teen Equation Cards have been used to reinforce that 17 is 10 + 7. Children's Unit 4 Teen Number Books also help to reinforce this concept as children show and write the 10 ones and extra ones in teen numbers. Encourage children to share their Teen Number Books with their families. This is a good opportunity for **English Language Learners** to practice math vocabulary outside of school.

ACTIVITY 1

Complete the Teen Number Book

▶ Finish the Teen Number Book [WHOLE CLASS]

Today children will complete their Unit 4 Teen Number Books.

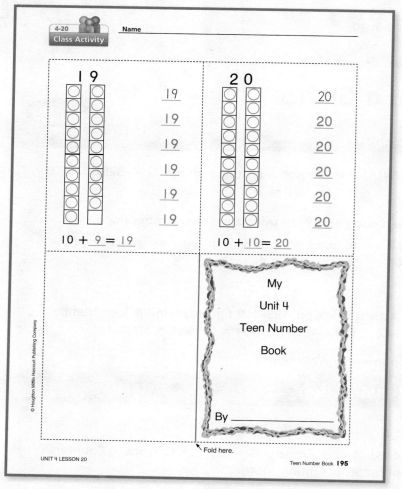

Student Activity Book page 195

MP.6 Attend to Precision Discuss with children how they will complete the top of Student Activity Book page 195. Then focus their attention on the bottom of the page and discuss how they might decorate the front cover.

While children complete the page, hand out the Teen Number Book pages that children completed in Lessons 16 and 18.

Have children cut on the dashed lines of Student Activity Book page 195. First, children should cut off the bottom half on the dashed lines, and fold it to make a cover. Then they should cut out the top half, making sure to cut along the vertical dashed line.

Next, have everyone cut along the dashed lines on the other two Teen Number Book pages. Have each child order the Teen Number Book Pages (numbers 11–20) and put them inside the cover.

You can complete each book by putting two staples along the left side.

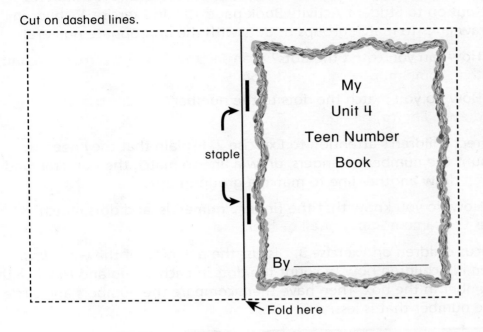

Cut on dashed lines.

My
Unit 4
Teen Number
Book

staple

By _____

Fold here

MP.5 Use Appropriate Tools After the book has been assembled, allow children to explore various ways to use it. Show children how to turn the pages to say the numbers in order from 11 to 20. Ask questions such as the following.

• Point to the page that shows the teen partners for 13.

• What is an equation for 17?

• Find the number that shows a group of 10 ones and 5 more ones.

• How can you use the Teen Number Book to play the *Teen Number Game*?

You may want to post the Teen Number Books in the classroom or in the hallway for several days before sending them home.

English Language Learners

Use 10-sticks to review *greater* and *less*.

BEGINNING

Point to 20 then 19. Ask: **How many 10-sticks are there?** 2,1 Say: **20 has a *greater* quantity of 10-sticks than 19. So 19 is *less* than than 20.** Have children repeat.

INTERMEDIATE

Ask: **Is 19 *greater* than or *less* than 20?** less than

ADVANCED

Have children make short sentences with *greater* and *less* to compare 19 and 20.

Alternate Approach

You may wish to have children glue each small cut-out Teen Number Book page onto a larger sheet of construction paper. Then you can complete each book by stapling together the construction paper pages.

Learning Community— Best Practices

MATH TALK In math conversations, encourage children to respond before you do. Allow time for children to make comments or ask questions about one another's work before you begin to speak. If you tend to speak first, children will give up ownership as active participants and will expect you to provide all of the answers and feedback.

COMMON CORE

Mathematical Practice
CC.K–12.MP.4, CC.K–12.MP.7

Mathematical Content
CC.K.CC.4a, CC.K.CC.4b,
CC.K.CC.2, CC.K.CC.6,
CC.K.CC.7

25 MINUTES

FOCUS Match pictures to numbers, compare groups, and practice addition within 10.

MATERIALS Student Activity Book page 197

 Whiteboard Lesson

ACTIVITY 2

Draw Lines to Match

▶ Match Numbers to Pictures INDIVIDUALS

MP.7 Look for Structure Identify Relationships Direct children's attention to Student Activity Book page 197. In Exercise 1, children draw lines to match groups of dots with the appropriate numeral.

• **How can you count the dots?** I can see that there is a row of 5 and then some more. I can count from 5.

• **How do you match the dots to the number?** I count the dots. Then I draw a line to the number.

Direct children's attention to Exercise 2. Explain that they need to count the number of fingers, draw a line to match the numeral, and then draw another line to match a group of dots.

• **How do you know that the fingers, numerals, and dots match?** There is the same number of all of them.

Focus children on Exercise 3. Discuss the meaning of the word *less*. Remind children how to count the dots in each group and to write the number in the box. Then have them compare the numbers and circle the number that is less.

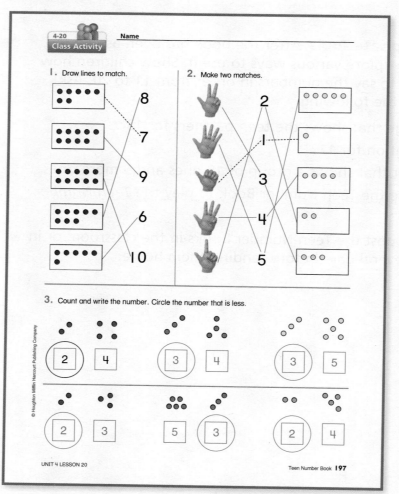

Student Activity Book page 197

▶ Practice Addition Equations Within 10 $\boxed{\text{INDIVIDUALS}}$

MP.4 Model with Mathematics Direct children's attention to Student Activity Book page 198. Connect addition equations to children's experiences. Ask children to give a story problem for each of the first three equations to monitor understanding of addition situations.

You may want to invite children to first complete the equations in the top five rows to build fluency of addition within 5. Then have them go back and use strategies that they have learned to complete the remaining equations. Some children may choose to use fingers, use counters, or draw pictures to add correctly.

4-20
Class Activity

Name _____

PATH to FLUENCY

4. Add the numbers.

1 + 3 = 4	3 + 1 = 4	5 + 0 = 5
4 + 0 = 4	0 + 2 = 2	2 + 1 = 3
1 + 2 = 3	3 + 2 = 5	2 + 3 = 5
1 + 4 = 5	2 + 2 = 4	1 + 1 = 2
2 + 1 = 3	1 + 2 = 3	4 + 1 = 5
5 + 3 = 8	5 + 1 = 6	8 + 2 = 10
2 + 6 = 8	6 + 4 = 10	3 + 7 = 10
6 + 1 = 7	4 + 5 = 9	1 + 8 = 9
3 + 7 = 10	4 + 4 = 8	6 + 3 = 9

198 UNIT 4 LESSON 20   Teen Number Book

© Houghton Mifflin Harcourt Publishing Company

Student Activity Book page 198

✓ Formative Assessment: Check Understanding

Student Summary Write 8 + 2 = ___ on the board and ask children to explain how they would solve the equation.

▲ On Level ▲ RtI Tier 1
for students having success

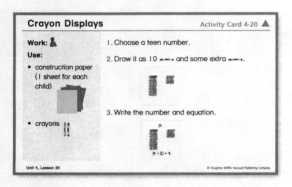

Activity Notes Assign teen numbers. Review teen number quantities.

 Math Writing Prompt

Teen Partners Have children choose a teen number. Then have them write the partners for their teen number.

 MegaMath

Software Support
Country Countdown: Counting Critters, Level P

■ Challenge
for students seeking a challenge

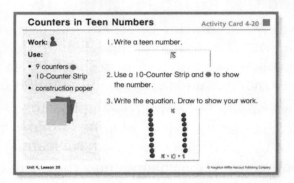

Activity Notes Assign teen numbers. Review the 10-Counter Strip.

 Math Writing Prompt

Write an Equation Challenge children to write a different equation using the same numbers in $19 = 9 + 10$.

 Destination Math®

Software Support
Course I: Module 2: Unit 1: Session 3: Sums Within 20, with 10 as One Addend

 Language Arts Connection

Teen Numbers As you read books or other printed materials with children, look for teen numbers. Encourage children to identify each number and tell how the number is a group of 10 ones and extra ones. Children can look up these teen numbers in their Teen Number Books. Ask children to continue looking for teen numbers when they read at home with family.

15 is a teen number. It is a group of 10 ones and 5 extra ones.

Identify Cones and Cylinders

LESSON FOCUS

- Describe cones and cylinders and compose three-dimensional shapes.

VOCABULARY

cone
cylinder

COMMON CORE

Mathematical Practice
CC.K–12.MP.1, CC.K–12.MP.3, CC.K–12.MP.4,
CC.K–12.MP.5, CC.K–12.MP.6, CC.K–12.MP.7
Mathematical Content
CC.K.G.1, CC.K.G.2, CC.K.G.3, CC.K.G.6

The Day at a Glance

Teaching the Lesson

USE MATH TALK TODAY!

MATH BACKGROUND for this lesson is included on p. 329MM.

ACTIVITY FOCUS

Activity 1   Use defining attributes to describe a cone.

Activity 2   Use defining attributes to describe a cylinder.

Activity 3   Compose three-dimensional shapes from cubes, cones, and cylinders.

MATERIALS

- Cones, cone-shaped objects • Cylinders, cylinder-shaped objects • Cubes, cube-shaped objects • Math Journals

- *i*Tools: Geometry • Whiteboard

Differentiated Instruction

MATERIALS

- Activity Cards 4-21 • Cylinder-shaped objects • Three-dimensional-shaped objects

- Soar to Success Math Intervention • MegaMath • Destination Math®

- **RtI** Tier 1 • Tier 2 • Tier 3

Home or School Activity

MATERIALS

- Music Connection p. 448

QUICK PRACTICE ⏱ 5 MINUTES

Repeated Quick Practice Use these Quick Practices from previous lessons.
Practice −1 Orally
(See Unit 4, Lesson 15.)
Count to 100 by Tens
(See Unit 4, Lesson 11.)

DAILY ROUTINES
Counting Tens and Ones
(See pp. xxxi–xxxii.)

DIGITAL RESOURCES

Use these digital resources along with your eSAB and eTE to support your students' learning experiences.

Professional Development

Whiteboard Lesson

*i*Tools

Soar to Success Math Intervention

MegaMath

Destination Math®

COMMON CORE

Mathematical Practice
CC.K–12.MP.3, CC.K–12.MP.6,
CC.K–12.MP.7

Mathematical Content
CC.K.G.1, CC.K.G.2, CC.K.G.3

20 MINUTES

FOCUS Use defining attributes to describe a cone.

MATERIALS Cones and cone-shaped objects

Whiteboard Lesson

Class Management

Pacing Provide children with sufficient time to explore the attributes of the cones and cylinders (in the next activity). It is important for building understanding of visual spatial relationships.

 MATH TALK *in ACTION* | **What can you say about cones?**

Nina: All the cones have a circle on the bottom.

Adrienne: Yes, and they all have a point on top.

Sam: Wait a minute. The one I am holding has a circle on the top and a point on the bottom.

Alex: I am confused. Which is the right way?

Sam: Oh, I know now! They all have a circle and a point. You can hold the shape in any direction so the circle and the point can be anywhere: top, bottom, or side. They are all still cones.

That is right. It does not matter what position a shape is in. It is still the same shape.

ACTIVITY 1

Attributes of Cones

▶ Describe Shapes WHOLE CLASS   MATH TALK

MP.3, MP.6 Attend to Precision Invite volunteers to name the solid shapes they have learned about so far and tell what they know about each of them. Responses from children should include attributes of a sphere and a cube, such as the following:

▶ A cube has square faces that are all the same size.

▶ A cube has 6 faces.

▶ A cube can stack, but it does not roll.

▶ A sphere is round all over.

▶ A sphere can roll, but it does not stack.

▶ Explore and Describe Cones SMALL GROUPS

MP.7 Look for Structure Give each group of children a variety of cones, including different sized cone-shaped objects. Display a cone.

• Who knows the name of this shape? a cone

• Is the cone two-dimensional (flat) or three-dimensional (solid)? three-dimensional, solid How do you know? It is not flat. It goes across, back, and down. It takes up space.

MP.6 Attend to Precision Explain a Representation Allow time for children to hold and study a cone. Then have them tell what they discovered about a cone.

• What can you say about a cone? A cone rolls. A cone rolls in a circle. Cones are different sizes. A cone has a face that is a circle. A cone has a point.

• What have you seen that is shaped like a cone? an ice cream cone, a big orange cone on the road, cones on a soccer field

• What can you say about the face on the end of the cone? The face is a circle.

• Do your cones look different when you move them around? (Show one cone with the face toward the children and then move it slowly until they just see it from the side.) Does it really change or is it just a different way of looking at it? It looks different, but it does not change its size or shape. For a solid shape, we have to turn it around to see all of the shape.

Attributes of Cylinders

▶ Explore and Describe Cylinders SMALL GROUPS

MP.6 Attend to Precision Explain a Representation Give each group of children a variety of cylinders, including different sized cylinder-shaped objects.

- Who knows the name of these shapes? cylinders Explore the cylinders for a few minutes and then you can share what you discovered about them.

- What did you see that is the same about all of the cylinders? They can roll. They have a circle on both ends. They all look the same but the sizes are different.

- A cylinder can be any height. It can be tall or short. It can be wide or narrow.

- What have you seen that is shaped like a cylinder? a roll of paper towels, a can, a roll of wrapping paper, a glass

- Are cylinders solid shapes? How do you know? They are solid shapes because they go across, backward and forward, and up and down. They take up space.

- How did the cylinders look different when you moved them around? (Show one cylinder with a face toward the children and then move it slowly until they just see the long side.) It looked like a circle from one end.

- Does the cylinder change when you move it? It looks different, but it does not change its size or shape. For a solid shape, we have to turn it around to see all of the shape.

COMMON CORE

Mathematical Practice
CC.K–12.MP.1, CC.K–12.MP.6
Mathematical Content
CC.K.G.1, CC.K.G.2, CC.K.G.3

20 MINUTES

FOCUS Use defining attributes to describe a cylinder.

MATERIALS Cylinders and cylinder-shaped objects

 Whiteboard Lesson

English Language Learners

Write *circle, cylinder,* and *cone* on the board. Display examples of each shape. Explain that a circle is flat. Point out that a *cylinder* and a *cone* are solid.

BEGINNING

Display a *circle*. Say: **This is a *circle*.** Ask children to repeat. Continue the process for *cylinder* and *cone*.

INTERMEDIATE

Display a *circle*, a *cylinder*, and a *cone*. Ask: **What are the names of these shapes?** circle, cylinder, and cone

ADVANCED

Ask children to describe a *circle*. A circle is a flat, round shape. Ask them to tell one way cylinders and cones are alike. Cylinders and cones are solid.

Activity continued ▶

Digital Resource

*i*Tools Choose 'Geometry' on the Menu. Use Activity 1 'Solid Figures' with the tab for 'Activities.' Children can see and identify three-dimensional shapes.

▶ ## Cylinders and Cones in Relative Positions

SMALL GROUPS

MP.1 Make Sense of Problems Act it Out Give each group of children a cylinder and a cone or cylinder- and cone-shaped objects. Explain that they will take turns being the leader and holding the shapes, but all children in the group should check and participate in how the shapes are displayed as you describe the positions.

• This can is shaped like a cylinder. This party hat is shaped like a cone. I will call the can a cylinder and the hat a cone. Use your shapes the same way.

• We are going to practice some math words, so we will use the words *cylinder* and *cone* instead of naming the objects with those shapes.

• Now the leader will hold the cylinder in one hand and the cone in the other hand.

• Do what I do with my cylinder and cone and everyone should say what I say.

Hold and move your shapes to show the relative positional words as you say them and check what children do and say. You should show all relative positions from the children's point of view as they show relative positions from their own point of view.

• My cylinder is *above* my cone. (move shapes) My cylinder is *below* my cone.

• My cylinder is *in front of* my cone. My cylinder is *in back of* my cone.

• My cylinder is *behind* my cone. My cylinder is *in front of* my cone.

Repeat as needed with a child leading. Make sure everyone has an opportunity to position the shapes.

Compose 3-Dimensional Shapes

▶ **Combine Solid Shapes** | SMALL GROUPS |

MP.4, MP.5 Use Appropriate Tools/Model with Mathematics
Provide each group with cubes, cones, cylinders, and cube-, cone-, and cylinder-shaped objects. Children will compose three-dimensional shapes using cubes, cones, and cylinders.

• What types of shapes do you see in front of you? cubes, cylinders, and cones

• You will be combining these shapes to make new shapes. You are going to build with them. You can stack them, one on top of another, like this (demonstrate for children how to stack). You can put the shapes *next to* one another.

• Explore the shapes a little to see which shapes might be used for which positions.

Let children experiment with the shapes to determine which shapes can stack and how they can stack.

• Which shapes will probably be on the bottom? Explain. Cylinders or cubes will be on the bottom because those shapes can stack.

• Why would either of those shapes probably be the bottom shape? Those shapes have a face on the bottom and top and you can stack them. If the cone was put on the bottom, then the face would be at the bottom and I could not stack a shape on the point at the top because it would fall off.

• Now it is time to make stacks of shapes. See what creative and different shapes you can make. Be sure everyone in your group gets to share ideas for what to build.

Allow time for children to share the shapes they made and describe them to the class using the proper shape names and positions words. Some shapes may be composed of just 2 three-dimensional shapes while others may combine 3 or more shapes.

 Formative Assessment: Check Understanding

Student Summary Ask children to explain the difference between a cylinder and a cone.

 COMMON CORE

Mathematical Practice
CC.K–12.MP.4, CC.K–12.MP.5

Mathematical Content
CC.K.G.6

20 MINUTES

FOCUS Compose three-dimensional shapes from cubes, cones, and cylinders.

MATERIALS Cubes, cones, cylinders, and cube-, cone-, and cylinder-shaped objects

Whiteboard Lesson

Teaching Note

Geometry Center Activities
Center activities for geometry will focus on free exploration with all of the solid shapes used so far. Children can build whatever they envision with the geometry materials. The cones and cylinders are especially appropriate for such exploration and play.

▲ On Level ▲RtI Tier 1
for students having success

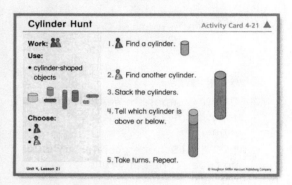

Cylinder Hunt — Activity Card 4-21 ▲

Work: 👥

Use:
• cylinder-shaped objects

Choose:
• 👤
• 👤

1. 👤 Find a cylinder.
2. 👤 Find another cylinder.
3. Stack the cylinders.
4. Tell which cylinder is above or below.
5. Take turns. Repeat.

Unit 4, Lesson 21 © Houghton Mifflin Harcourt Publishing Company

Activity Notes Provide various sizes of cylinders and distribute them around the room. Remind children of the meanings of *above* and *below*.

 Math Writing Prompt

Name cylinders Have children write about objects they have seen that are shaped like cylinders.

 MegaMath

Software Support
Shapes Ahoy: Undersea 3D, Level C

■ Challenge
for students seeking a challenge

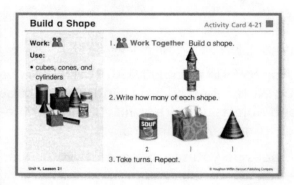

Build a Shape — Activity Card 4-21 ■

Work: 👥

Use:
• cubes, cones, and cylinders

1. 👥 Work Together Build a shape.
2. Write how many of each shape.

SOUP 2   1   1

3. Take turns. Repeat.

Unit 4, Lesson 21 © Houghton Mifflin Harcourt Publishing Company

Activity Notes Demonstrate how to compose shapes. Have children write how many of each shape they used in their models.

 Math Writing Prompt

Compare Have children use pictures or words to explain the difference between a sphere and a cylinder.

 Destination Math®

Software Support
Course I: Module 3: Unit 2: Session 2: Three-Dimensional Shapes

 ## Music Connection

Instrument Shapes Have children think about or look at pictures of instruments and see how many shapes they can find in an instrument as a whole or a part of an instrument. For example, a drum and a tambourine are both cylinders. Cymbals are circles, and a triangle is a triangle.

Focus on Mathematical Practices

LESSON FOCUS
- Use the Common Core Content Standards and Practices in a variety of real world problem solving situations.

COMMON CORE
Mathematical Practice
CC.K–12.MP.1, CC.K–12.MP.2, CC.K–12.MP.3, CC.K–12.MP.4, CC.K–12.MP.5, CC.K–12.MP.6, CC.K–12.MP.7, CC.K–12.MP.8
Mathematical Content
CC.K.MD.3, CC.K.G.1, CC.K.G.2, CC.K.G.4

The Day at a Glance

Teaching the Lesson

MATH BACKGROUND for this lesson is included on p. 329MM.

ACTIVITY FOCUS

Activity 1 Mathematical Practices
1 Make sense of problems and persevere in solving them.
3 Construct viable arguments and critique the reasoning of others.
6 Attend to precision.
7 Look for and make use of structure.
8 Look for and express regularity in repeated reasoning.

Activity 2 Mathematical Practices
2 Reason abstractly and quantitatively.
5 Use appropriate tools strategically.

6 Attend to precision.
7 Look for and make use of structure.

Activity 3 Mathematical Practices
3 Construct viable arguments and critique the reasoning of others.
4 Model with mathematics.
5 Use appropriate tools strategically.
7 Look for and make use of structure.

MATERIALS

- Student Activity Book pp. 199–200 • Fluency Check 4 (Assessment Guide) • Spheres, cubes, cones, cylinders • Three-dimensional shaped objectss • Crayons • Math Journals

- iTools: Geometry • Whiteboard

Differentiated Instruction

MATERIALS

- Activity Cards 4-22 • Three-dimensional-shaped objects

- Soar to Success Math Intervention • MegaMath • Destination Math®

- **RtI** Tier 1 • Tier 2 • Tier 3

Home or School Activity

MATERIALS

- Science Connection p. 454

QUICK PRACTICE 5 MINUTES

Repeated Quick Practice Use these Quick Practices from previous lessons.

Count to 100 by Tens Point to the numbers in the bottom row of the 120 Poster while children count and flash 10 fingers with each count. A **Student Leader** wears the "How Many Tens?" Card and raises one finger for each decade number that is counted. (See Unit 4, Lesson 11.)

Partners of 4, 5, 6, or 7 (See Unit 4, Lesson 3, 4, 5, or 6.)

DAILY ROUTINES

Counting Tens and Ones
(See pp. xxxi–xxxii.)

DIGITAL RESOURCES

Use these digital resources along with your eSAB and eTE to support your students' learning experiences.

Professional Development

Whiteboard Lesson

iTools

Soar to Success Math Intervention

MegaMath

Destination Math®

COMMON CORE

Mathematical Practice
CC.K–12.MP.1, CC.K–12.MP.3,
CC.K–12.MP.6, CC.K–12.MP.7,
CC.K–12.MP.8

Mathematical Content
CC.K.G.2

30 MINUTES

FOCUS Identify cubes, cylinders, and spheres.

MATERIALS Student Activity Book pp. 199–200, crayons (red, blue, yellow, green)

Whiteboard Lesson

Digital Resource

*i*Tools Choose 'Geometry' on the Menu. Use Activity 1 'Solid Figures' with the tab for 'Activities.' Children can see and identify three-dimensional shapes.

ACTIVITY 1

Finding Shapes in Our Classroom

▶ **Hunt for Shapes** WHOLE CLASS MATH TALK

Ask for Ideas Invite volunteers to go on a shape hunt. Instruct them to look around the classroom for objects shaped like spheres, cubes, cones, and cylinders.

MP.8 Use Repeated Reasoning Ask questions to encourage children to describe the attributes of each of the objects they find. For example:

• How do you know this block is a cube? I know because all the faces are square and the same size. There are 6 faces.

MP.1 Make Sense of Problems Analyze the Problem Invite children to look at Student Activity Book page 199. Tell them that for each shelf on the bookcase, you will name a shape, and they will carefully look at each shape, and then circle the objects that have that shape. You may wish to tell the children to use a crayon of a particular color when they circle the objects.

MP.7 Look for Structure Allow time for children to study all the objects on the page before beginning.

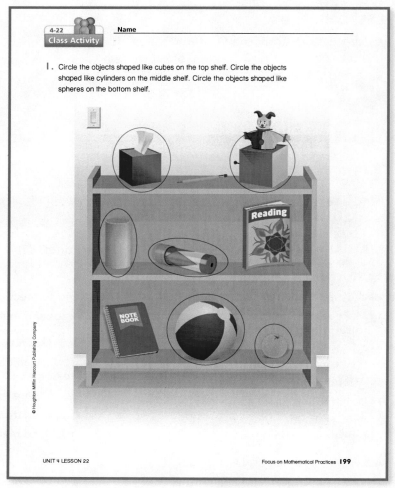

Student Activity Book page 199

• Look at the top row (shelf). Describe the different shapes of the objects you see. Now circle all the objects that are cubes.

Check that children have circled the correct objects. tissue box, jack-in-the-box

• Look at the middle shelf. Describe the shapes of the objects you see.

• Now circle all the objects that are cylinders. can, kaleidoscope

When children are ready, invite them to look at the bottom shelf.

• Describe the shapes of the objects you see. Now circle all the objects that are spheres. ball, orange

MP.3 Construct a Viable Argument Justify Conclusions Ask children to explain why they have circled the objects they did. Children should be able to justify their thinking by describing the attributes of the circled shapes.

▶ Identify and Describe Shapes

Children will need green, red, yellow, and blue crayons to complete Student Activity Book page 200. Invite children to talk about the different shapes they see on the page. Encourage children to name and describe the shapes using math terms they have learned.

Then have volunteers point to the cubes, cylinders, cones, and spheres, one at a time. Ask questions as each child volunteers.

- How do you know it is a cube? It has 6 faces. It stacks.
- How do you know it is a cylinder? It has 2 faces that are circles. It rolls.
- How do you know it is a cone? It has 1 face that is a circle. It has a point. It rolls.
- How do you know it is a sphere? It is round all over. It rolls.

Teaching Note

Watch for! Some children may not recognize shapes that do not stand vertically on a face, such as the cylinders and the cone (right side) on Student Activity Book page 200. Remind children that shapes can be shown in different positions, and that position does not change the shape of an object.

English Language Learners

Write *circle, cylinder,* and *cone* on the board. Display examples of each shape and discuss the attributes with children. Elicit that circles are flat and that cylinders and cones are not flat.

BEGINNING

Hold up each shape as you name it. Ask children to repeat.

INTERMEDIATE

Ask: **What types of shapes do you see?** circle, cylinder, and cone

ADVANCED

Ask children to describe a circle. A circle is a flat, round shape. Ask them to tell one way cylinders and cones are alike. Possible answer: Cylinders and cones are not flat.

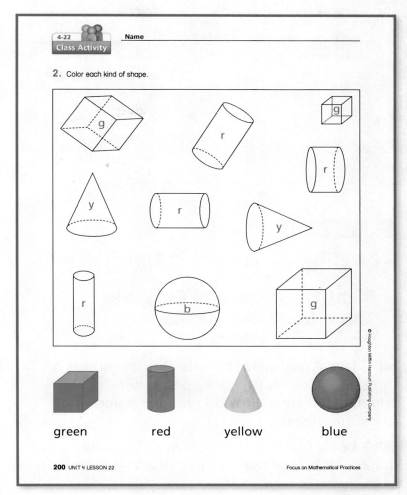

Student Activity Book page 200

MP.6 Attend to Precision Direct children's attention to the color code at the bottom of the page.

- What color should you use for the cubes? green
- Point to a cube.

Check that children are pointing to a cube.

- Color it green. Do you see any other cubes? yes Color them green, too.
- Check to make sure you have colored all of the cubes green.
- Now look back at the color code again. What shape will you look for next? cylinder What color crayon should you use? red

Have children complete the page by finding all the cylinders and coloring them red. Then have them identify and color the cones yellow and the spheres blue.

COMMON CORE

Mathematical Practice
CC.K–12.MP.2, CC.K–12.MP.5,
CC.K–12.MP.6, CC.K–12.MP.7

Mathematical Content
CC.K.G.4

15 MINUTES

FOCUS Describe and compare attributes of three-dimensional shapes.

MATERIALS Sphere, cube, cone, cylinder, three-dimensional-shaped objects

 Whiteboard Lesson

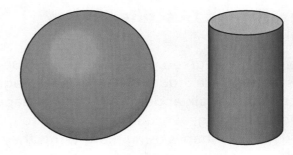

 ACTIVITY 2

Compare Attributes

▶ **Identify, Name, and Compare Three-Dimensional Shapes**

WHOLE CLASS MATH TALK

MP.5 Use Appropriate Tools Display models of three-dimensional (solid) shapes: sphere, cube, cylinder, and cone. Provide time for children to study the shapes.

MP.7 Look for Structure Have children name each shape. Encourage them to describe the shape using as many math terms as they can.

MP.6 Attend to Precision Display a model of a sphere and a cylinder.

• What objects in our classroom are shaped like a cylinder? cup, can

• Point to a sphere. How do you know it is a sphere? I know because it rolls.

• What other shapes roll? cone, cylinder

• How are a cone and a cylinder alike? They both roll.

• How are a cylinder and a sphere different? The cylinder has two faces; the sphere does not have any.

MP.2 Reason Abstractly Point out that a shape has many attributes and may be described in different ways. For example, a sphere is round all over, it rolls, and it is a solid shape. Make sure children understand that there are many different ways to describe the same shape.

Repeat with similar questioning about the attributes for the cube, cylinder, and cone. Knowing the attributes of each shape will aid children in identifying, naming, and comparing three-dimensional shapes.

COMMON CORE

Mathematical Practice
CC.K–12.MP.3, CC.K–12.MP.4,
CC.K–12.MP.5, CC.K–12.MP.7

Mathematical Content
CC.K.MD.3, CC.K.G.1

15 MINUTES

FOCUS Sort and identify positions of three-dimensional shapes.

MATERIALS Spheres, cubes, cones, cylinders, three-dimensional-shaped objects

Whiteboard Lesson

ACTIVITY 3

Establish a Position

MP.4, MP.5 Use Appropriate Tools/Model with Mathematics Take a shape such as a sphere and hold it above another shape such as a cube.

- Which shape is *above* the other one? The sphere is *above* the cube.

- Which shape is *below* the other? The cube is *below* the sphere.

Repeat with other pairs of shapes. Hold the shapes in different ways to include the terms *beside, next to, in front of, behind,* and any other appropriate positions children name.

MP.3 Construct a Viable Argument Children should be able to explain whether they agree or disagree with other children's responses to the positions of the shapes.

▶ **Sort Three-Dimensional Shapes**

SMALL GROUPS

MP.7 Look for Structure Provide groups of children with 10 assorted three-dimensional shapes (spheres, cubes, cones, and cylinders) or objects shaped like three-dimensional shapes. Tell children to sort the shapes into groups.

Provide time for children to decide how to sort the shapes into groups. Then have them sort the shapes according to their plan. When all of the small groups have completed their shape sorting have groups explain what they did.

- How did you sort your shapes? Children may sort by shapes that roll/do not roll or stack/do not stack.

After groups have explained how they sorted the shapes, have them try to sort the shapes a different way. Then have them explain how they sorted.

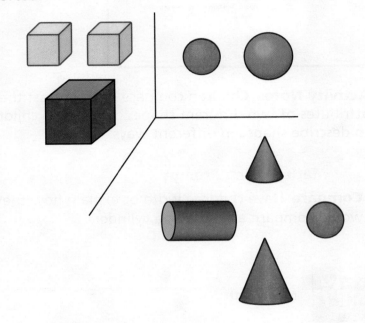

 Formative Assessment: Check Understanding

Student Summary What are some different words you can use to describe the positions of objects? above, below, beside, next to, in front of, behind Ask volunteers to use cubes, spheres, cones, or cylinders to demonstrate a position. They should name the shapes and their positions.

✓ **Fluency Check**

See Assessment Guide for Fluency Check 4 on p. 79.

▲ On Level  RtI Tier 1

for students having success

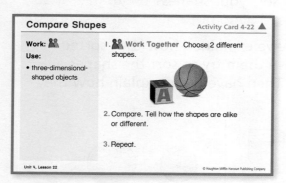

Activity Notes Children compare and contrast the attributes of two different shapes. Encourage children to describe shapes in different ways.

 Math Writing Prompt

Compare Have children write or explain how they would compare a cone and a cylinder.

 MegaMath

Software Support
Shapes Ahoy: Undersea 3D, Level F

■ Challenge

for students seeking a challenge

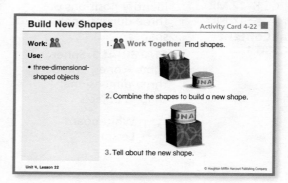

Activity Notes Children find three-dimensional classroom objects of different shapes. They combine the shapes to build a model of a real life object.

Math Writing Prompt

Write to Build Have children write or explain about a way they would use shapes to build a model of a house.

 Destination Math®

Software Support
Course I: Module 3: Unit 2: Session 2: Three-Dimensional Shapes

 Science Connection

Position Words Remind children that they have been using position words to describe the position of shapes. Explain that now they will use position words to describe the positions of living things, such as animals and plants. For example, The red flower is growing *next to* the green bush; A mother duck may walk *in front of* the ducklings; Some birds can fly *above* the trees.

Have children choose one example to draw.

Unit Review and Test

UNIT TEST OBJECTIVES

4A Count objects and compare the number of objects in groups. [CC.K.CC.1, CC.K.CC.3, CC.K.CC.4, CC.K.CC.4a, CC.K.CC.4b, CC.K.CC.4c, CC.K.CC.5, CC.K.CC.6, CC.K.CC.7]

4B Add and subtract within 10 by composing and decomposing numbers. [CC.K.OA.1, CC.K.OA.2, CC.K.OA.3, CC.K.OA.4, CC.K.OA.5]

4C Decompose teen numbers into a group of ten ones and extra ones. [CC.K.NBT.1]

4D Identify and describe three-dimensional shapes, and describe shapes in relative positions. [CC.K.G.1, CC.K.G.2, CC.K.G.3, CC.K.G. 5, CC.K.G.6]

The Day at a Glance

Today's Goals

ASSESSING THE UNIT: SUMMATIVE ASSESSMENT

• Review and assess progress on unit test objectives.

DIFFERENTIATED INSTRUCTION

• Use activities from unit lessons to reteach content.
• Use prescriptions for common errors.

ONLINE PRACTICE

• Additional practice is provided online at www.thinkcentral.com/.

MATERIALS

 Student Activity Book pp. 201–204 • Unit 4 Test Form A (open response) and Form B (multiple choice), Assessment Guide (optional) • Unit 4 Performance Assessment with rubric, Assessment Guide (optional) • Math Journals (optional)

USING THE ASSESSMENT

You can use this Unit Review/Test as an end-of-unit review to determine if children have mastered all the unit objectives.

You can assess children's knowledge with a secure, formal assessment that is provided in the Assessment Guide.

VOCABULARY

Choose a vocabulary activity from the Teacher Resources section (page T10) to review words from the unit.

Assess Unit Objectives

45 MINUTES (more if schedule permits)

FOCUS Review and assess progress on unit objectives.

MATERIALS Student Activity Book pp. 201–204

▶ Review and Assessment

If children are ready for assessment on the unit test objectives, you may use either the Unit Review/Test in the Student Activity Book or one of the forms of the Unit 4 Test in the Assessment Guide.

If children would benefit from review, use the Student Activity Book pages to review the content, and then use one of the forms of the Unit 4 Test in the Assessment Guide.

Scoring To provide a numerical score for this assessment, assign 10 points for each item.

▶ Reteaching Resources

The chart below lists the objectives for each test item.

Reteaching The lesson activities in which the objective is covered are provided so you may revisit these activities with children who do not show mastery of the objectives.

Common Errors You will find common errors and prescriptions on the last two pages of this lesson.

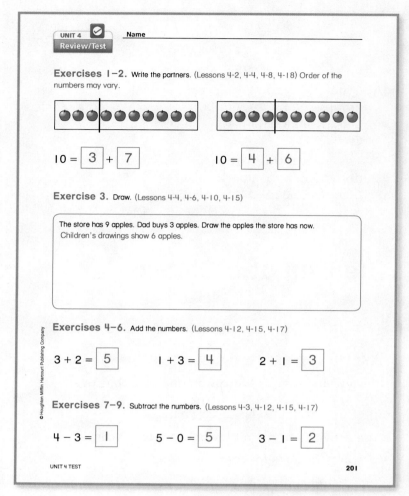

Student Activity Book page 201

Test Items	Unit Test Objective	Reteaching Activities
1–2	**4B** Add and subtract within 10 by composing and decomposing numbers.	Lesson 2 Activity 2 Lesson 4 Activity 2 Lesson 8 Activity 1 Lesson 18 Activity 1
3	**4B** Add and subtract within 10 by composing and decomposing numbers.	Lesson 4 Activity 1 Lesson 6 Activity 1 Lesson 10 Activity 1 Lesson 15 Activity 1
4–6	**4B** Add and subtract within 10 by composing and decomposing numbers.	Lesson 12 Activity 3 Lesson 17 Activity 1
7–9	**4B** Add and subtract within 10 by composing and decomposing numbers.	Lesson 3 Activity 3 Lesson 12 Activity 3 Lesson 17 Activity 2

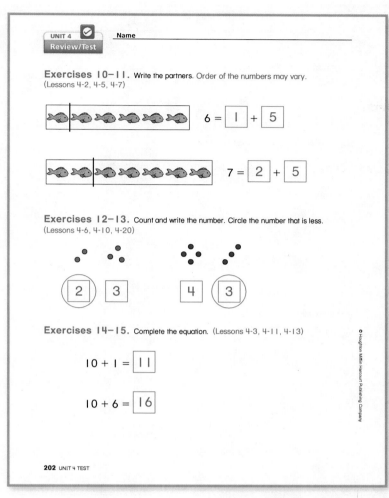

Student Activity Book page 202

▶ Assessment Options

SUMMATIVE ASSESSMENT

Open Response Test
Unit 4 Test, Form A, is provided in the Assessment Guide.

Multiple Choice Test
Unit 4 Test, Form B, is provided in the Assessment Guide.

Performance Assessment
Unit 4 Performance Task, with rubric, is provided in the Assessment Guide.

Online Assessment
www.thinkcentral.com

FORMATIVE ASSESSMENT

Portfolio Assessment

> **Teacher Selected Items:**
> Homework for Lessons 3, 8, 10, 19
> Class Activity work for Lessons 2, 6, 12, 22

> **Student Selected Items:** Allow children to choose a favorite Home or School Activity and a best writing prompt.

Check Understanding: in every lesson

Test Items	Unit Test Objective	Reteaching Activities
10–11	**4B** Add and subtract within 10 by composing and decomposing numbers.	Lesson 2 Activity 1 Lesson 5 Activity 3 Lesson 7 Activity 3
12–13	**4A** Count objects and compare the number of objects in groups.	Lesson 6 Activity 2 Lesson 10 Activity 2 Lesson 20 Activity 2
14–15	**4C** Decompose teen numbers into a group of ten ones and extra ones.	Lesson 3 Activities 2 and 3 Lesson 11 Activity 1 Lesson 13 Activity 1

Assessing the Unit continued ▶

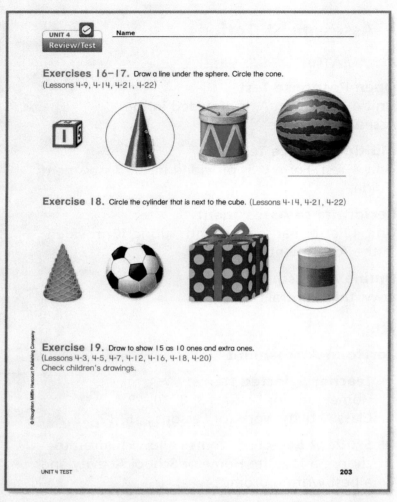

Student Activity Book page 203

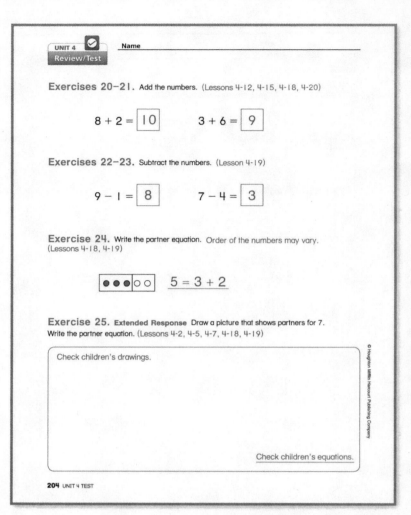

Student Activity Book page 204

Test Items	Unit Test Objective	Reteaching Activities
16–18	**4D** Identify and describe three-dimensional shapes, and describe shapes in relative positions.	Lesson 9 Activity 2 Lesson 14 Activity 1
19	**4C** Decompose teen numbers into a group of ten ones and extra ones.	Lesson 3 Activity 1 Lesson 5 Activity 1
20–23	**4B** Add and subtract within 10 by composing and decomposing numbers.	Lesson 12 Activity 3 Lesson 15 Activity 2
24	**4B** Add and subtract within 10 by composing and decomposing numbers.	Lesson 18 Activities 1 and 2 Lesson 19 Activity 1
25	**4B** Add and subtract within 10 by composing and decomposing numbers.	Lesson 2 Activity 1 Lesson 5 Activity 3

Differentiated Instruction

Common Errors and Prescriptions

Items	Common Error	Prescription
1–2	May count all ten objects at once	Encourage children to count the objects on the left side of the Break-Apart Stick and write the number. Then have them count the objects on the right side of the Break-Apart Stick and write the number.
3	May not draw the correct number of objects	Encourage children to draw very simple objects and to focus on creating the correct number of objects rather than the actual drawing. Remind them to check their work by counting the objects that they drew.
4–6	May not add fluently within 5	Invite children to show the partners with fingers to help them.
7–9	May not subtract fluently within 5	Invite children to show the first number with fingers and to hold down the number they are subtracting. Remind them that the fingers pointing up is the number to write.
10–11	May be confused at seeing the partners on the right side of the equal sign	Remind children that the equal sign shows that both sides of the equation have the same quantity.
12–13	May not identify the number that is less	Remind children to choose the number that shows fewer objects.
14–15	May not add ten ones and extra ones correctly	Provide children with the 1–20 Board and the Teen Equation Cards to help them complete the equation.
16–17	May not identify shapes correctly	Encourage children to describe attributes of three-dimensional shapes. Then have them apply those attributes to real world shapes.
18	May not understand position words	Remind children that *next to* means beside. Demonstrate for children the meaning of *next to* with objects.
19	May draw an incorrect number of objects	Provide children with a 10-stick and centimeter cubes to model their work.
20–21	May not add within 10	Invite children to draw simple objects to represent the partners. Then have them count the objects they drew.
22–23	May not subtract within 10	Invite children to decompose numbers into partners and then write the partner.
24	May not write the equation correctly	Invite children to use Number Tiles and the + and = tiles to represent the picture. Then have them write the equation.
25	May not draw the partners correctly	Encourage children to use tiles to show partners. Remind them that there are several ways to show partners of 7.

Online Practice

Additional practice is provided online at www.thinkcentral.com/.

NOTES:

UNIT 5 · Consolidation of Concepts

Learning Progressions for the Common Core Standards
Counting and Cardinality, Operations and Algebraic Thinking, Number and Operations in Base Ten, and Measurement and Data

In Grade K, children will

- create and solve story problems and make drawings or write equations to represent problem situations.
- identify all partners of numbers from 2–10 and teen numbers and write addition equations to represent the partners.
- achieve fluency adding and subtracting within 5.

In Grade 1, children will

- represent a situation or numerical problem with groups of objects, a drawing, or fingers.
- model the situation by composing two addend groups or decomposing a total group.
- use subitizing with 5-groups to omit the counting of one addend.
- work toward fluency for addition and subtraction within 10.

Content Standards Across the Grades

Grade K

- Know number names and the count sequence. [CC.K.CC.1, 2, 3]
- Count to tell the number of objects. [CC.K.CC.4, 4a, 4b, 4c, 5]
- Compare numbers. [CC.K.CC.6, 7]
- Understand addition as putting together and adding to, and understand subtraction as taking apart and taking from. [CC.K.OA 1, 2, 3, 4, 5]
- Work with numbers 11–19 to gain foundations for place value [CC.K.NBT.1]
- Describe and compare measurable attributes. [CC.K.MD 1, 2]

Grade 1

- Represent and solve problems involving addition and subtraction. [CC.1.OA.1, 2]
- Understand and apply properties of operations and the relationship between addition and subtraction. [CC.1.OA.3, 4]
- Add and subtract within 20. [CC.1.OA.5, 6]
- Work with addition and subtraction equations. [CC.1.OA.7, 8]
- Extend the counting sequence. [CC.1.NBT.1]
- Understand place value. [CC.1.NBT.2]
- Measure lengths indirectly and by iterating length units. [CC.1.MD.1, 2]

UNIT 5 CONSOLIDATION OF CONCEPTS

REAL WORLD PROBLEM SOLVING

BIG IDEA 1   More Partners of 10

Common Core State Standards CC.K.CC.1, CC.K.CC.3, CC.K.CC.4a, CC.K.CC.5, CC.K.CC.7, CC.K.OA.1, CC.K.OA.2, CC.K.OA.3, CC.K.OA.4, CC.K.OA.5, CC.K.NBT.1

1 **Math Stories and Scenes with Teen Numbers** **461**
FOCUS Create addition and subtraction story problems; Visualize and represent teen numbers as ten ones and extra ones.

2 **Partners of 10: Stars in the Night Sky** **465**
FOCUS Create and count stars to make partners of 10 for a classroom display; Count the number of objects in a group through 20.

3 **More Partners of 10: Stars in the Night Sky** **471**
FOCUS Write equations to show partners of 10 and identify an unknown partner of 10; Count by tens to 100 and show teen numbers as a group of ten ones and extra ones.

4 **Solve and Retell Story Problems** **477**
FOCUS Tell, retell, and solve addition and subtraction story problems with drawings and equations; Visualize teen numbers as 10 (two 5-groups) and extra ones.

REAL WORLD PROBLEM SOLVING

BIG IDEA 2   Numbers 1 Through 20

Common Core State Standards CC.K.CC.1, CC.K.CC.3, CC.K.CC.4, CC.K.CC.4c, CC.K.CC.5, CC.K.OA.1, CC.K.OA.2, CC.K.OA.3, CC.K.OA.4, CC.K.OA.5, CC.K.NBT.1

5 **Make Quantities 1–20** **481**
FOCUS Show numbers 1–20 as a group of ten ones and more ones; Practice partners for numbers 7–9, and find the unknown partner when the total and one partner are known.

6 **More Solve and Retell Story Problems** **485**
FOCUS Tell, retell, and write equations for addition and subtraction stories; Visualize teen numbers as ten ones and extra ones.

7 **Numbers 1–20** **491**
FOCUS Show numbers 1–20; show the teen numbers as a group of ten ones and further ones; Find the unknown partner when the total and one partner are known.

REAL WORLD
PROBLEM SOLVING

BIG IDEA 3 — More Teen Numbers and Partners

Common Core State Standards CC.K.CC.1, CC.K.CC.2, CC.K.CC.3, CC.K.CC.5, CC.K.OA.1, CC.K.OA.2, CC.K.OA.3, CC.K.OA.4, CC.K.OA.5, CC.K.NBT.1

REAL WORLD
PROBLEM SOLVING

BIG IDEA 4 — More Story Problems and Equations

Common Core State Standards CC.K.CC.3, CC.K.CC.4, CC.K.CC.4c, CC.K.CC.5, CC.K.CC.6, CC.K.CC.7, CC.K.OA.1, CC.K.OA.2, CC.K.OA.3, CC.K.OA.4, CC.K.OA.5, CC.K.NBT.1, CC.K.MD.1, CC.K.MD.2

UNIT 5 CONTENTS

Contents | Planning | Research & Math Background

Assessment

Math Expressions provides Diagnostic Tools for both Formative Assessment and Summative Assessment as well as Review Opportunities to support the learning needs of your students.

 Unit 5 Test Objectives

5A Count objects and compare the number of objects in groups. [CC.K.CC.1, CC.K.CC.2, CC.K.CC.3, CC.K.CC.4, CC.K.CC.4a, CC.K.CC.4b, CC.K.CC.4c, CC.K.CC.5, CC.K.CC.6, CC.K.CC.7]

5B Add and subtract within 10 by composing and decomposing numbers. [CC.K.OA.1, CC.K.OA.2, CC.K.OA.3, CC.K.OA.4, CC.K.OA.5]

5C Decompose teen numbers into a group of ten ones and extra ones. [CC.K.NBT.1]

5D Identify and compare measurable attributes. [CC.K.MD.1, CC.K.MD.2]

Assessment and Review Resources

DIAGNOSTIC TOOLS

Student Activity Book
- Unit Review and Test (pp. 265–268)

Assessment Guide
- Test A— Open Response
- Unit 5—Observational Assessment
- Performance Task

Online Test Generator
- Open Response Test
- Multiple Choice Test
- Test Bank Items

FORMATIVE ASSESSMENT

Teacher Edition
- Check Understanding (in every lesson)
- Quick Practice (in every lesson)
- Math Talk (in every lesson)
- Portfolio Suggestions (pp. 470, 500, 514, 573)

SUMMATIVE ASSESSMENT

Assessment Guide
- Test A—Open Response
- Unit 5—Observational Assessment
- Performance Task

REVIEW OPPORTUNITIES

Homework and Remembering
- Review of recently taught topics
- Spiral Review

Teacher Edition
- Unit Review and Test (pp. 571–576)

Assessment Guide
- Fluency Check

Online Test Generator
- Custom review sheets

PLANNING GUIDE FOR UNIT 5
Consolidation of Concepts

LESSONS	Print Resources	Materials
BIG IDEA 1 More Partners of 10		
1 **Math Stories and Scenes with Teen Numbers** **Common Core State Standards** CC.K.CC.5, CC.K.OA.2, CC.K.OA.5, CC.K.NBT.1 **FOCUS** Create addition and subtraction story problems; Visualize and represent teen numbers as ten ones and extra ones.	TE pp. 461–464 SAB pp. 205–206 AC 5-1	✓ *Anno's Counting Book* by Mitsumasa Anno Crayons or markers
2 **Partners of 10: Stars in the Night Sky** **Common Core State Standards** CC.K.CC.1, CC.K.CC.3, CC.K.CC.5, CC.K.CC.7, CC.K.OA.4 **FOCUS** Create and count stars to make partners of 10 for a classroom display; Count the number of objects in a group through 20.	TE pp. 465–470 SAB pp. 207–210 H&R pp. 89–90 AC 5-2	Stars (TRB M53) Crayons or markers (purple and yellow) Scissors Glue stick
3 **More Partners of 10: Stars in the Night Sky** **Common Core State Standards** CC.K.CC.1, CC.K.OA.1, CC.K.OA.3, CC.K.OA.4, CC.K.OA.5, CC.K.NBT.1 **FOCUS** Write equations to show partners of 10 and identify an unknown partner of 10; Count by tens to 100 and show teen numbers as a group of ten ones and extra ones.	TE pp. 471–476 SAB pp. 211–214 AC 5-3	Night Sky display ✓ Pointer Equations strips Decade number cards Sticky notes "How Many Tens?" Card
4 **Solve and Retell Story Problems** **Common Core State Standards** CC.K.CC.3, CC.K.CC.5, CC.K.OA.2, CC.K.OA.3, CC.K.OA.4, CC.K.NBT.1 **FOCUS** Tell, retell, and solve addition and subtraction story problems with drawings and equations; Visualize teen numbers as 10 (two 5-groups) and extra ones.	TE pp. 477–480 SAB pp. 215–216 H&R pp. 91–92 AC 5-4 MCC 17	*none*
BIG IDEA 2 Number 1 Through 20		
5 **Make Quantities 1–20** **Common Core State Standards** CC.K.CC.1, CC.K.CC.3, CC.K.OA.3, CC.K.NBT.1 **FOCUS** Show numbers 1–20 as a group of ten ones and more ones; Practice partners for numbers 7–9, and find the unknown partner when the total and one partner are known.	TE pp. 481–484 SAB pp. 217–218 H&R pp. 93–94 AC 5-5	✓ 1–20 Boards ✓ Centimeter cubes ✓ 10-sticks ✓ Number Tiles 1–9 Break-Apart Sticks ✓ +/− Tiles ✓ 120 Poster

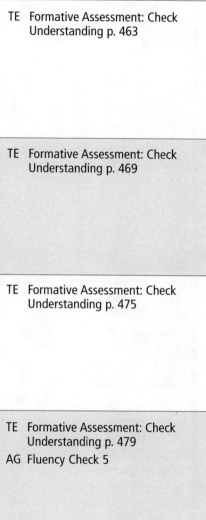

Digital Resources	**Assessment**
Interactive Whiteboard *i*Tools: Counters Warm-Up 1.13 Country Countdown: Counting Critters, Level P Course I: Module 2: Unit 1: Session 3	TE Formative Assessment: Check Understanding p. 463
Interactive Whiteboard *i*Tools: Counters Warm-Up 1.11 Country Countdown: Counting Critters, Level C Course I: Module 1: Unit 2: Session 3	TE Formative Assessment: Check Understanding p. 469
Interactive Whiteboard *i*Tools: Counters Warm-Up 1.13 Country Countdown: Block Busters, Level G Course I: Module 2: Unit 1: Session 3	TE Formative Assessment: Check Understanding p. 475
Interactive Whiteboard *i*Tools: Counters Warm-Up 11.17 Country Countdown: Block Busters, Level G Course I: Module 2: Unit 1: Session 3	TE Formative Assessment: Check Understanding p. 479 AG Fluency Check 5
Interactive Whiteboard *i*Tools: Counters Warm-Up 1.13 Country Countdown: Counting Critters, Level P Course I: Module 2: Unit 1: Session 3	TE Formative Assessment: Check Understanding p. 483

COMMON CORE STATE STANDARDS FOR MATHEMATICAL CONTENT KEY

CC.K.CC Counting and Cardinality

CC.K.OA Operations and Algebraic Thinking

CC.K.NBT Number and Operations in Base Ten

CC.K.MD Measurement and Data

CC.K.G Geometry

PRINT KEY

TE: Teacher Edition

SAB: Student Activity Book

H&R: Homework and Remembering

AC: Activity Cards

MCC: Math Center Challenge

AG: Assessment Guide

TRB: Teacher's Resource Book

✓: Grade K kits

DIGITAL KEY

*i*T   *i*Tools

Soar to Success Math Intervention

HMH MegaMath

Destination Math®

Interactive Whiteboard

Online Assessment

EV   ExamView

*See RtI p. 461T

UNIT 5   PLANNING

PLANNING UNIT 5: **Consolidation of Concepts** (continued)

LESSONS	Print Resources	Materials
BIG IDEA 2 Numbers 1 Through 20 (continued)		
6 **More Solve and Retell Story Problems** Common Core State Standards CC.K.OA.1, CC.K.OA.2, CC.K.OA.3, CC.K.OA.4, CC.K.NBT.1 **FOCUS** Tell, retell, and write equations for addition and subtraction stories; Visualize teen numbers as ten ones and extra ones.	TE pp. 485–490 SAB pp. 219–224 AC 5-6 MCC 18	✓ Counters ✓ Number Tiles 1–10 ✓ +/− Tiles Night Sky display *Hiding Zero* Gameboard ✓ Giant Number Cards
7 **Numbers 1–20** Common Core State Standards CC.K.CC.3, CC.K.CC.4, CC.K.CC.4c, CC.K.CC.5, CC.K.OA.1, CC.K.OA.2, CC.K.OA.3, CC.K.OA.5, CC.K.NBT.1 **FOCUS** Show numbers 1–20; show the teen numbers as a group of ten ones and further ones; Find the unknown partner when the total and one partner are known.	TE pp. 491–496 SAB pp. 225–226 H&R pp. 95–96 AC 5-7	✓ 1–20 Boards ✓ 10-sticks ✓ Centimeter cubes ✓ Number Tiles 1–9 Break-Apart Sticks ✓ +/− Tiles
BIG IDEA 3 More Teen Numbers and Partners		
8 **Review Partners** Common Core State Standards CC.K.CC.3, CC.K.OA.1, CC.K.OA.3, CC.K.OA.4 **FOCUS** Find all the partners of 2, 3, 4, 5, 6, and 10; View teen numbers as ten ones and extra ones, and practice finding 10-partners.	TE pp. 497–500 SAB pp. 227–228 H&R pp. 97–98 AC 5-8	✓ Counters ✓ Number Tiles 1–10 ✓ +/− Tiles Night Sky display
9 **Partners of 6, 7, 8, and 9** Common Core State Standards CC.K.OA.3, CC.K.OA.4, CC.K.NBT.1 **FOCUS** Visualize teen numbers in sequence as ten ones and extra ones and find the unknown partner when the total and one partner are known; Identify partners of the numbers 6 through 9.	TE pp. 501–506 SAB pp. 229–230 H&R pp. 99–100 AC 5-9	✓ 1–20 Boards ✓ 10-sticks ✓ Centimeter cubes ✓ Number Tiles 1–10 Break-Apart Sticks ✓ +/− Tiles
10 **Tens in Teen Numbers: A Game** Common Core State Standards CC.K.CC.3, CC.K.OA.1, CC.K.OA.2, CC.K.OA.3, CC.K.NBT.1 **FOCUS** Solve addition and subtraction story problems, and visualize teen numbers as ten ones and extra ones; Use the = and ≠ signs in comparing.	TE pp. 507–510 SAB pp. 231–232 H&R pp. 101–102 AC 5-10	*Hiding Zero* Gameboard ✓ Number Tiles 1–10 ✓ Giant Number Cards
11 **Tens in Teen Numbers Book** Common Core State Standards CC.K.CC.3, CC.K.OA.3, CC.K.OA.4 **FOCUS** Visualize teen numbers as ten ones and extra ones, and find 10-partners.	TE pp. 511–514 SAB pp. 233–238 H&R pp. 103–104 AC 5-11	Scissors ✓ Counters ✓ Number Tiles 1–10 ✓ +/− Tiles Night Sky display

<table>
<tr><td>

 Digital Resources

</td><td>

 Assessment

</td></tr>
<tr><td>

 Interactive Whiteboard
*i*T *i*Tools: Counters
Warm-Up 11.17
Country Countdown: Block Busters, Level G
Course I: Module 2: Unit 1: Session 3

</td><td>

TE Formative Assessment: Check Understanding p. 489

</td></tr>
<tr><td>

Interactive Whiteboard
*i*T *i*Tools: Counters
Warm-Up 1.13
Country Countdown: Counting Critters, Level P
Course I: Module 2: Unit 1: Session 3

</td><td>

TE Formative Assessment: Check Understanding p. 495
AG Fluency Check 6

</td></tr>
<tr><td>

Interactive Whiteboard
*i*T *i*Tools: Counters
Warm-Up 1.11
Country Countdown: Counting Critters, Level G
Course I: Module 2: Unit 1: Session 1

</td><td>

TE Formative Assessment: Check Understanding p. 499

</td></tr>
<tr><td>

Interactive Whiteboard
*i*T *i*Tools: Counters
Warm-Up 10.3
Country Countdown: Counting Critters, Level G
Course I: Module 2: Unit 1: Session 1

</td><td>

TE Formative Assessment: Check Understanding p. 505

</td></tr>
<tr><td>

Interactive Whiteboard
*i*T *i*Tools: Counters
Warm-Up 7.10
Country Countdown: Counting Critters, Level P
Course I: Module 2: Unit 2: Session 2

</td><td>

TE Formative Assessment: Check Understanding p. 509

</td></tr>
<tr><td>

 Interactive Whiteboard
*i*T *i*Tools: Counters
Warm-Up 1.13
Country Countdown: Counting Critters, Level P
Course I: Module 2: Unit 2: Session 2

</td><td>

TE Formative Assessment: Check Understanding p. 513

</td></tr>
</table>

COMMON CORE STATE STANDARDS FOR MATHEMATICAL CONTENT KEY

CC.K.CC Counting and Cardinality
CC.K.OA Operations and Algebraic Thinking
CC.K.NBT Number and Operations in Base Ten
CC.K.MD Measurement and Data
CC.K.G Geometry

PRINT KEY

TE: Teacher Edition
SAB: Student Activity Book
H&R: Homework and Remembering
AC: Activity Cards
MCC: Math Center Challenge
AG: Assessment Guide
TRB: Teacher's Resource Book
✓: Grade K kits

DIGITAL KEY

*i*T *i*Tools
Soar to Success Math Intervention*
HMH MegaMath
Destination Math®
Interactive Whiteboard
Online Assessment
EV ExamView
*See RtI p. 461T

UNIT 5 PLANNING

PLANNING UNIT 5: **Consolidation of Concepts** (continued)

LESSONS	Print Resources	Materials
BIG IDEA 3 More Teen Numbers and Partners (continued)		
12 **Partners of 10: Class Project** **Common Core State Standards** CC.K.OA.2, CC.K.OA.3, CC.K.OA.4, CC.K.OA.5 **FOCUS** Relate 10-partner drawings to addition equations and find changes in the partners of ten.	TE pp. 515–518 SAB pp. 239–242 H&R pp. 105–106 AC 5-12 MCC 19	10-Partner Showcase Crayons or markers
13 **Introduction to Counting and Grouping Routines** **Common Core State Standards** CC.K.CC.1, CC.K.CC.2, CC.K.OA.2, CC.K.OA.3, CC.K.OA.4, CC.K.OA.5 **FOCUS** Count by ones and tens to 100; Find partners of 10 and write and discuss 7-partners.	TE pp. 519–522 SAB pp. 246–244 H&R pp. 107–108 AC 5-13	✓ 120 Poster ✓ Pointer 10-Partner Showcase Sticky notes
14 **Practice: Number Activities** **Common Core State Standards** CC.K.CC.3, CC.K.CC.5, CC.K.OA.1, CC.K.OA.3, CC.K.OA.5 **FOCUS** Equalize groups by adding, and find partners of 7, 8, and 9.	TE pp. 523–526 SAB pp. 245–246 AC 5-14	*none*
BIG IDEA 4 More Story Problems and Equations		
15 **Add Partners to Find Totals** **Common Core State Standards** CC.K.CC.4, CC.K.CC.4c, CC.K.CC.5, CC.K.OA.1, CC.K.OA.2, CC.K.OA.3, CC.K.OA.5, CC.K.NBT.1 **FOCUS** Show numbers 1–20; show the teen numbers as a group of ten ones and further ones; Find the unknown partner when the total and one partner are known and find the total of two partners.	TE pp. 527–532 SAB pp. 247–248 H&R pp. 109–110 AC 5-15	✓ 1–20 Boards ✓ 10-sticks ✓ Centimeter cubes ✓ Number Tiles 1–9 Break-Apart Sticks ✓ +/– Tiles

Digital Resources	Assessment
Interactive Whiteboard iT iTools: Counters Warm-Up 1.11 Country Countdown: Block Busters, Level C Course I: Module 1: Unit 2: Session 3	TE Formative Assessment: Check Understanding p. 517
Interactive Whiteboard iT iTools: Counters Warm-Up 2.14 Country Countdown: Block Busters, Level I Course II: Module 1: Unit 1: Session 1	TE Formative Assessment: Check Understanding p. 521
Interactive Whiteboard iT iTools: Counters Warm-Up 7.13 Country Countdown: Harrison's Comparisons, Level D Course I: Module 1: Unit 4: Session 1	TE Formative Assessment: Check Understanding p. 525 AG Fluency Check 7
Interactive Whiteboard iT iTools: Counters Warm-Up 1.9 Country Countdown: Counting Critters, Level D Course I: Module 1: Unit 3: Session 1	TE Formative Assessment: Check Understanding p. 531

COMMON CORE STATE STANDARDS FOR MATHEMATICAL CONTENT KEY

CC.K.CC Counting and Cardinality

CC.K.OA Operations and Algebraic Thinking

CC.K.NBT Number and Operations in Base Ten

CC.K.MD Measurement and Data

CC.K.G Geometry

PRINT KEY

TE: Teacher Edition

SAB: Student Activity Book

H&R: Homework and Remembering

AC: Activity Cards

MCC: Math Center Challenge

AG: Assessment Guide

TRB: Teacher's Resource Book

✓: Grade K kits

DIGITAL KEY

iT iTools

Soar to Success Math Intervention*

HMH MegaMath

Destination Math®

Interactive Whiteboard

Online Assessment

EV ExamView

*See RtI p. 461T

PLANNING UNIT 5: Consolidation of Concepts (continued)

LESSONS	Print Resources	Materials

BIG IDEA 4 More Story Problems and Equations (continued)

16 **Story Problems and Comparing: Totals Through 10**

Common Core State Standards CC.K.CC.3, CC.K.CC.5, CC.K.CC.6, CC.K.OA.1, CC.K.OA.2

FOCUS Tell, retell, and solve addition and subtraction stories; Compare the number of objects in two groups, and take away objects to make groups equal.

Print Resources	Materials
TE pp. 533–536 SAB pp. 249–250 H&R pp. 111–112 AC 5-16	*none*

17 **Subtract to Make Equal Groups**

Common Core State Standards CC.K.CC.3, CC.K.CC.5, CC.K.CC.6, CC.K.CC.7, CC.K.NBT.1

FOCUS Visualize teen numbers as ten ones and further ones; Compare the number of objects in groups and compare numbers.

Print Resources	Materials
TE pp. 537–542 SAB pp. 251–252 H&R pp. 113–114 AC 5-17	Crayons or markers *Hiding Zero* Gameboard ✓ Number Tiles 1–10 ✓ Giant Number Cards

18 **Tens and Ones**

Common Core State Standards CC.K.OA.3, CC.K.OA.4, CC.K.OA.5, CC.K.NBT.1

FOCUS Visualize teen numbers as a group of ten ones and further ones.

Print Resources	Materials
TE pp. 543–548 SAB pp. 253–256 AC 5-18	Crayons or markers

19 **Teen Numbers, Partners, and Equations**

Common Core State Standards CC.K.CC.4, CC.K.CC.5, CC.K.OA.1, CC.K.OA.2, CC.K.NBT.1

FOCUS Tell, retell, and solve addition and subtraction stories; Show teen numbers as a group of ten ones and further ones.

Print Resources	Materials
TE pp. 549–552 SAB pp. 257–258 AC 5-19	*none*

20 **More Tens in Teen Numbers: A Game**

Common Core State Standards CC.K.CC.3, CC.K.CC.5, CC.K.CC.6, CC.K.CC.7, CC.K.NBT.1

FOCUS Compare the number of objects in groups and compare numbers; Visualize teen numbers as ten ones and extra ones.

Print Resources	Materials
TE pp. 553–556 SAB pp. 259–262 AC 5-20	*Hiding Zero* Gameboard ✓ Number Tiles 1–10 ✓ Giant Number Cards 1–10

Interactive Whiteboard _i_**T** _i_Tools: Counters Warm-Up 10.5 **MM** Numberopolis: Carnival Stories, Level C Course 1: Module 2: Unit 1: Session 1	TE Formative Assessment: Check Understanding p. 535	
Interactive Whiteboard _i_**T** _i_Tools: Counters Warm-Up 4.6 **MM** Country Countdown: Harrison's Comparisons, Level H Course 1: Module 1: Unit 3: Session 1	TE Formative Assessment: Check Understanding p. 541	
Interactive Whiteboard _i_**T** _i_Tools: Counters Warm-Up 1.15 **MM** Country Countdown: Block Busters, Level G Course 1: Module 1: Unit 3: Session 1	TE Formative Assessment: Check Understanding p. 547	
Interactive Whiteboard _i_**T** _i_Tools: Counters Warm-Up 1.15 **MM** Numberopolis: Carnival Stories, Level M Course 1: Module 1: Unit 3: Session 1	TE Formative Assessment: Check Understanding p. 551	
Interactive Whiteboard _i_**T** _i_Tools: Counters Warm-Up 7.10 **MM** Country Countdown: Counting Critters, Level P Course 1: Module 2: Unit 2: Session 2	TE Formative Assessment: Check Understanding p. 555	

COMMON CORE STATE STANDARDS FOR MATHEMATICAL CONTENT KEY

CC.K.CC Counting and Cardinality

CC.K.OA Operations and Algebraic Thinking

CC.K.NBT Number and Operations in Base Ten

CC.K.MD Measurement and Data

CC.K.G Geometry

PRINT KEY

TE: Teacher Edition

SAB: Student Activity Book

H&R: Homework and Remembering

AC: Activity Cards

MCC: Math Center Challenge

AG: Assessment Guide

TRB: Teacher's Resource Book

✓: Grade K kits

DIGITAL KEY

_i_**T** _i_Tools

Soar to Success Math Intervention*

MM HMH MegaMath

Destination Math®

Interactive Whiteboard

✓ Online Assessment

EV ExamView

*See RtI p. 461T

PLANNING UNIT 5: **Consolidation of Concepts** (continued)

LESSONS	📖 Print Resources	🗑 Materials
BIG IDEA 4 More Story Problems and Equations (continued)		
21 **Compare Length and Compare Height** Common Core State Standards CC.K.MD.1, CC.K.MD.2 **FOCUS** Compare two objects and identify which is longer or shorter; Compare two objects and identify which is taller or shorter.	TE pp. 557–560 AC 5-21 MCC 20	Pencils and other objects for comparing length and height
22 **Compare Weight and Compare Capacity** Common Core State Standards CC.K.MD.2, CC.K.MD.2 **FOCUS** Compare two objects and identify which is heavier or lighter; Compare two containers and identify which has more or less capacity.	TE pp. 561–564 AC 5-22	Classroom objects Beach ball Tennis ball Containers of various sizes Water, rice, or sand Spill tray
23 **Focus on Mathematical Practices** Common Core State Standards CC.K.CC.3, CC.K.CC.4, CC.K.NBT.1, CC.K.MD.1, CC.K.MD.2 **FOCUS** Apply mathematical concepts and skills in meaningful contexts; Reinforce the Common Core Mathematical Content Standards and Mathematical Practices with a variety of problem-solving situations.	TE pp. 565–570 SAB pp. 263–264 AC 5-23	Index cards Crayons
UNIT REVIEW/TEST	TE Unit 5 Review and Test, pp. 571–576 SAB Unit 5 Review and Test, pp. 265–268	

Digital Resources

 Interactive Whiteboard
iT iTools: Counters
Warm-Up 41.2
MM Shapes Ahoy: Made to Measure, Level A
Course I: Module 3: Unit 1: Session 1

Interactive Whiteboard
iT iTools: Counters
Warm-Up 42.4
MM Country Countdown: Harrison's Comparisons, Level F
Course I: Module 3: Unit 1: Session 2

Interactive Whiteboard
iT iTools: Counters
Warm-Up 1.15
MM Shapes Ahoy: Made to Measure, Level A
Course I: Module 3: Unit 1: Session 1

Online Assessment
EV ExamView

Assessment

TE Formative Assessment: Check Understanding p. 559

TE Formative Assessment: Check Understanding p. 563

TE Formative Assessment: Check Understanding p. 569
AG Fluency Check 8

AG Unit 5 Test A—Open Response
AG Unit 5 Test B—Observational Assessment
AG Unit 5 Performance Assessment

COMMON CORE STATE STANDARDS FOR MATHEMATICAL CONTENT KEY

CC.K.CC Counting and Cardinality

CC.K.OA Operations and Algebraic Thinking

CC.K.NBT Number and Operations in Base Ten

CC.K.MD Measurement and Data

CC.K.G Geometry

PRINT KEY

TE: Teacher Edition

SAB: Student Activity Book

H&R: Homework and Remembering

AC: Activity Cards

MCC: Math Center Challenge

AG: Assessment Guide

TRB: Teacher's Resource Book

✓: Grade K kits

DIGITAL KEY

iT iTools

Soar to Success Math Intervention*

MM HMH MegaMath

Destination Math®

Interactive Whiteboard

✓ Online Assessment

EV ExamView

*See RtI p. 461T

Common Core State Standards for Mathematics

Math Expressions integrates the Mathematical Practices throughout every teaching lesson. This program correlates fully to the concepts, skills, and problems listed in the Common Core Content Standards.

Common Core State Standards for Mathematical Practice in This Unit

CC.K–12.MP.1	Make sense of problems and persevere in solving them.	Lessons 1, 2, 4, 5, 10, 15, 16, 19, 21, 22, 23
CC.K–12.MP.2	Reason abstractly and quantitatively.	Lessons 7, 15, 17, 18, 20, 23
CC.K–12.MP.3	Construct viable arguments and critique the reasoning of others.	Lessons 1, 2, 6, 8, 12, 13, 14, 16, 17, 21, 22, 23
CC.K–12.MP.4	Model with mathematics.	Lessons 3, 4, 5, 6, 7, 9, 10, 11, 12, 13, 19, 23
CC.K–12.MP.5	Use appropriate tools strategically.	Lessons 5, 6, 10, 19, 23
CC.K–12.MP.6	Attend to precision.	Lessons 2, 6, 7, 9, 10, 11, 13, 15, 16, 17, 19, 20, 21, 22, 23
CC.K–12.MP.7	Look for and make use of structure.	Lessons 3, 6, 7, 9, 11, 12, 13, 14, 15, 17, 18, 20, 23
CC.K–12.MP.8	Look for and express regularity in repeated reasoning.	Lessons 15, 16, 17, 18, 20, 23

Common Core State Standards for Mathematical Content in This Unit

CC.K.CC Counting and Cardinality

Know number names and the count sequence.

K.CC.1	Count to 100 by ones and by tens.	Lessons 2, 3, 5, 13
K.CC.2	Count forward beginning from a given number within the known sequence (instead of having to begin at 1).	Lesson 13
K.CC.3	Write numbers from 0 to 20. Represent a number of objects with a written numeral 0–20 (with 0 representing a count of no objects).	Lessons 2, 4, 5, 7, 8, 10, 11, 14, 16, 17, 20, 23

Count to tell the number of objects.

K.CC.4	Understand the relationship between numbers and quantities; connect counting to cardinality.	Lessons 7, 15, 19, 23
K.CC.4a	When counting objects, say the number names in the standard order, pairing each object with one and only one number name and each number name with one and only one object.	Lesson 3
K.CC.4c	Understand that each successive number name refers to a quantity that is one larger.	Lessons 7, 15
K.CC.5	Count to answer "how many?" questions about as many as 20 things arranged in a line, a rectangular array, or a circle, or as many as 10 things in a scattered configuration; given a number from 1–20, count out that many objects.	Lessons 1, 2, 3, 4, 7, 14, 15, 16, 17, 19, 20

Compare numbers.

K.CC.6	Identify whether the number of objects in one group is greater than, less than, or equal to the number of objects in another group, e.g., by using matching and counting strategies.	Lessons 16, 17, 20
K.CC.7	Compare two numbers between 1 and 10 presented as written numerals.	Lessons 2, 17, 20

CC.K.OA Operations and Algebraic Thinking

Understand addition as putting together and adding to, and understand subtraction as taking apart and taking from.

K.OA.1	Represent addition and subtraction with objects, fingers, mental images, drawings, sounds, acting out situations, verbal explanations, expressions, or equations.	Lessons 3, 6, 7, 8, 10, 14, 15, 16, 19
K.OA.2	Solve addition and subtraction word problems, and add and subtract within 10, e.g., by using objects or drawings to represent the problem.	Lessons 1, 3, 4, 6, 7, 10, 12, 13, 15, 16, 19
K.OA.3	Decompose numbers less than or equal to 10 into pairs in more than one way, e.g., by using objects or drawings, and record each decomposition by a drawing or equation.	Lessons 3, 4, 5, 6, 7, 8, 9, 10, 11, 12, 13, 14, 15, 18
K.OA.4	For any number from 1 to 9, find the number that makes 10 when added to the given number, e.g., by using objects or drawings, and record the answer with a drawing or equation.	Lessons 2, 3, 4, 6, 8, 9, 11, 12, 13, 18
K.OA.5	Fluently add and subtract within 5.	Lessons 1, 3, 7, 12, 13, 14, 15, 18

CC.K.NBT Number and Operations in Base Ten

Work with numbers 11–19 to gain foundations for place value.

K.NBT.1	Compose and decompose numbers from 11 to 19 into ten ones and some further ones, e.g., by using objects or drawings, and record each composition or decomposition by a drawing or equation; understand that these numbers are composed of ten ones and one, two, three, four, five, six, seven, eight, or nine ones.	Lessons 1, 3, 4, 5, 6, 7, 9, 10, 15, 17, 18, 19, 20, 23

CC.K.MD Measurement and Data

Describe and compare measurable attributes.

K.MD.1	Describe measurable attributes of objects, such as length or weight. Describe several measurable attributes of a single object.	Lessons 21, 22, 23
K.MD.2	Directly compare two objects with a measurable attribute in common, to see which object has "more of"/"less of" the attribute, and describe the difference.	Lessons 21, 22, 23

Differentiated Instruction

Math Expressions lessons are designed to accommodate a wide range of student learning styles and academic skills. A variety of lesson features and program resources incorporate strategies and opportunities for differentiating instruction.

English Language Learners

Present this problem to all children. Offer the different levels of support to meet children's levels of language proficiency.

Objective Review vocabulary used to compare two numbers.

Problem Write **greater than, less than,** and **equal to** on the board. Write 6 and 4. Ask children to use connecting cubes to make a cube train to show each number. Guide children to compare the two groups.

BEGINNING

Ask: **Which number is greater?** 6 Say: **6 is greater than 4.** Ask children to repeat. Ask: **Which number is less?** 4 Say: **4 is less than 6.** Ask children to repeat. Guide children to add 2 cubes so the trains have the same number of cubes. Say: **6 is equal to 6.** Ask children to repeat.

INTERMEDIATE

Point to 6. Ask: **Greater than or less than?** greater than Point to 4. Ask: **Greater than or less than?** less than Guide children to add 2 cubes so the trains have the same number of cubes. Ask: **Is 6 equal to 6?** yes

ADVANCED

Ask children to use *greater than* and *less than* to describe the two groups. 6 is greater than 4. 4 is less than 6. Guide children to add 2 cubes so the trains have the same number of cubes. Ask them to use *equal to* as they describe the two groups. 6 is equal to 6.

Differentiated Instruction: Individualizing Instruction Activities

Differentiated Instruction Cards	*On Level • Challenge in every lesson*
Math Writing Prompts	*On Level • Challenge in every lesson*
Math Center Challenges	*Advanced: 4 in every unit*
English Language Learners	*In every lesson*

Ready-Made Math Challenge Centers

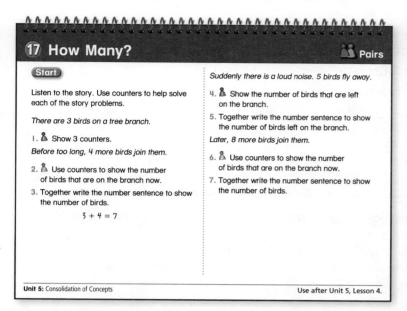

Grouping Pairs

Materials Counters

Objective Model and write math facts for addition and subtraction up to 10.

Common Core State Standards CC.K.OA.1, CC.K.OA.2, CC.K–12.MP.1, CC.K–12.MP.2, CC.K–12.MP.4

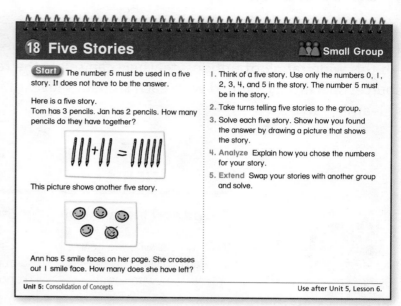

Grouping Small Groups

Materials Crayons or markers

Objective Tell and solve addition and subtraction stories using 5.

Common Core State Standards CC.K.OA.1, CC.K.OA.5, CC.K–12.MP.1, CC.K–12.MP.4

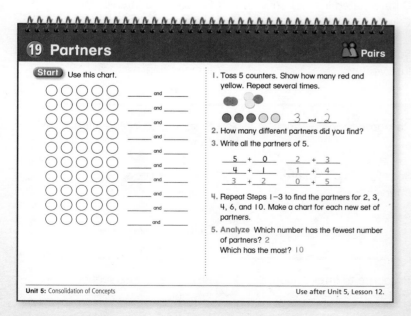

Grouping Pairs

Materials 10 Two-Color Counters

Objective Find number partners for 2, 3, 4, 5, 6, and 10.

Common Core State Standards CC.K.OA.3, CC.K–12.MP.2, CC.K–12.MP.7

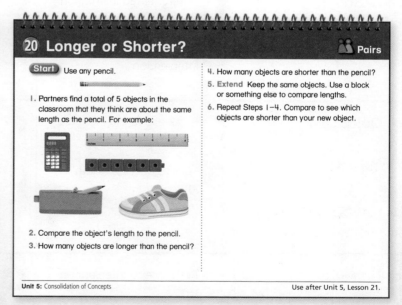

Grouping Pairs

Materials Pencil

Objective Compare lengths using a nonstandard measuring tool.

Common Core State Standards CC.K.MD.2, CC.K–12.MP.4, CC.K–12.MP.6

Response to Intervention

Throughout *Math Expressions*, activities and materials for all levels of RtI engage learners with focused print and online intervention options. With this wide range of options, teachers can select the resource or resources specifically aligned with each student's level of understanding and learning style.

RtI	TIER 1 **On-Level Intervention** For students who are generally at grade level but need early intervention with specific concepts.	TIER 2 **Strategic Intervention** For students who need small group instruction to review concepts and skills.	TIER 3 **Intensive Intervention** For students who need one-on-one instruction to build foundational skills.
Beginning of Each Unit		Response to Intervention Skill Soar to Success: Math Intervention	Response to Intervention Example Soar to Success: Math Intervention
Each Lesson	Differentiated Instruction Cards – On Level Soar to Success: Math Intervention	Differentiated Instruction Cards – Intervention Soar to Success: Math Intervention	Response to Intervention Example Soar to Success: Math Intervention
Each Quick Quiz	Response to Intervention Lesson Soar to Success: Math Intervention	Response to Intervention Skill Soar to Success: Math Intervention	Response to Intervention Example Soar to Success: Math Intervention Diagnostic Interview
Each Unit Test	Response to Intervention Lesson Soar to Success: Math Intervention	Response to Intervention Skill Soar to Success: Math Intervention	Response to Intervention Example Soar to Success: Math Intervention Diagnostic Interview

Cross-Curricular Connections

Cross-curricular connections are included at the end of each lesson with a Home or School Activity.

Connections

LITERATURE LINKS

Math Literature Library

Rumble Bus

Rumble Bus
Hop aboard and take a seat on Larry Dane Brimner's *Rumble Bus*! At each stop along the bus route, simple equations demonstrate a practical use of subtraction.

Literature Connections

Anno's Counting Book by Mitsumasa Anno (HarperCollins Publishers, 1977, or Big Book edition, 1992)

Dr. Karen C. Fuson,
Math Expressions Author

Putting Research into Practice

Relations: More Than, Equal to, Less Than

Kindergarten children make three kinds of advances. They

• extend their use of matching and counting to sets ≤ 10,

• count or match pictures or drawings instead of objects,

• find out and say both relations using full sentences, such as "Eight circles are more than six circles. Six circles are less than eight circles."

National Council of Teachers of Mathematics (NCTM).
Focus in Kindergarten. Reston, Va.: NCTM, 2010, p. 34.

Learning Paths

Children in *Math Expressions* have been building their knowledge of the relations greater than, equal to, and less than throughout the year. They began by matching and counting small sets of objects and moved to larger sets. They later made math drawings to compare two numbers. In Unit 5, they continue to build on this earlier knowledge by practicing comparing two numbers between 1 and 10 presented as written numerals. They understand and use both *greater than* and *less than*. Such use of comparing language is vital for the extension in Grade 1 to additive comparison situations that ask *How much more/less?* instead of just *Which is more/less?*

Children extend their understanding of adding and subtracting situations by telling, retelling, and solving such problems with larger numbers and in any situation. They solve such situations with fingers and math drawings and represent the situations with expressions $(9 - 3$ or $5 + 4)$ or with equations $(9 - 3 = 6$ or $5 + 4 = 9)$. They move to fluency with numbers with totals of 5 or less by solving numerical addition or subtraction equations, by knowing, or by using fingers or drawings. Knowing may draw on the patterns developed earlier of $+1$ and -1 and doubles $(1 + 1$ and $2 + 2)$.

Children continue to find an unknown partner by drawing Tiny Tumblers on Math Mountains, and telling and solving unknown partner stories. The Unit 4 knowledge of teen numbers and partners of 10 and of other numbers is strengthened and extended with games, structured activities, and classroom visual supports such as the Teen Number Book, 10-Partner Showcase, and Stars in the Night Sky.

Other Useful References

Cross, C. T., Woods, T. A, Schweingruber, H. (Eds.) (2009). *Mathematics learning in early childhood: Paths toward excellence and equity.* Center for Education, Division of Behavioral and Social Sciences and Education. Washington, DC: National Academy Press.

Getting Ready to Teach Unit 5

Using the Common Core Standards for Mathematical Practice

The Common Core State Standards for Mathematical Content indicate what concepts, skills, and problem solving children should learn. The Common Core State Standards for Mathematical Practice indicate how children should demonstrate understanding. These *Mathematical Practices* are embedded directly into the Student and Teacher Editions for each unit in *Math Expressions*. As you use the teaching suggestions, you will automatically implement a teaching style that encourages children to demonstrate a thorough understanding of concepts, skills, and problems. In this program, Math Talk suggestions are a vehicle used to encourage discussion that supports all eight Mathematical Practices. See examples in Mathematical Practice 6.

COMMON CORE
Mathematical Practice 1
Make sense of problems and persevere in solving them.

Children analyze and make conjectures about how to solve a problem. They plan, monitor, and check their solutions. They determine if their answers are reasonable and can justify their reasoning.

TEACHER EDITION: Examples from Unit 5

MP.1 Make Sense of Problems Solve a Similar Problem Introduce a new aspect of story problems for this unit: retelling the same story, using different words that mean the same thing. This kind of language exercise allows more children an opportunity to talk, and it helps review mathematical language. Focus on having children ask the question in different ways. (See the common addition and subtraction words below.) This also helps children learn to ask the question for an addition story and for a subtraction story.

Lesson 1 ACTIVITY 1

MP.1 Make Sense of Problems Have children tell addition or subtraction story problems, solve them with math drawings, and write the corresponding equations. Try to have as many children as possible work at the board while other children work on paper.

MP.6 Attend to Precision Explain Solutions For each story problem, select two children to explain their drawings and equations. Encourage other children to ask them questions.

Lesson 19 ACTIVITY 1

Mathematical Practice 1 is integrated into Unit 5 in the following ways:

Act It Out	Analyze the Problem	Analyze Relationships
Check Answers	Make Sense of Problems	Solve a Similar Problem

Mathematical Practice 2
Reason abstractly and quantitatively.

Children make sense of quantities and their relationships in problem situations. They can connect models, drawings, expressions, and equations to a given situation. Quantitative reasoning entails attending to the meaning of quantities. Children are also learning to think abstractly—reasoning without always relying on physical representations. In this unit, this involves determining the unknown partner when the total and one partner are known, visualizing partners as a operational component of an equation and other visualization practice, and comparing two numbers presented as written numerals.

TEACHER EDITION: Examples from Unit 5

• What partner of 8 did I take?

MP.2 Reason Abstractly and Quantitatively The second child now looks at the centimeter cubes to find the partner that has been taken. Children can count the cubes they see and then count on to 8 with their fingers, or they may be able to visualize 8 cubes and mentally "see" how many are missing. There may be some children who still need to place the cubes as they count on. The second child now names the two partners and puts the appropriate Number Tiles and the +/− Tile in place below the cubes.

Lesson **15** **ACTIVITY 2**

MP.2 Reason Abstractly and Quantitatively In this activity, they are comparing the first number with the second number, and writing the comparison letter between the two numbers. Stress that direction is important in writing the comparison. They must determine whether the number on the left is greater than, equal to, or less than the number on the right.

Write 5 __ 4, 8 __ 10, and 6 __ 6 on the board. Ask volunteers to write the correct comparison letter for each pair of numbers. Ask the others in the class whether they agree with the comparisons and discuss, as needed. Reinforce the order by having the class say the comparison aloud.

Lesson **17** **ACTIVITY 3**

Mathematical Practice 2 is integrated into Unit 5 in the following ways:

Reason Abstractly
Reason Abstractly and Quantitatively

Mathematical Practice 3
Construct viable arguments and critique the reasoning of others.

Children use stated assumptions, definitions, and previously established results in constructing arguments. They are able to analyze situations and can recognize and use counterexamples. They justify their conclusions, communicate them to others, and respond to the arguments of others.

Children are also able to distinguish correct logic or reasoning from that which is flawed, and—if there is a flaw in an argument—explain what it is. Children can listen or read the arguments of others, decide whether they make sense, and ask useful questions to clarify or improve the arguments.

Math Talk is a conversation tool by which children formulate ideas and analyze responses and engage in discourse. See also MP.6 Attend to Precision.

TEACHER EDITION: Examples from Unit 5

▶ What's the Error?   WHOLE CLASS

MP.3, MP.6 Construct Viable Arguments/Critique the Reasoning of Others Puzzled Penguin Explain that Puzzled Penguin placed a Number Tile on top of the zero in each 10 on the Hiding Zero Gameboard. Then Puzzled Penguin was asked to read an equation as a Student Leader called out 15.

$$15 = 1\ 5 + \boxed{}$$

$$15 = 10 + 5$$

- Puzzled Penguin moved the 5.
- Then Puzzled Penguin said that the equation is 15 plus 10 equals 5. Is Puzzled Penguin correct? Why? No. Puzzled Penguin read the equation wrong.

Lesson **6** ACTIVITY 3

MP.3, MP.6 Construct Viable Arguments/Critique the Reasoning of Others Puzzled Penguin This Puzzled Penguin activity addresses the error of incorrectly identifying whether the first number is greater than or less than the second number when comparing two numbers.

MATH TALK Discuss with children whether Puzzled Penguin's work is correct or not, and how they can help.

- Puzzled Penguin compared pairs of numbers, as we have just done.
- Let's look at Puzzled Penguin's work.

Write **6 L 4** on the board.

- In the first comparison, Puzzled Penguin wrote that 6 is less than 4. Is that correct? no
- What letter should be shown instead of the L? G

Lesson **17** ACTIVITY 3

Mathematical Practice 3 is integrated into Unit 5 in the following ways:

| Compare Methods | Compare Representations | Critique the Reasoning of |
| Justify Conclusions | | Others |

Mathematical Practice 4
Model with mathematics.

Children can apply the mathematics they know to solve problems that arise in everyday life. This might be as simple as writing an expression or an equation to solve a problem. Children might use objects or draw pictures to lead them to a solution for a problem.

Children apply what they know and are comfortable making assumptions and approximations to simplify a complicated situation. They are able to identify important quantities in a practical situation and represent their relationships using such tools as sketches and tables.

TEACHER EDITION: Examples from Unit 5

MP.4 Model Mathematics Write an Equation Have children tell the equation for each collection of stars as All Stars = Big Stars + Little Stars (for example, $10 = 1 + 9$) and then write that equation. For each equation, have children show the partners with their fingers by wiggling fingers for one partner and then the other partner.

After all the equations are filled in on the page, have children switch the partners for each equation (for example, $9 + 1$ and $1 + 9$).

Lesson **3** ACTIVITY 1

▶ **Create and Solve Story Problems** MATH TALK

MP.4 Model Mathematics Write an Equation Use **Solve and Discuss** for this activity.

Have children tell addition and subtraction story problems, solve them with math drawings, and write the corresponding equations. Have as many children as possible work at the board while other children work on paper. Select two children to explain their drawings and equations for each story. The other children can ask them questions. Remind children to check to see if the answer is reasonable. If it is not, they should reevaluate the approach they used to solve the problem.

Lesson **4** ACTIVITY 1

Mathematical Practice 4 is integrated into Unit 5 in the following ways:

| Build a Model | Draw a Model | Write an Equation |

Mathematical Practice 5
Use appropriate tools strategically.

Children consider the available tools and models when solving mathematical problems. Children make sound decisions about when each of these tools might be helpful. These tools might include paper and pencil for drawings and computation, manipulatives, or even their fingers. They recognize both the insight to be gained from using the tool and the tool's limitations. When making mathematical models, children are able to identify quantities in a practical situation and represent relationships using such modeling tools as tables, expressions, and equations.

Modeling numbers in problems and in computations is a central focus in *Math Expressions* lessons. Children learn and develop models to solve numerical problems and to model problem situations. Children continually use both kinds of modeling throughout the program.

TEACHER EDITION: Examples from Unit 5

MP.5 Use Appropriate Tools Hand out copies of the three Hiding Zero Gameboard pages. Have Student Pairs arrange their three pages in order, vertically or horizontally. Then have them work together to put a Number Tile on top of the 0 in each 10 (for example, 14 = 14 + blank rectangle).

Hiding Zero Gameboard
(Student Activity Book
pages 219–224)

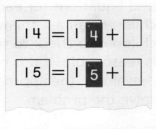

Lesson **6** ACTIVITY 3

MP.4, MP.5 Use Appropriate Tools/ Model with Mathematics Instruct children to put the cards in order from 1–20 by looking at the number of dots. Ask questions about how the numbers change from one number to the next. Children should verbalize the following ideas:

▶ Each card has one more dot than the one before it.

▶ Each card is one more than the number before it.

Have children mix up the cards and place the cards in order, either by dots or by numerals. Allow each child in the group to order the cards, but not every child in the group should order them the same way.

Lesson **23** ACTIVITY 2

Mathematical Practice 5 is integrated into Unit 5 in the following ways:

Model with Mathematics | **Use Appropriate Tools**

Mathematical Practice 6
Attend to precision.

Children try to communicate precisely to others. They try to use clear definitions in discussion with others and in their own reasoning. They state the meaning of the symbols they choose. They are careful about specifying units of measure to clarify the correspondence with quantities in a problem. They calculate accurately and efficiently, and express numerical answers with a degree of precision appropriate for the problem context. Children give carefully formulated explanations to each other.

TEACHER EDITION: Examples from Unit 5

MP.6 Attend to Precision Children play *The 10-Partners Game* in **Student Pairs** with 10 counters. They place the counters in two rows of 5 or in towers of 5 (in a 5-group pattern). One child closes and covers his or her eyes. The other child takes some of the counters and hides them. Then he or she says the following rhyme, stating how many counters are left. Then have both children record the equation on a sheet of paper, $6 + 4 = 10$.

• Oink, oink, 6 pigs in the pen. Tell me, what's the partner of ten?

The first child looks and says the number he or she sees, and then finishes the rhyme.

• I see 6 pigs in the pen. 6 and 4 are partners of ten.

Lesson **6** ACTIVITY 2

Ask volunteers to name other objects that are longer, shorter, or the same length.

• Do you agree with this choice?

MP.1 Make Sense of Problems Analyze the Problem Children should be able to explain why they agree that a statement is true or why they think it is false. Allow class discussion for children to present their thoughts.

MP.6 Attend to Precision Children should include accurate words and facts in their explanation. They can use models or drawings to support their position.

When all children have agreed with the description, add the object to the correct list. Children should name 5 or 6 objects for each category, if possible.

Lesson **23** ACTIVITY 3

Mathematical Practice 6 is integrated into Unit 5 in the following ways:

Explain Solutions | **Attend to Precision**

COMMON CORE
Mathematical Practice 7
Look for structure.

Children analyze problems to discern a pattern or structure. They draw conclusions about the structure of the relationships they have identified.

TEACHER EDITION: Examples from Unit 5

▶ **Add Shapes to the Smaller Group** WHOLE CLASS

MP.7 Look for Structure Work through the example with children, drawing and writing the numbers as you proceed. Guide children to see that the number of shapes in the second row, and the additional number needed, are partners.

Lesson 14 ACTIVITY 1

MP.7 Look for Structure Identify Relationships Begin by doing finger wiggles to review partners for numbers 7, 8, and 9. For each pair of partners, do the finger wiggle at least four times. If desired, ask a volunteer to write the expression for each pair on the board.

Have everyone hold up 8 fingers and choose partners of 8 (for example, 1 and 7). Do finger wiggles with the class.

• Wiggle (or bend) 1 finger. Now wiggle the other 7 fingers.

It is important that children wiggle all of the other fingers for the second partner. This helps them feel that 1 and 7 come from 8 and together make 8.

Ask children to wiggle 1 and 7 at least three more times.

Lesson 15 ACTIVITY 2

Mathematical Practice 7 is integrated into Unit 2 in the following ways:

Generalize	Identify Relationships
Look for and Make Use of Structure	Use Structure

Mathematical Practice 8
Look for and express regularity in repeated reasoning.

Children use repeated reasoning as they analyze patterns, relationships, and calculations to generalize methods, rules, and shortcuts. As they work to solve a problem, children maintain oversight of the process while attending to the details. They continually evaluate the reasonableness of their intermediate results.

TEACHER EDITION: Examples from Unit 5

MP.8 Use Repeated Reasoning
Generalize Ask children to describe what they see when they have placed the 10-sticks and cubes on all of the numbers. There are many observations they can make. Encourage discussion.

• How is each number different from the number before it? Each number is one greater (has one more cube) as you move right on the board.

Lesson **7** ACTIVITY 1

MP.8 Use Repeated Reasoning
Conclude The mathematical goal is for children to realize they can make two groups equal either by adding to the group that has less or taking away from the one that has the greater number. It is important for children to experience both processes.

Lesson **17** ACTIVITY 2

Mathematical Practice 8 is integrated into Unit 5 in the following ways:

Conclude
Generalize

FOCUS on Mathematical Practices
Unit 5 includes a special lesson that involves solving real world problems and incorporates all 8 Mathematical Practices. In this lesson children use what they know about comparing measurable attributes and justifying conclusions.

STUDENT EDITION: LESSON 23 PAGES 263–264

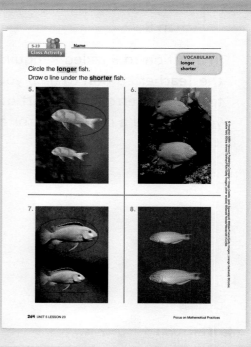

Getting Ready to Teach Unit 5

Learning Path in the Common Core Standards

In this unit, children continue to work with teen numbers and to create and solve story problems involving contexts chosen by the children. Work with partners of numbers 2–10 and teen numbers culminates in children writing equations to represent partner situations and in comparing a number as greater than or less than another number and showing how to make equal groups. In measurement, they have hands-on experiences comparing lengths, heights, weights, and capacities.

Help Students Avoid Common Errors

Math Expressions gives children opportunities to analyze and correct errors, explaining why the reasoning was flawed.

In this unit, we use Puzzled Penguin to show typical errors that children make. Children enjoy teaching Puzzled Penguin the correct way, telling why this way is correct, and explaining why the error is wrong. The common errors are presented as requests for help from Puzzled Penguin to the children:

▸ **Lesson 2:** writing 14, 17, and 19 with transposed digits as 41, 71, and 91

▸ **Lesson 6:** reading the equation for 15 in the *Hiding Zero Game* incorrectly

▸ **Lesson 16:** writing that 8 is Greater than 10 and 10 is Less than 8; writing that 7 is Less than 5 and 5 is Greater than 7

▸ **Lesson 17:** in comparing 6 and 4 writing that 6 is Less than 4; in comparing 6 and 8 writing that 6 is Greater than 8

In addition to Puzzled Penguin, other suggestions are listed in the Teacher Edition to help you watch for situations that may lead to common errors. As a part of the Unit Test Teacher Edition pages, you will find a common error and prescription listed for each test item.

Math Expressions
VOCABULARY

As you teach this unit, emphasize understanding of these terms.

- addition
- subtraction
- partner
- equation
- match

See the Teacher Glossary.

Story Problems

Lessons

Create Story Problems Children make up their own addition and subtraction story problems—in Lesson 1 about situations in *Anno's Counting Book* and in later lessons about any situation they choose. At first, let children use numbers for adding and subtracting within 5, but encourage them as you move through the unit to use numbers for adding and subtracting within 10.

Solve Story Problems Guide children to begin to analyze story situations by asking them to restate a problem using other words. This will help them build their math language skills. As before, children may use drawings, expressions, or equations to solve problems. In this unit, use Math Talk to discuss story problem solutions (see the discussion of Math Talk below).

These activities are designed to help the class work toward Math Talk Level 2, although some children may still be at Level 1. Encourage children who may be reluctant to share their ideas to ask a question or to comment on something that someone else said.

Math Talk In the NSF research project that led to the development of *Math Expressions*, much work was done with helping teachers and children build learning communities within their classrooms. An important aspect of doing this is Math Talk. The researchers found three levels of Math Talk that go beyond the usual classroom routine of children simply solving problems and giving answers and the teacher asking questions and offering explanations. Although an example is given for Level 3, it is not expected that kindergarten classes will reach this level very often.

Math Talk Level 1: A child briefly explains his or her thinking to others. The teacher helps children listen to and help others, models fuller explaining and questioning by others, and briefly probes and extends children's ideas.

Example Story Problem: 2 kittens sit in the window. 1 more kitten jumps up to join them. How many kittens are in the window now?

Who can tell us how many kittens are in the window?

Billy: There are 3 kittens.

How do you know?

Billy: I know that 2 and 1 more is 3.

from THE PROGRESSIONS FOR THE COMMON CORE STATE STANDARDS ON OPERATIONS AND ALGEBRAIC THINKING

Kindergarten Students learn and use mathematical and non-mathematical language, especially when they make up problems and explain their representation and solution. The teacher can write expressions (e.g., $3 - 1$) to represent operations, as well as writing equations that represent the whole situation before the solution (e.g., $3 - 1 = \square$) or after (e.g., $3 - 1 = 2$). Expressions like $3 - 1$ or $2 + 1$ show the operation, and it is helpful for students to have experience just with the expression so they can conceptually chunk this part of an equation.

Who found a different way to answer the question?

Lucy: I made a drawing with 2 circles and 1 circle, and then counted the circles to find 3.

Math Talk Level 2: A child gives a fuller explanation and answers questions from other children. The teacher helps children listen to and ask good questions, models full explaining and questioning (especially for new topics), and probes more deeply to help children compare and contrast methods.

Example Story Problem:

Snow has 8 marbles and 2 boxes. How many marbles can she put in each box?

How can we find the answer to this problem?

Ruth: We can draw the boxes and then draw marbles in the boxes. But what I don't know is if there should be the same number in each box.

Jake: Is this a problem that has more than one answer?

Why do you ask that, Jake?

Jake: Because I know more than 1 way to break apart 8.

Ruth: If we break apart 8, we can make a list of the ways. Do you think that is what we are supposed to do?

Nancy: I think so, because we have been learning about break-aparts.

Ruth: And it does not say the boxes have to be the same.

What is one way to start the list?

Caleb: Let's start with 1 and 7, and then change by 1 more each time.

Nancy: I agree with Caleb.

---

from THE PROGRESSIONS FOR THE COMMON CORE STATE STANDARDS ON OPERATIONS AND ALGEBRAIC THINKING

Working within 10 Later in the year, students solve addition and subtraction equations for numbers within 5, for example, $2 + 1 = \square$ or $3 - 1 = \square$, while still connecting these equations to situations verbally or with drawings. Experience with decompositions of numbers and with Add To and Take From situations enables students to begin to fluently add and subtract within 5.

Math Talk Level 3: The explaining child manages the questioning and justifying. Children assist each other in understanding and correcting errors and in explaining more fully. The teacher monitors and assists and extends only as needed.

Example Story Problem:

Joe ate 4 green grapes and 5 purple grapes. How many grapes did he eat?

Who will show us how to find the answer?

Julia: I know that green grapes and purple grapes are both grapes, so I have to add 4 + 5. I know that is 9, so the answer is 9 grapes. I also made a drawing to be sure I was right. Here is my drawing.

O   O   O   O
O   O   O   O

Bob: I think your answer is right, but your drawing only shows 8. You need to fix your drawing.

Nancy: Yes, when I count your circles, you are showing 4 + 4. So, draw another circle.

How can we be sure that we make the right drawing?

Julia: I should have checked my drawing to be sure I made 4 + 5. So we should always check what we do.

Nancy: We need to count each thing when we make drawings. We have to be sure and not guess that it looks right.

MATH TALK is important not only for discussing solutions to story problems but also for any kind of mathematical thinking children do, such as explaining why each number in the count sequence is 1 more than the number before it, how to use a drawing to subtract, or how to put two right triangles together to make a rectangle.

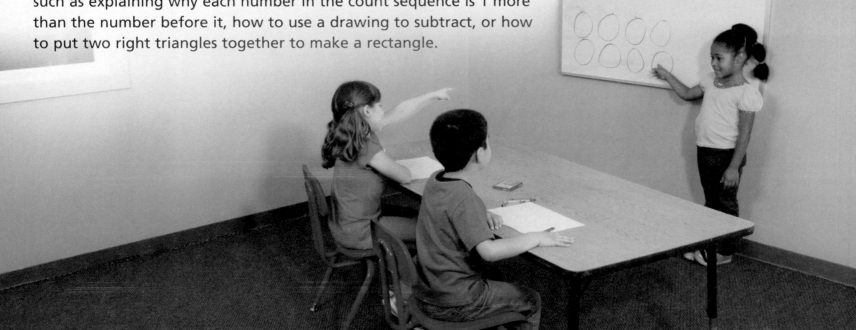

Teen Numbers as Ten Ones and More Ones

As in earlier units, children spend much time building their concepts of teen numbers as ten ones and more ones. This strong foundation will help them with place value concepts in Grade 1, where they will learn that 10 ones are the same as 1 ten and that tens are used to build 2-digit numbers.

Draw Ten Ones and More Ones In this unit, children make drawings of teen numbers, first with pictures of objects and later with circles or dots to represent ones.

Use Models Children use these models from earlier units for activities with teen numbers: Number Tiles, 1–20 Board with 10-sticks and centimeter cubes, and counters. With all these models, children form teen numbers with a 10 ones part and a more ones part. As they model numbers in order, they see that each number is 1 more than the number before it.

Teen Number Book Children make another Teen Number Book for this unit. On the page for each teen number, they draw that many objects and circle ten of the objects so that the number is represented as ten ones and more ones. After children complete all the pages for the Teen Number Book, they will assemble the pages for you to staple together.

> *from* **THE PROGRESSIONS FOR THE COMMON CORE STATE STANDARDS ON NUMBER AND OPERATIONS IN BASE TEN**
>
> **Work with numbers from 11 to 19 to gain foundations for place value** Children use objects, math drawings, and equations to describe, explore, and explain how the "teen numbers," the counting numbers from 11 through 19, are ten ones and some more ones.

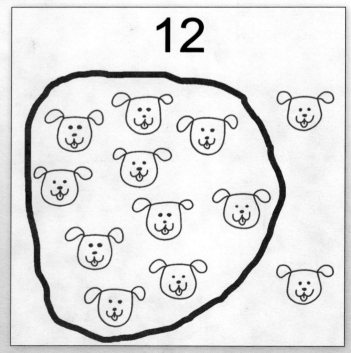

Hiding Zero Game This game is designed to help children see the ten in teen numbers. As children work in pairs, they first form the teen numbers on the *Hiding Zero* Gameboards by covering the zero in the 10 with the appropriate Number Tile for a given teen number.

$$14 = 1\ 4 + \square$$

$$15 = 1\ 5 + \square$$

Then children visualize how a teen number is composed of 10 ones and more ones as they move the Number Tile to complete the teen number partner equation. They reinforce their understanding with verbalization by reading the equation and reciting what each part of the teen number represents.

$$14 = 10 + 4$$

$$15 = 10 + 5$$

Counting

Lessons
2 **13** **14** **23**

Children continue to practice counting numbers in this unit. They now count by ones and by tens to 100. Keeping the Night Sky Display posted gives the children continual reference to the visual representations of 100 as 10 groups of ten ones and of all the possible partners of 10.

The Night Sky

from **THE PROGRESSIONS FOR THE COMMON CORE STATE STANDARDS ON COUNTING AND CARDINALITY**

From saying the counting words to counting out objects Counting objects arranged in a line is easiest; with more practice, students learn to count objects in more difficult arrangements, such as rectangular arrays (they need to ensure they reach every row or column and do not repeat rows or columns).

Children's earlier work with counting, especially with counting to 20, has prepared them for the repetition of digits in each of the different "tens" decades. Continue to emphasize the nature of the count sequence—that each number is 1 greater than the one before it and that each time a new decade number is made and named, the digits from 1 through 9 replace the zero in the decade number to form the next nine numbers that lead to the next decade number.

Partners and Equations

Finger Wiggles for Partners of 10 This activity uses a kinesthetic approach to support children's learning of the partners of 10. Using all the senses helps children cement their learning of these fundamental relationships of numbers.

Equations Children will complete or write equations for the partners of numbers through 10 and for the partners of teen numbers where one partner is 10. This is a big step for kindergarten children. Not all children will be ready to do this at the same time. Some children may still write expressions, but encourage all children to use the models on their Student Activity Book pages to write equations.

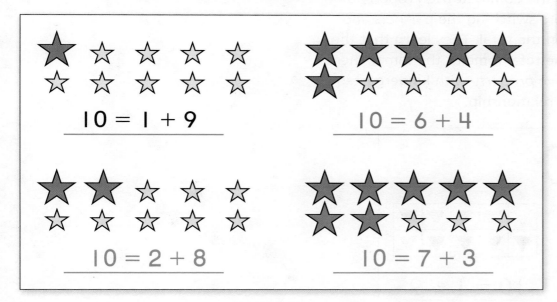

from **THE PROGRESSIONS FOR THE COMMON CORE STATE STANDARDS ON COUNTING AND CARDINALITY**

From subitizing to single-digit arithmetic fluency Perceptual subitizing develops into conceptual subitizing—recognizing that a collection of objects is composed of two subcollections and quickly combining their cardinalities to find the cardinality of the collection (e.g., seeing a set as two subsets of cardinality 2 and saying "four").

UNIT 5

MATH BACKGROUND

Unknown Partners Children will use the Tiny Tumblers on the Math Mountains model to find an unknown partner, given a number at the top of the Math Mountain and one partner. Children may have different strategies for doing this, so encourage discussion.

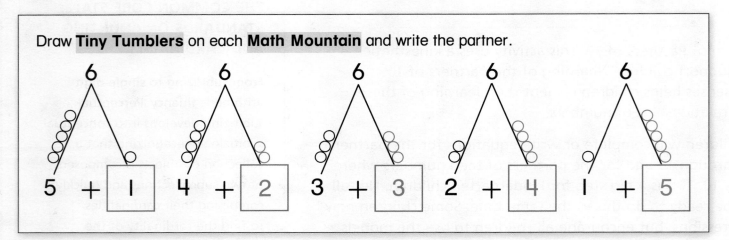

Draw **Tiny Tumblers** on each **Math Mountain** and write the partner.

6   6   6   6   6

5 + 1   4 + 2   3 + 3   2 + 4   1 + 5

Switch Partners Informal exposure to the Commutative Property of Addition takes place as children explore switching the partners and observing whether there is a change in the total. They learn that the partners can be in either order and the total remains the same. There is no need to use the term *commutative property* with kindergarten children or to expect them to use the relationship.

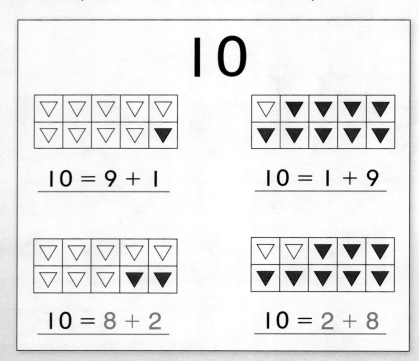

10

$10 = 9 + 1$ $10 = 1 + 9$

$10 = 8 + 2$ $10 = 2 + 8$

Numbers 1–20

Lessons
5 7 15

Model Numbers Children use the 1–20 Board with 10-sticks and centimeter cubes to model all the numbers from 1 through 20. They observe how the numbers change and how arrangements of the digits repeat. As in earlier units, children model the teen numbers using a 10-stick to show 10 ones and cubes to show more ones.

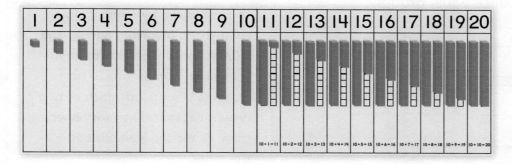

Understanding how the numbers change from 1 through 20 adds to the strong foundation children are building for place value concepts in later grades.

Path to Fluency

Lessons
7 9 12 13 15 18

Because the Common Core State Standards require that children fluently add and subtract within 5 by the end of kindergarten, this unit continues to include practice sets designed to help children acquire this fluency. As in earlier units, the *Path to Fluency* exercise sets provide practice with addition and subtraction within 5 to help children achieve this goal.

$2 + 1 = \boxed{3}$ $3 + 1 = \boxed{4}$ $2 + 2 = \boxed{4}$

$2 + 3 = \boxed{5}$ $1 + 3 = \boxed{4}$ $3 + 2 = \boxed{5}$

Compare Numbers

Lessons

Comparing Children know how to compare two sets of objects by counting or by matching. In Unit 4, they learned to add objects to the group with fewer objects to make equal groups. In this unit they will continue to add objects to make equal groups but will also learn to subtract objects to make equal groups. It is important for children to see that they can use either process to produce equal groups.

In this unit as in Unit 4, children will use *G* for *Greater than* and *L* for *Less than*. They will use the mathematical symbols >, <, and = for recording comparisons in Grade 1.

Measurement

Lessons

The Kindergarten Common Core State Standards for Measurement say that children will describe and compare measurable attributes. These lessons engage children in hands-on activities in measuring and comparing lengths, heights, weights, and capacities. By measuring and comparing real objects rather than pictures, children gain a truer sense of the measurable attribute.

> *from* **THE PROGRESSIONS FOR THE COMMON CORE STATE STANDARDS ON COUNTING AND CARDINALITY**
>
> **From comparison by matching to comparison by numbers to comparison involving adding and subtracting** The standards about comparing numbers focus on students identifying which of two groups has more than (or fewer than, or the same amount as) the other.

Math Stories and Scenes with Teen Numbers

LESSON FOCUS

- Create addition and subtraction story problems.
- Visualize and represent teen numbers as ten ones and extra ones.

VOCABULARY

partners
addition
subtraction
teen number

COMMON CORE

Mathematical Practice
CC.K–12.MP.1, CC.K–12.MP.3
Mathematical Content
CC.K.CC.5, CC.K.OA.2, CC.K.OA.5, CC.K.NBT.1

The Day at a Glance

USE
MATH TALK
TODAY!

Teaching the Lesson

MATH BACKGROUND for this lesson is included on pp. 461GG–461KK.

ACTIVITY FOCUS

Activity 1 Create story problems using *Anno's Counting Book.*

Activity 2 Draw scenes that show teen numbers as a group of ten ones and some extra ones.

MATERIALS

Student Activity Book pp. 205–206 (includes Family Letter) • *Anno's Counting Book* by Mitsumasa Anno • Crayons or markers

*i*Tools: Counters • Whiteboard

Differentiated Instruction

MATERIALS

Activity Cards 5-1 • Strips of paper • Crayons or markers • Math Journals

Soar to Success Math Intervention • MegaMath • Destination Math®

RtI Tier 1 • Tier 2 • Tier 3

Home and School Connection

MATERIALS

Family Letter (Student Activity Book pp. 205–206)

QUICK PRACTICE 5 MINUTES

Repeated Quick Practice Use these Quick Practices from previous lessons.

Practice −1 Orally Present several −1 problems, such as 4 −1, 6 −1, and 3 −1. Children show the first number on fingers and then lower one finger to subtract 1. Point to the Number Parade to reinforce the pattern that −1 is the number before. (See Unit 4, Lesson 15.)

Count to 100 by Tens Point to the numbers in the bottom row of the 120 Poster while children count by tens and flash 10 fingers for each decade number. Meanwhile, a Student Leader wears the "How Many Tens?" card and counts the tens with single fingers. (See Unit 4, Lesson 11.)

DAILY ROUTINES

Counting Tens and Ones
(See pp. xxxi–xxxii.)

DIGITAL RESOURCES

Use these digital resources along with your eSAB and eTE to support your students' learning experiences.

Professional Development

Whiteboard Lesson

*i*Tools

Soar to Success Math Intervention

MegaMath

Destination Math®

COMMON CORE

Mathematical Practice
CC.K–12.MP.1

Mathematical Content
CC.K.OA.2, CC.K.OA.5

35 MINUTES

FOCUS Create story problems using *Anno's Counting Book.*

MATERIALS *Anno's Counting Book* by Mitsumasa Anno

iT *i*Tools: Counters

 Whiteboard Lesson

Digital Resource

***i*Tools** Choose 'Counters' on the Menu. Use Activity 3 'Add' with the tab for 'Activities.' Children can use counters to help them add two numbers. Then they enter the total.

Use Activity 4 'Subtract' with the tab for 'Activities.' Children can use counters to help them subtract. Then they enter the partner.

Class Management

Looking Ahead In Unit 5, Lesson 2 and throughout this unit, you will make a Night Sky display on the classroom wall. You may want to prepare ahead of time. Use large, blue bulletin-board paper or a tablecloth, approximately 4 feet by 5 feet. Gather glue sticks and ten sheets of 11 by 17 inch construction paper. Glue the stars (from Unit 5, Lesson 2) to the construction paper before mounting them to the backing.

ACTIVITY 1 📖 Literature Connection

Find Break-Apart Partners and Tell Stories

▶ **Revisit *Anno's Counting Book*** | WHOLE CLASS | MATH TALK

Return to *Anno's Counting Book* and revisit each page with your class. Focus on finding all of the partners and telling addition and subtraction "what if" stories about each page.

As you move to each new number, find partners of that number in the drawing. Then have children identify any partners of that number that are not in the drawing.

Ask children to make up one addition story and one subtraction story for each page. Here is a possible example for page 1:

• What if 5 more houses were built? How many houses would we see?

Stating the question is the most difficult part of telling a story. If a child needs assistance, have a peer help to state the question.

MP.1 Make Sense of Problems Solve a Similar Problem Introduce the new aspect of story problems for this unit: retelling the same story, using different words that mean the same thing. This kind of language exercise allows more children an opportunity to talk, and it helps review mathematical language. Focus on having children ask the question in different ways. (See the common addition and subtraction words shown below.) This also helps children learn how to ask the question for an addition story and for a subtraction story.

Common Addition and Subtraction Words Below are some common words that may indicate addition or subtraction. Help children use them during different retellings.

Addition (I see 7 cows and 1 dog.)

• How many animals are there *altogether?*

• How many animals are there *in all?*

• There is a *total* of how many animals?

• If we *put them together*, how many animals are there?

Subtraction (There were 9 sheep in the field, but 4 of them went into the barn.)

• How many sheep are *left* in the field?

• How many sheep are *still* in the field?

Draw a Teen Scene

▶ **Brainstorm Ideas** SMALL GROUPS

Discuss the cubes on the final two pages of *Anno's Counting Book,* pages 11 and 12.

- What do you notice about the cubes stacked at the edge of the picture? There is a group of ten cubes and one more for 11, and a group of ten ones and 2 more ones for 12.

MP.3 Construct a Viable Argument Compare Representations
How is this like the way you made teen numbers in Unit 4? We made a group of 10 ones and then we showed the extra ones.

Ask for Ideas Explain that each child is going to draw a Teen Scene that shows a teen number as a group of ten ones and some extra ones. Brainstorm things children can draw in their Teen Scenes. Children can make these scenes as colorful as they wish.

Designate a place in the classroom for displaying a couple of Teen Scenes at a time. There will be several wall displays in this unit, so you probably will not have space to display all of the Teen Scenes at once.

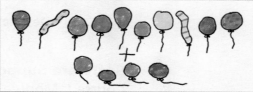

 Formative Assessment: Check Understanding

Student Summary Ask pairs of children to count each other's teen scenes from the activity above. Have each child compare the scenes telling which has more and which has fewer.

⟨ COMMON CORE

Mathematical Practice
CC.K–12.MP.3
Mathematical Content
CC.K.CC.5, CC.K.NBT.1

20 MINUTES

FOCUS Draw scenes that show teen numbers as a group of ten ones and some extra ones.

MATERIALS crayons or markers

◥ Whiteboard Lesson

English Language Learners

Write *addition* and *subtraction* on the board. Say *add* and *subtract* as you circle each part. Display five books. Say: **Two books are mine. Three books are library books. How many books do I have altogether?** 5 books

BEGINNING

Say: **We add to find how many books altogether. This is an addition story.** Have children repeat *addition.* Then repeat with a subtraction story.

INTERMEDIATE

Ask children to say *addition* or *subtraction* for the story. addition Repeat with a subtraction story.

ADVANCED

Say: **Why is this an addition story?** It is an addition story because we are putting two groups together. **Repeat with a subtraction story.**

Class Management

Throughout Unit 5, keep at least two of the children's Teen Scenes up in the classroom. Change pictures during the unit so that all of the children's pictures can be displayed.

▲ On Level   🔺 RtI Tier 1

for students having success

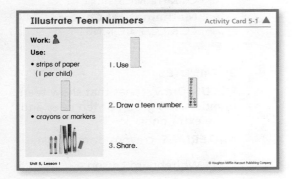

Activity Notes Use *Anno's Counting Book,* giving attention to the stacked cubes in the side column. Explain that children will do the same.

✏️ Math Writing Prompt

Before and After Challenge children to write the number before and after the teen number they draw on the strip.

 MegaMath

Software Support
Country Countdown
Counting Critters, Level P

■ Challenge

for students seeking a challenge

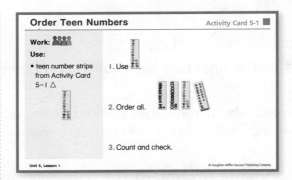

Activity Notes Be sure that children have successfully completed the On Level activity.

✏️ Math Writing Prompt

Say the Number Extend the lesson by saying a number and having children write the number that comes either before or after.

 Destination Math®

Software Support
Course I: Module 2: Unit 1: Session 3: Sums within 20, with 10 as One Addend

---

Family Letter Have children take home the Family Letter on Student Activity Book page 205. This letter explains how the concept of teen numbers is developed in *Math Expressions.* It gives parents and guardians a better under-standing of the learning that goes on in math class and creates a bridge between home and school. A Spanish translation of this letter is on the following page in the Student Activity Book.

Student Activity Book page 205

Student Activity Book page 206

Partners of 10: Stars in the Night Sky

LESSON FOCUS
- Create and count stars to make partners of 10 for a classroom display.
- Count the number of objects in a group through 20.

VOCABULARY
big
small

COMMON CORE

Mathematical Practice
CC.K–12.MP.1, CC.K–12.MP.3, CC.K–12.MP.6
Mathematical Content
CC.K.CC.1, CC.K.CC.3, CC.K.CC.5, CC.K.CC.7, CC.K.OA.4

The Day at a Glance

USE MATH TALK TODAY!

Teaching the Lesson

MATH BACKGROUND for this lesson is included on pp. 461LL–461NN.

ACTIVITY FOCUS

Activity 1   Make and count stars to make partners of 10 for the Night Sky display.

Activity 2   Count the number of objects in a group through 20.

MATERIALS

Student Activity Book pp. 207–210 (includes Stars) • Stars (TRB M53) • Crayons or markers (purple and yellow) • Scissors • Glue stick

*i*Tools: Counters • Whiteboard

Differentiated Instruction

MATERIALS

Activity Cards 5-2 • Paper strips (red and yellow) • Number Tiles • Math Journals

Soar to Success Math Intervention • MegaMath • Destination Math®

RtI   Tier 1 • Tier 2 • Tier 3

Homework

MATERIALS

Homework and Remembering pp. 89–90

QUICK PRACTICE   5 MINUTES

Repeated Quick Practice Use these Quick Practices from previous lessons.

Count to 100 by Tens (See Unit 4, Lesson 11.)

Practice −1 Orally (See Unit 4, Lesson 15.)

DAILY ROUTINES
Counting Tens and Ones
(See pp. xxxi–xxxii.)

DIGITAL RESOURCES

Use these digital resources along with your eSAB and eTE to support your students' learning experiences.

Professional Development

Whiteboard Lesson

*i*Tools

Soar to Success Math Intervention

MegaMath

Destination Math®

COMMON CORE

Mathematical Practice
CC.K–12.MP.1
Mathematical Content
CC.K.CC.1, CC.K.OA.4

20 MINUTES

FOCUS Make and count stars to make partners of 10 for the Night Sky display.

MATERIALS Stars (Student Activity Book page 207 or TRB M53; 1 per child), crayons or markers (purple and yellow), scissors (1 per child), glue stick

 Whiteboard Lesson

Teaching Note

Math Background The Night Sky display is a major source for building numerical understandings in Unit 5. It serves as the focus for key concepts: counting by tens, learning the decade numbers, and practicing 10-partners.

ACTIVITY 1

Color and Cut Out Stars for the Night Sky Display

Distribute Student Activity Book page 207.

Student Activity Book page 207

Discuss the page with the children.

• What shapes and sizes do you see? big stars and little stars

• How many stars are on the page? 10

Explain that the big math project for Unit 5 is to make a Night Sky on the classroom wall. Today, children will color and cut out stars. Then the stars will be placed on the wall to make a beautiful Night Sky display.

Have children color the small stars yellow and the big stars purple. Some children may be able to cut out their own stars, but many may need assistance. You will need 50 small yellow stars and 50 large purple stars for the Night Sky display.

MP.1 Make Sense of Problems Check Answers Ask children to help you count all of the stars to check that you have 100.

To make the Night Sky display in your classroom, use a glue stick to fasten 100 stars to the background you have prepared (see Unit 5, Lesson 1, Activity 1 Class Management: Looking Ahead). The stars should be in groups of 10. Mix little stars and big stars in each group of 10, as demonstrated below, to show the different partners of 10. Glue each set of 10 onto individual sheets of 11-inch by 17-inch construction paper.

Leave room for adding an Equation Strip under each star group and a Decade Number Card at the left of each star group (see Class Management: Looking Ahead on this page).

The Night Sky

Class Management

Looking Ahead Before Lesson 3, prepare Equation Strips and Decade Number Cards to add to the Night Sky display.

Equation Strips: Write equations on posterboard or construction paper to fit under the star groups.

$10 = 1 + 9$
$10 = 2 + 8$
$10 = 3 + 7$
$10 = 4 + 6$
$10 = 5 + 5$

$10 = 5 + 5$
$10 = 6 + 4$
$10 = 7 + 3$
$10 = 8 + 2$
$10 = 9 + 1$

Decade Number Cards: Write decade numbers 10–100 on sticky notes, posterboard, or construction paper.

10	20	30
40	50	60
70	80	90

100

It is helpful to make all of the Equation Strips one color and all of the Decade Number Cards another color.

COMMON CORE

Mathematical Practice
CC.K–12.MP.1, CC.K–12.MP.3, CC.K–12.MP.6

Mathematical Content
CC.K.CC.1, CC.K.CC.3, CC.K.CC.5, CC.K.CC.7

FOCUS Count the number of objects in a group through 20.

MATERIALS Student Activity Book pages 209 and 210

 iTools: Counters

Whiteboard Lesson

Digital Resource

*i*Tools Choose 'Counters' on the Menu. Use Activity 1 'Count' with the tab for 'Activities'. Children can use counters to count.

ACTIVITY 2

Count How Many

▶ Count How Many WHOLE CLASS

Ask children to look at the first group of stars on Student Activity Book page 209, count how many there are in all, and write that number in the box.

MP.1 Make Sense of Problems Check Answers Suggest that children make a small mark in the stars to keep track of the ones they have counted.

Allow time for children to complete the page independently.

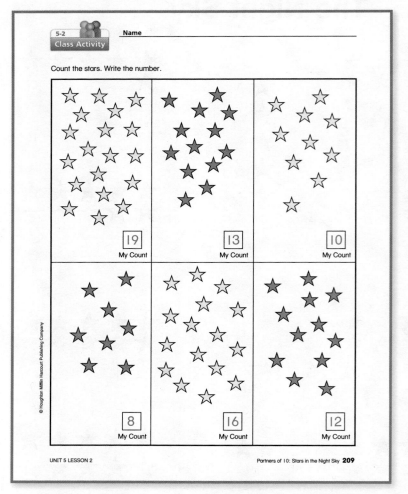

Student Activity Book page 209

▶ What's the Error? | WHOLE CLASS | MATH TALK

MP.3, MP.6 Construct Viable Arguments/Critique the Reasoning of Others Puzzled Penguin Explain that Puzzled Penguin was asked to write the numbers 14, 17, and 19.

• Puzzled Penguin is not sure that each number was written correctly. Help Puzzled Penguin look at the first number to see if it is correct.

Student Activity Book page 210

• **Is the number written fourteen?** No, it is 4 and 1 or forty-one.
• **How do we write the number fourteen correctly?** 1 for the ten ones and 4 for four more ones
• **Now help Puzzled Penguin write the number correctly.**

Repeat for the numbers 17 and 19. Ask children to explain why they think Puzzled Penguin made the mistake.

 Formative Assessment: Check Understanding

Student Summary Ask a child to draw a group of objects for a number that you say, using the numbers 11 through 20.

English Language Learners

Draw a big circle and a small square on the board. Label them *big* and *small*. Point to each shape as you say: **Big means large. Small means little.** Ask children to draw a big circle and a small square on their paper.

BEGINNING

Say: **The circle is big. The square is small.** Have children repeat.

INTERMEDIATE

Ask: **What is the size of the circle?** big **What is the size of the square?** small

ADVANCED

Say: **Tell about your drawing.** It's a big circle and a small square.

▲ On Level    **RtI** Tier 1
for students having success

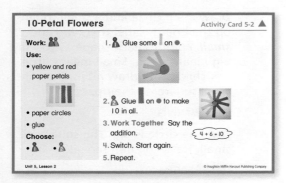

Activity Notes Children make partners of 10 by adding petals to a circle to make a 10-petal flower. Encourage children to make many partners for 10.

 Math Writing Prompt

Explain Your Thinking Are there more partners for 6 or for 10? Explain why.

 MegaMath

Software Support
Country Countdown
Counting Critters, Level C

■ Challenge
for students seeking a challenge

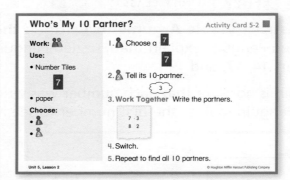

Activity Notes Ask pairs of children to take turns finding the 10-partner for a given number. Then record all the possible partners for 10.

 Math Writing Prompt

Think About It What would be the easiest way to find all the partners of 10?

 Destination Math®

Software Support
Course I: Module 1: Unit 2: Session 3: Creating Representations of the Numbers from 5 to 10

The Homework activity on page 89 gives children practice counting numbers through 19. Page 90 asks children to practice adding partners of 10.

Include children's completed homework page as part of their portfolios.

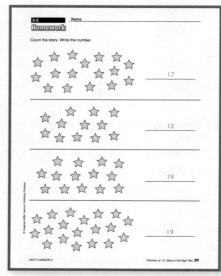

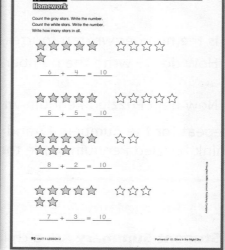

Homework and Remembering page 89   Homework and Remembering page 90

More Partners of 10: Stars in the Night Sky

LESSON FOCUS

- Write equations to show partners of 10 and identify an unknown partner of 10.
- Count by tens to 100 and show teen numbers as a group of ten ones and extra ones.

VOCABULARY

partners
decade numbers
teen numbers
ten
one
equation

COMMON CORE

Mathematical Practice
CC.K–12.MP.4, CC.K–12.MP.7
Mathematical Content
CC.K.CC.1, CC.K.OA.1, CC.K.OA.3, CC.K.OA.4, CC.K.OA.5, CC.K.NBT.1

The Day at a Glance

USE
MATH TALK
TODAY!

Teaching the Lesson

MATH BACKGROUND for this lesson is included on pp. 461JJ–461KK.

ACTIVITY FOCUS

Activity 1: Write equations and do finger wiggles for partners of 10.

Activity 2: Count by tens to 100 and practice partners of 10 to learn new Quick Practice routines using the Night Sky display.

Activity 3: Show teen numbers as a group of ten ones and extra ones.

MATERIALS

- Student Activity Book pp. 211–214 (includes Family Letter) • Night Sky display • Pointer • Equation Strips • Decade Number Cards • Sticky notes • "How Many Tens?" Card

- *i*Tools: Counters • Whiteboard

Differentiated Instruction

MATERIALS

- Activity Cards 5-3 • Math Journals

- Soar to Success Math Intervention • MegaMath • Destination Math®

- **RtI** Tier 1 • Tier 2 • Tier 3

Home and School Connection

MATERIALS

- Family Letter (Student Activity Book pp. 211–212)

QUICK PRACTICE 5 MINUTES

The new Quick Practice routines for Unit 5 are introduced in Activity 2 of this lesson.

Partner Peek: Tell the Unknown Partner

Count to 100 by Tens and Tell How Many

Say Groups of 10 and Decade Numbers (and Reverse).

DAILY ROUTINES
Counting Tens and Ones
(See pp. xxxi–xxxii.)

DIGITAL RESOURCES

Use these digital resources along with your eSAB and eTE to support your students' learning experiences.

 Professional Development

 Whiteboard Lesson

 *i*Tools

 Soar to Success Math Intervention

 MegaMath

 Destination Math®

COMMON CORE

Mathematical Practice
CC.K–12.MP.4

Mathematical Content
CC.K.OA.1, CC.K.OA.3,
CC.K.OA.4, CC.K.OA.5

15 MINUTES

FOCUS Write equations and do finger wiggles for partners of 10.

MATERIALS Student Activity Book page 213

 *i*Tools: Counters

Whiteboard Lesson

Digital Resource

*i***Tools** Choose 'Counters' on the Menu. Use Activity 4 'Subtract' with the tab for 'Activities.' Children can use counters to help them subtract. Then they enter the partner.

Teaching Note

What to Expect from Students
It may still be a bit difficult for some children to wiggle their fingers to show the different partners of 10. However, making the effort provides valuable kinesthetic information that reinforces number concepts and improves fine-motor coordination. Continue to encourage the children.

ACTIVITY 1

See 10-Partners in the Night Sky

▶ **Write Equations** WHOLE CLASS

Student Activity Book page 213 shows patterns of stars in the Night Sky.

Student Activity Book page 213

Have children look at the page and count to see that each group has 10 stars, and then discuss the partners they see.

• How can you quickly tell how many stars are in each group? I can see there two 5-groups, so there are 10 in every group.

MP.4 Model with Mathematics Write an Equation Have children tell the equation for each collection of stars as All Stars = Big Stars + Little Stars (for example, 10 = 1 + 9) and then write that equation. For each equation, have children show the partners with their fingers by wiggling fingers for one partner and then the other partner.

After all the equations are filled in on the page, have children switch the partners for each equation (for example, 9 + 1 and 1 + 9).

Introduce the Unit 5 Quick Practice Activities

▶ **Practice Naming the 10-Partners** [WHOLE CLASS]

A **Student Leader** uses the pointer to point to a group of stars in the Night Sky display and calls on a volunteer to tell the partners of 10 shown by the big and little stars of one group (for example, "8 and 2 make 10"). The class repeats the partners while wiggling or bending fingers. Tape the appropriate Equation Strip under the 10-group. Continue the activity with the remaining groups of stars.

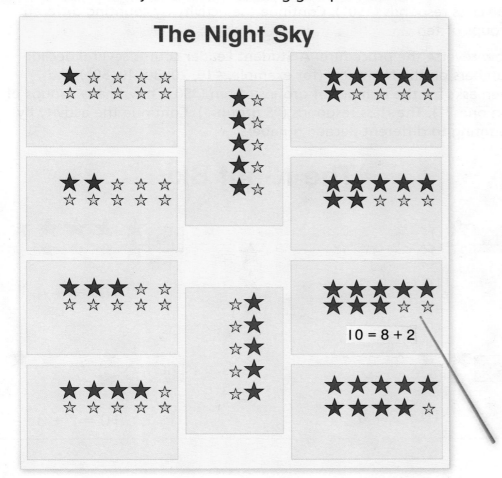

The Night Sky

$10 = 8 + 2$

▶ **Partner Peek: Tell the Unknown Partner** [WHOLE CLASS]

MP.7 Look for Structure Cover one partner in each Night Sky equation with a sticky note. A **Student Leader** names one partner and asks for the other ("10 = 8 and how many?"). At a signal from the Student Leader, the class names the other partner ("10 = 8 and 2"). Continue the activity with the other equations. Identify equations in which the partners are switched (1 + 9 and 9 + 1).

Activity continued ▶

COMMON CORE

Mathematical Practice
CC.K–12.MP.7
Mathematical Content
CC.K.CC.1, CC.K.OA.1,
CC.K.OA.3, CC.K.OA.4,
CC.K.OA.5

15 MINUTES

FOCUS Count by tens to 100 and practice partners of 10 to learn new Quick Practice routines using the Night Sky display.

MATERIALS Night Sky display, pointer, Equation Strips, Decade Number Cards

 Whiteboard Lesson

English Language Learners

Write *decade numbers* on the board. Say: **When we group ten ones together, we make decade numbers.** Distribute 10-sticks to children. Invite a volunteer to give you his or her 10-stick (1 group of ten ones). Write 10 on the board and say: **Ten is a decade number.** Have children repeat. Then invite another child to give you his or her 10-stick (ten more ones) and write 20 on the board. Say: **Twenty is a decade number.** Have children repeat. Continue in this way until you reach 100.

Class Management

We use a signal from the **Student Leader** for the class response to give more children a chance to think of the answer. This could be indicated by raising and then lowering an arm.

Teaching Note

Math Background The Unit 5 Quick Practice routines are designed to build on the connections begun in Unit 4. Children will continue to learn the decade numbers and connect them to groups of ten ones (for example, 60 is 6 groups of ten ones, 3 groups of ten ones make 30). Counting skills will be practiced and reinforced, and children will continue to grow in their understanding of partners.

▶ Count to 100 by Tens and Tell How Many $\boxed{\text{WHOLE CLASS}}$

Fasten Decade Number Cards in order next to 10-groups on the Night Sky. A **Student Leader** points to each group of ten with a pointer while the class counts by tens ("10, 20, . . . 100"). Children flash ten fingers with each count.

▶ Say Groups of 10 and Decade Numbers (and Reverse) $\boxed{\text{WHOLE CLASS}}$ **MATH TALK**

A **Student Leader** counts several groups of ten on the Night Sky and then asks for the decade number ("5 groups of ten ones make . . ."). The class responds ("50"). Continue the activity by counting different groups of ten.

Now reverse the procedure. A **Student Leader** counts several decade numbers on the Night Sky (for example, "10, 20, 30, 40, 50") and then asks for the number of groups of ten ("50 is how many groups of ten ones?"). The class responds ("5 groups"). Continue the activity by counting to different decade numbers.

The Night Sky

Show Teen Numbers

▶ Complete a Teen Board

Discuss the Teen Board layout on Student Activity Book page 214. This is similar to the back of the 1–20 Board.

MP.4 Model with Mathematics Draw a Model Remind children of when they made their Unit 4 Teen Number Books. They can draw small circles or dots in the 10-sticks. Then, under each group of ten, the children will write 10 plus the partner needed to make the teen total. They should also complete the partner equations at the bottom of the page.

When children have finished the page, practice linking the teen number at the top to the equation at the bottom, for example:

• Put your finger on 15. 15 is a group of 10 plus how many? 5
• Show the 10 circles you drew. Show the 5 circles you drew.

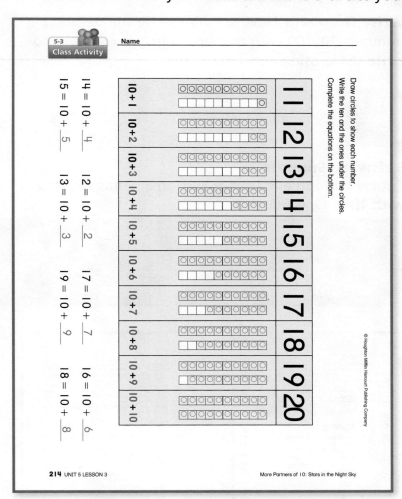

Student Activity Book page 214

COMMON CORE

Mathematical Practice
CC.K–12.MP.4
Mathematical Content
CC.K.OA.1, CC.K.NBT.1

10 MINUTES

FOCUS Show teen numbers as a group of ten ones and extra ones.
MATERIALS Student Activity Book page 214

 Whiteboard Lesson

Class Management

Looking Ahead Save Student Activity Book page 214. Children will make similar drawings throughout this unit. If you wish, you can post these teen drawings around the room.

 Formative Assessment: Check Understanding

Student Summary Ask a child to draw a group of ten ones and some extra ones, then tell you the number.

▲ On Level    Tier 1
for students having success

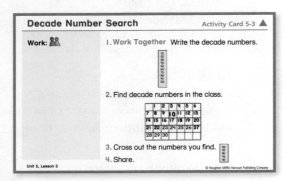

Activity Notes Children may only find one item per number. They should be given time to complete the search.

✏️ **Math Writing Prompt**

Draw a Picture Challenge children to draw pictures of places outside school where they would see decade numbers.

 MegaMath

Software Support
Country Countdown
Block Busters, Level G

■ Challenge
for students seeking a challenge

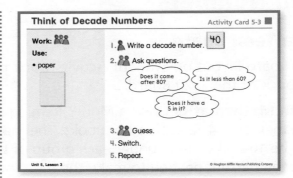

Activity Notes Walk children through a sample of this activity, modeling the types of questions to ask.

✏️ **Math Writing Prompt**

Write Numbers Have children write the decade numbers 10–100 with numbers missing. Ask pairs to write the missing numbers.

 Destination Math®

Software Support
Course I: Module 2: Unit 1: Session 3: Sums within 20, with 10 as One Addend

---

Family Letter Have children take home the Family Letter on Student Activity Book page 211. This letter explains how the concept of ten ones in teen numbers is developed in *Math Expressions*. It gives parents and guardians a better understanding of the learning that goes on in math class and creates a bridge between school and home. A Spanish translation of this letter is on the following page in the Student Activity Book.

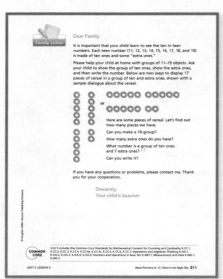

Student Activity Book page 211

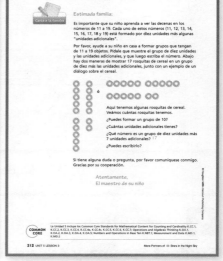

Student Activity Book page 212

Solve and Retell Story Problems

LESSON FOCUS

- Tell, retell, and solve addition and subtraction story problems with drawings and equations.
- Visualize teen numbers as 10 (two 5-groups) and extra ones.

VOCABULARY

ten
one
equation

COMMON CORE

Mathematical Practice
CC.K–12.MP.1, CC.K–12.MP.4, CC.K–12.MP.6
Mathematical Content
CC.K.CC.3, CC.K.CC.5, CC.K.OA.2, CC.K.OA.3, CC.K.OA.4, CC.K.NBT.1

The Day at a Glance

Teaching the Lesson

MATH BACKGROUND for this lesson is included on pp. 461GG–461KK, 461MM–461NN.

ACTIVITY FOCUS

Activity 1 Tell, retell, and solve story problems with drawings and equations.

Activity 2 Visualize 11–20 animal pictures as a group of ten ones and extra ones.

MATERIALS

- Student Activity Book pp. 215–216 • Fluency Check 5 (Assessment Guide)

- *i*Tools: Counters • Whiteboard

Differentiated Instruction

MATERIALS

- Activity Cards 5-4 • Math Journals

- Soar to Success Math Intervention • MegaMath • Destination Math®

- **RtI** Tier 1 • Tier 2 • Tier 3

Homework

MATERIALS

- Homework and Remembering pp. 91–92

QUICK PRACTICE 5 MINUTES

Partner Peek: Tell the Unknown Partner Cover one partner in each Night Sky equation. A **Student Leader** names one partner and asks for the other. At a signal from the Student Leader, the class answers. Repeat for other partners. (See Unit 5, Lesson 3.)

Count to 100 by Tens and Tell How Many A **Student Leader** points to each group of ten ones on the Night Sky display while the class counts by tens, flashing ten fingers with each count. A second Student Leader wears the "How Many Tens?" Card and raises one finger with each ten. At the end, the first Student Leader summarizes, "10 groups of ten ones is 100." (See Unit 5, Lesson 3.)

Say Groups of 10 and Decade Numbers (and Reverse) A **Student Leader** counts several groups of ten ones on the Night Sky display and then asks for the decade number ("4 groups of ten ones make ..."). The class responds ("40"). The Student Leader repeats this activity, counting to a different 10-group each time. A second Student Leader reverses the procedure. (See Unit 5, Lesson 3.)

DAILY ROUTINES

Counting Tens and Ones (See pp. xxxi–xxxii.)

DIGITAL RESOURCES

Use these digital resources along with your eSAB and eTE to support your students' learning experiences.

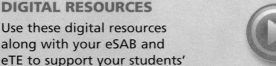

Professional Development

Whiteboard Lesson

*i*Tools

Soar to Success Math Intervention

MegaMath

Destination Math®

COMMON CORE
Mathematical Practice
CC.K–12.MP.1, CC.K–12.MP.4,
CC.K–12.MP.6
Mathematical Content
CC.K.OA.2, CC.K.OA.3, CC.K.OA.4

25 MINUTES
FOCUS Tell, retell, and solve story problems with drawings and equations.

 Whiteboard Lesson

Learning Community— Best Practices

Building Concepts Remember when you model subtraction with math drawings to cross out using a minus sign instead of Xs. Also, be sure to subtract the first objects in the drawing to support counting on from the number taken away.

COMMON CORE
Mathematical Practice
CC.K–12.MP.1
Mathematical Content
CC.K.CC.3, CC.K.CC.5, CC.K.OA.2,
CC.K.OA.3, CC.K.OA.4, CC.K.NBT.1

15 MINUTES
FOCUS Visualize 11–20 animal pictures as a group of ten ones and extra ones.
Materials Student Activity Book pages 215–216

iT *i*Tools: Counters

 Whiteboard Lesson

Digital Resource

*i*Tools Choose 'Counters' on the Menu. Use Activity 1 'Count' with the tab for 'Activities.' Children can use counters to count.

ACTIVITY 1

Tell, Retell, and Solve Math Stories

▶ Create and Solve Story Problems WHOLE CLASS   MATH TALK

Use **Solve and Discuss** for this activity.

MP.4 Model with Mathematics Write an Equation Have children tell addition and subtraction story problems with numbers through 10, solve them with math drawings, and write the corresponding equations. Have as many children as possible work at the board while the other children work on paper. Select two children to explain their drawings and equations for their stories. The other children can ask them questions. Remind children to check to see if the answer is reasonable. If it is not, they should reevaluate the approach they used to solve the problem.

MP.1, MP.6 Make Sense of Problems/Attend to Precision Solve a Similar Problem Have the children retell each story using different words that mean the same thing. This kind of language exercise allows more children an opportunity to talk, and it helps review mathematical language. Focus on having the children ask the question in different ways. (See Unit 5, Lesson 1, Activity 1.)

Activity 1 will be repeated four more times during this unit. By the end of Unit 5, all children should have had multiple turns at the board, retelling someone else's story and telling their own stories.

ACTIVITY 2 Science Connection

See Tens in Groups of Teen Animals

▶ Practice with Teen Numbers WHOLE CLASS

Student Activity Book page 215 uses 5-groups to show animals arranged in groups of ten with some extra ones to make a teen number. Children may count the animals if they wish, but focus on helping them see and describe the two 5-groups that make ten and the extra ones for each teen number.

Have children discuss the example at the top left of the Student Activity Book page.

- What kind of animal do you see at the top left? horses
- What do you know about horses?
- Can you see 10 horses and then 2 more horses?

Point out that someone has circled the 10 horses. Then relate the 10-group to the equation 10 + 2 = 12.

Ask for Ideas Work through each group of animals together. Discuss what kind of animal it is, and have children tell what they know about that animal. Then have them circle the 10-group for that animal. Encourage children to try to see how many there are by using 5-groups, instead of by counting. Children can count to check if they wish.

MP.1 Make Sense of Problems Check Answers When the page is complete, review the equations by having children do number flashes for each equation (for example, say "10 and 9 make 19" as children show fingers).

On Student Activity Book page 216, invite children to practice counting the stars. Ask children to note that in the first box and the last box, the number of stars is the same even though the groups are arranged differently.

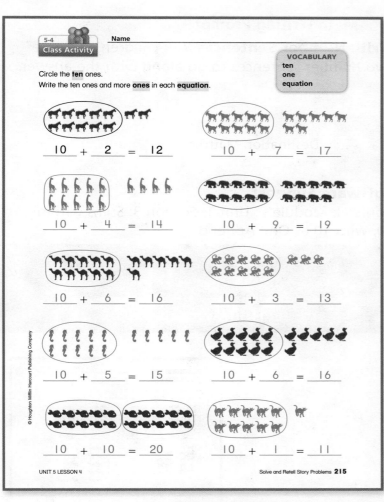
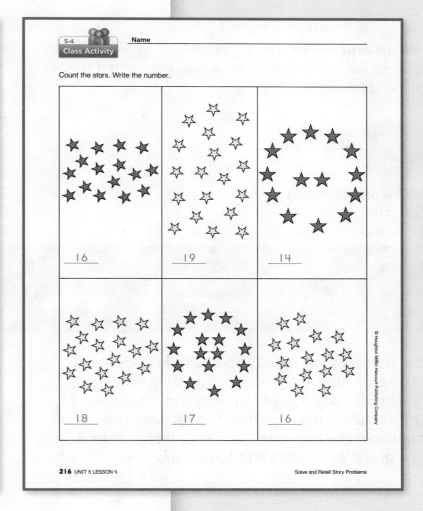

Student Activity Book pages 215–216

✓ Formative Assessment: Check Understanding

Student Summary Ask a child to tell addition and subtraction story problems, solve them with math drawings, and write the corresponding equations.

✓ Fluency Check

See Assessment Guide for Fluency Check 5 on addition/subtraction within 5.

▲ On Level  Tier 1
for students having success

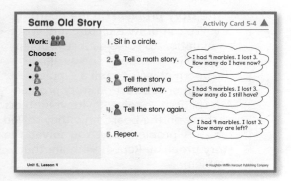

Activity Notes Model the activity for children by telling a story, and then telling the story a different way.

 Math Writing Prompt

Write and Solve Invite children to record all of the stories being told and then solve them when the list is complete.

 MegaMath

Software Support
Country Countdown
Block Busters, Level G

■ Challenge
for students seeking a challenge

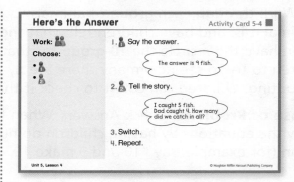

Activity Notes Choose a child to participate in the activity with you. He or she says an answer, and you make up a number story.

 Math Writing Prompt

Write Number Sentences Ask children to create two number sentences to go along with the answer.

 Destination Math®

Software Support
Course I: Module 2: Unit 1: Session 3: Sums within 20, with 10 as One Addend

---

Use Homework pages 91 and 92 to provide children with more practice visualizing teen numbers as a group of ten ones and extra ones. Once children have practiced visualizing, they can begin the back page, drawing teen numbers as a group of 10 ones and some extra ones.

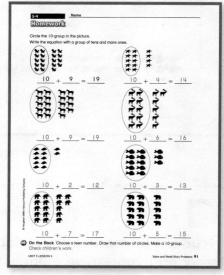

Homework and Remembering page 91

Make Quantities 1–20

LESSON FOCUS

- Show numbers 1–20 as a group of ten ones and more ones.
- Practice partners for numbers 7–9, and find the unknown partner when the total and one partner are known.

VOCABULARY

partner

COMMON CORE

Mathematical Practice
CC.K–12.MP.1, CC.K–12.MP.4, CC.K–12.MP.5
Mathematical Content
CC.K.CC.1, CC.K.CC.3, CC.K.OA.3, CC.K.NBT.1

The Day at a Glance

USE MATH TALK TODAY!

Teaching the Lesson

MATH BACKGROUND for this lesson is included on pp. 461JJ–461KK, 461OO.

ACTIVITY FOCUS

Activity 1 Build numbers 1–20 with 10-sticks and centimeter cubes.

Activity 2 Practice showing partners for 7–9.

MATERIALS

Student Activity Book pp. 217–218 • 1–20 Boards (TRB M36) • Centimeter cubes • 10-sticks • Number Tiles 1–9 • Break-Apart Sticks • +/− Tiles • 120 Poster

iTools: Counters • Whiteboard

Differentiated Instruction

MATERIALS

Activity Cards 5-5 • Dot cubes • Math Journals

Soar to Success Math Intervention • MegaMath • Destination Math®

RtI Tier 1 • Tier 2 • Tier 3

Homework

MATERIALS

Homework and Remembering pp. 93–94

QUICK PRACTICE ⏱ 5 MINUTES

Repeated Quick Practice Use these Quick Practices from previous lessons.

Partner Peek: Tell the Unknown Partner (See Unit 5, Lesson 3.)

Count to 100 by Tens and Tell How Many (See Unit 5, Lesson 3.)

Say Groups of 10 and Decade Numbers (and Reverse) (See Unit 5, Lesson 3.)

DAILY ROUTINES

Counting Tens and Ones (See pp. xxxi–xxxii.)

DIGITAL RESOURCES

Use these digital resources along with your eSAB and eTE to support your students' learning experiences.

 Professional Development

 Whiteboard Lesson

 iTools

 Soar to Success Math Intervention

 MegaMath

Destination Math®

COMMON CORE

Mathematical Practice
CC.K–12.MP.4, CC.K–12.MP.5
Mathematical Content
CC.K.CC.1, CC.K.CC.3,
CC.K.OA.3, CC.K.NBT.1

30 MINUTES

FOCUS Build numbers 1–20 with 10-sticks and centimeter cubes.

MATERIALS Student Activity Book pages 217–218, 1–20 Boards (TRB M36; 1 per pair), centimeter cubes (90 per pair, or use bags of cubes from Unit 4), 10-sticks (12 per pair)

 Whiteboard Lesson

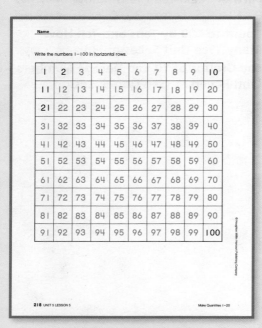

Student Activity Book page 218

ACTIVITY 1

Make Numbers on the 1–20 Board

▶ Build Numbers on the 1–20 Board [PAIRS] MATH TALK

This activity uses **Student Pairs.**

MP.4, MP.5 Use Appropriate Tools/Model with Mathematics Have each Student Pair place the 1–20 Board in front of them. Have children in each Student Pair work together to place centimeter cubes and 10-sticks on the boards to show the numbers 1 through 20.

After they have placed the cubes and 10-sticks on all of the numbers, have children discuss how the numbers change from one to the next.

▶ Write Numbers to 100

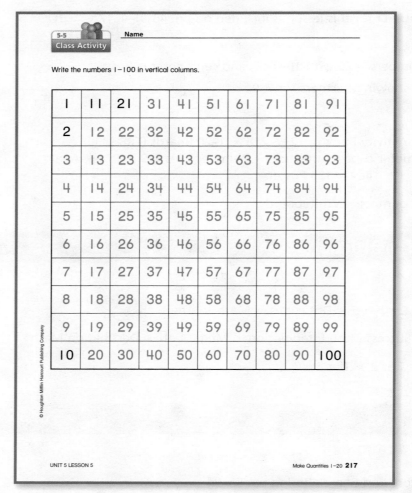

Student Activity Book page 217

Ask children to use Student Activity Book pages 217–218 to write the numbers from 1 to 100. Ask that they try to do so without looking at the 120 Poster, but suggest that they look occasionally to check.

Play *The Unknown Partner Game* for 7, 8, and 9

COMMON CORE

Mathematical Practice
CC.K–12.MP.1

Mathematical Content
CC.K.CC.3, CC.K.OA.3,
CC.K.NBT.1

▶ **Practice Partners with the Finger Wiggle** | WHOLE CLASS |

MP.1 Make Sense of Problems Act It Out Begin by having everyone hold up 8 fingers. Then have children choose partners for 8.

• Wiggle 1 finger. Now wiggle the other 7 fingers.

Continue with different partners for 8. Then do the partners for numbers 9 and 7.

▶ **Play *The Unknown Partner Game* for 7–9** | PAIRS |

Student Pairs sit beside each other facing the work space. On each turn, children take out only the number of centimeter cubes needed. Below is a sample turn for the number 8.

Children pull down Number Tile 8 and place 8 centimeter cubes under the tile. One child takes a Break-Apart Stick, while the other child turns away. The first child places the Break-Apart Stick to make any partners for 8 and then hides the cubes for one partner leaving the Break-Apart Stick and the other cubes in place.

When finished, the first child asks:

• What partner of 8 did I take?

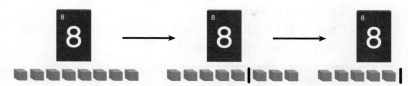

The second child uncovers his or her eyes. Children can count the cubes they see and then count on to 8 with their fingers. The second child puts the appropriate Number Tiles and the +/− Tile in place below the cubes and says, "5 and 3 are partners of 8." The first child replaces the cubes that were taken to confirm the unknown partner.

Second child places Number Tiles to show the partners.

Children then reverse roles and play the game for numbers 7, 8, and 9.

✅ Formative Assessment: Check Understanding

Student Summary Point to a column on the 120 Poster and ask a child to tell which number begins that column. Then ask the child to count the numbers in the column in order.

15 MINUTES

FOCUS Practice showing partners for 7–9.

MATERIALS Number Tiles 1–9 (1 set per pair), centimeter cubes (10 per pair), Break-Apart Sticks (1 per pair), +/− Tiles (1 per pair)

*i*T *i*Tools: Counters

📝 Whiteboard Lesson

English Language Learners

Write *partner* on the board. Say: **Find a friend to be your partner.** Explain that two numbers can also be partners. Write: 10 = 7 + 3. Say: **7 and 3 are partners of 10.**

BEGINNING

Write: 3 + 4 = 7. Say: **3 and 4 are partners of 7.** Have children repeat.

INTERMEDIATE

Write: 3 and 4 are _____ of 7. Say: **Complete the sentence and say it.** partners

ADVANCED

Write: 3 + 4 = 7. Ask: **What are 3 and 4?** 3 and 4 are partners of 7.

Digital Resource

*i***Tools** Choose 'Counters' on the Menu. Use Activity 3 'Add' with the tab for 'Activities.' Children can use counters to help them add two numbers. Then they enter the total.

▲ On Level  Tier 1

for students having success

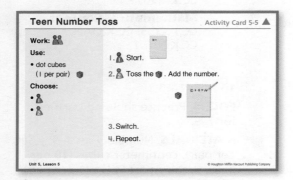

Activity Notes Model the activity for children by starting with 10 and then rolling the dot cube and adding to make a teen number.

✏️ Math Writing Prompt

Roll Again To extend the activity, have children start with another base number and then roll and add the rolled number.

 MegaMath

Software Support
Country Countdown
Counting Critters, Level P

■ Challenge

for students seeking a challenge

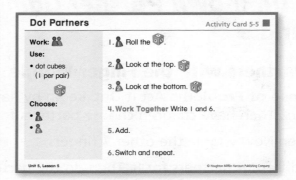

Activity Notes Show children how the opposite sides of the cube are partners for 7.

✏️ Math Writing Prompt

Write Partners Challenge children to write the partners and the total. Then have children switch partners and write the addition equations.

 Destination Math®

Software Support
Course I: Module 2: Unit 1: Session 3: Sums within 20, with 10 as One Addend

---

Children are asked to subtract the numbers on p. 93, then tell whether numbers, equations, and groups are equal or unequal. On p. 94, remind children that they will be writing numbers 1 through 100.

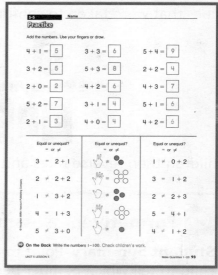

Homework and Remembering page 93

More Solve and Retell Story Problems

LESSON FOCUS

- Tell, retell, and write equations for addition and subtraction stories.
- Visualize teen numbers as ten ones and extra ones.

VOCABULARY

total
ten
teen number
equation

COMMON CORE

Mathematical Practice
CC.K–12.MP.3, CC.K–12.MP.4, CC.K–12.MP.5,
CC.K–12.MP.6, CC.K–12.MP.7
Mathematical Content
CC.K.OA.1, CC.K.OA.2, CC.K.OA.3,
CC.K.OA.4, CC.K.NBT.1

The Day at a Glance

Teaching the Lesson

USE MATH TALK TODAY!

MATH BACKGROUND for this lesson is included on pp. 461GG–461KK.

ACTIVITY FOCUS

Activity 1   Tell, retell, and write equations for addition and subtraction stories.

Activity 2   Show 10-partners with Number Tiles.

Activity 3   Visualize a group of ten ones in a teen number.

MATERIALS

- Student Activity Book pp. 219–224 • Counters • Number Tiles 1–10 • +/– Tiles • Night Sky display • Hiding Zero Gameboard • Giant Number Cards
- iTools: Counters • Whiteboard

Differentiated Instruction

MATERIALS

- Activity Cards 5-6 • Centimeter cubes • Math Journals
- Soar to Success Math Intervention • MegaMath • Destination Math®
- RtI   Tier 1 • Tier 2 • Tier 3

Home and School Activity

MATERIALS

- Technology Connection p. 490

QUICK PRACTICE   5 MINUTES

Use these Quick Practices from previous lessons.

Partner Peek: Tell the Unknown Partner (See Unit 5, Lesson 3.)

Count to 100 by Tens and Tell How Many (See Unit 5, Lesson 3.)

Say Groups of 10 and Decade Numbers (and Reverse) (See Unit 5, Lesson 3.)

DAILY ROUTINES

Counting Tens and Ones
(See pp. xxxi–xxxii.)

DIGITAL RESOURCES

Use these digital resources along with your eSAB and eTE to support your students' learning experiences.

 Professional Development

 Whiteboard Lesson

 iTools

 Soar to Success Math Intervention

 MegaMath

 Destination Math®

COMMON CORE

Mathematical Practice
CC.K–12.MP.4
Mathematical Content
CC.K.OA.2

30 MINUTES

FOCUS Tell, retell, and write equations for addition and subtraction stories.

 *i*Tools: Counters

Whiteboard Lesson

Digital Resource

*i***Tools** Choose 'Counters' on the Menu. Use Activity 3 'Add' with the tab for 'Activities.' Children can use counters to help them add two numbers. Then they enter the total.

Use Activity 4 'Subtract' with the tab for 'Activities.' Children can use counters to help them subtract. Then they enter the partner.

Teaching Note

Stories to Solve You may wish to help children analyze the simple addition and subtraction stories by asking them to retell the same story in a different way. This type of strategy helps build children's mathematical thinking skills. Guide them to see that addends can be used in a different order with the same results.

ACTIVITY 1 ABC Language Art Connection

Tell, Retell, and Solve Story Problems

▶ Talk About Story Problems WHOLE CLASS   MATH TALK

MP.4 Model with Mathematics Write an Equation This activity uses Step-by-Step at the Board.

Have children tell addition or subtraction story problems, solve them with math drawings, and write the corresponding equations. As many children as possible should work at the board while the other children work on paper. Select two children to explain their drawings and equations for their stories. The other children can ask questions.

As in Lessons 1 and 4 of this unit, have children retell each story using different words that mean the same thing. Focus children on asking the same question in different ways.

Addition

- I see 7 cows and 1 dog.
- How many animals do I see?
- How many animals are there?
- There is a *total* of how many animals?
- If we *put them together,* how many animals are there?

Subtraction

- There were 9 sheep in the field, but 4 of them went into the barn.
- How many sheep are *left* in the field?
- How many sheep are in the field *now*?
- How many sheep are *still* in the field?

You will do this activity three more times in this unit. By the end of the unit, all children should have had multiple turns at the board, retelling someone else's story and telling their own story. Concentrate on the greater numbers with totals up to 10. Modify the numbers in children's stories as necessary to include these more difficult numbers (for example, $5 + 4$, $9 - 7$, $10 - 4$).

Play *The Partners Game*

▶ Use Objects PAIRS

MP.6 Attend to Precision Children play *The 10-Partners Game* in **Student Pairs** with 10 counters. They place the counters in two rows of 5 or in towers of 5 (in a 5-group pattern). One child closes and covers his or her eyes. The other child takes some of the counters and hides them. Then he or she says the following rhyme, stating how many of the counters are left. Have both children record the equation, $10 = 6 + 4$, on a sheet of paper.

• Oink, oink, 6 pigs in the pen. Tell me, what's the partner of ten?

The first child looks and says the number he or she sees, and then finishes the rhyme.

• I see 6 pigs in the pen. 6 and 4 are partners of ten.

The rhyme lets children pretend that the counters are pigs in a pen. If you wish, you or your class can choose another animal with a one-syllable name. This way, you can continue the animal theme from Unit 1 and provide opportunities for children to use their imagination.

Be sure to have children arrange their 10 counters in two rows or towers of 5 so that they can see the 10-partners.

▶ Use Number Tiles PAIRS

Children play in pairs, using two sets of Number Tiles and the +/− Tile. Children turn all of

the Number Tiles in one set face down and all of the tiles in the other set face up in order.

MP.7 Use Structure One child turns over a face down tile, and the other child must tell the 10-partner for that number. Children may check the answers by looking on the Night Sky display or by using their fingers. When the children agree that the partner is correct, the second child uses the face up Number Tiles and the +/− Tile to show the partners (for example, $8 + 2$).

All Number Tiles are returned to their respective places. Then the second child turns over one of the face down tiles, and the first child says the 10-partner and shows both partners using the face up Number Tiles.

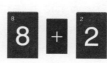

> COMMON CORE
>
> **Mathematical Practice**
> CC.K–12.MP.6, CC.K–12.MP.7
> **Mathematical Content**
> CC.K.OA.1, CC.K.OA.3,
> CC.K.OA.4

15 MINUTES

FOCUS Show 10-partners with Number Tiles.

MATERIALS Counters (10 per pair), Number Tiles 1–9 (2 sets per pair), +/− Tiles (1 per pair), Night Sky display

 Whiteboard Lesson

English Language Learners

Write *total* on the board. Say: **We put groups together to find the total.** Have 2 children stand on one side of you and 4 children stand on the other side. Bring the children together in one group.

BEGINNING

Have children count the total number of children. 6 Say: **The total is 6.** Have children repeat.

INTERMEDIATE

Have children count the total number of children. 6 **What is 6?** the total

ADVANCED

Ask: **How can we find the total number of children?** We find the total by counting the children when you put the groups together. **What is the total?** 6

Differentiated Instruction

Extra Help In this initial lesson, have children begin by playing the more concrete version of *The 10-Partners Game* with objects. When they are ready, they can move on to the more abstract version of the game with Number Tiles. This activity will be repeated in Unit 5, Lessons 8 and 11.

COMMON CORE

Mathematical Practice
CC.K–12.MP.3, CC.K–12.MP.5,
CC.K–12.MP.6, CC.K–12.MP.7

Mathematical Content
CC.K.NBT.1

10 MINUTES

FOCUS Visualize a group of ten ones in a teen number.

MATERIALS Hiding Zero Gameboard (Student Activity Book pages 219–224; 1 per pair), Number Tiles 1–10 (1 set per pair), Giant Number Cards; Puzzled Penguin Puppet (TRB M95)

 Whiteboard Lesson

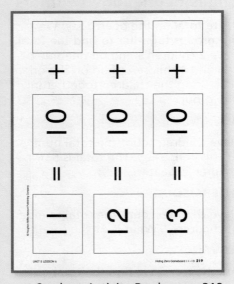

Student Activity Book page 219

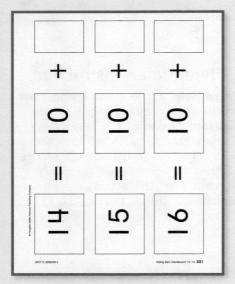

Student Activity Book page 221

ACTIVITY 3

The Hiding Zero Game

▶ **Set Up the Game** PAIRS

Tell children that the goal of *The Hiding Zero Game* is to see the group of ten in teen numbers.

MP.5 Use Appropriate Tools Hand out copies of the three Hiding Zero Gameboard pages. Have **Student Pairs** arrange their three pages in order, vertically or horizontally. Then have them work together to put a Number Tile on top of the 0 in each 10 (for example, $14 = 14 +$ blank rectangle).

Hiding Zero Gameboard (Student Activity Book pages 219–224)

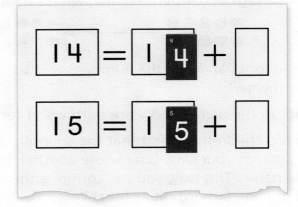

▶ **Play the Game** PAIRS MATH TALK

This activity uses **Whole Class Practice and Student Leaders.**

A **Student Leader** calls out a teen number (for example, 18) and one child in each **Student Pair** picks up Number Tile 8, which is covering the 0 in the 10, and puts it in the blank rectangle. Then both children read the equation together.

• 18 equals 10 plus 8.

The Student Leader continues calling out different numbers until all of the zeroes have been uncovered on children's gameboards. The Student Leader can hold up Giant Number Cards (10 plus a single-digit number) for each number as it is called. Student Pairs take turns removing the numbers covering the zeroes.

MP.7 Look for Structure You can have children play this game again if there is time. Both the visual and auditory components are important for this activity. Discuss any repeated changes that the children notice.

• What changes do you see from one number to the next? Each teen number is made by replacing the zero in ten with a number that tells how many extra ones there are.

▶ **What's the Error?** WHOLE CLASS

MP.3, MP.6 Construct Viable Arguments/Critique the Reasoning of Others Puzzled Penguin Use the Puzzled Penguin Puppet to begin this activity. Explain that Puzzled Penguin placed a Number Tile on top of the zero in each 10 on the Hiding Zero Gameboard. Then Puzzled Penguin was asked to read an equation as a **Student Leader** called out 15. Write the following gameboards on the board.

$$15 = 1\;5 + \boxed{}$$

$$15 = 10 + 5$$

Point to the first equation.

• Puzzled Penguin placed a 5 on top of the 0.

Point to the second equation.

• Puzzled Penguin moved the 5.

• Puzzled Penguin said that the equation is 15 plus 10 equals 5. Is Puzzled Penguin correct? Why? No. Puzzled Penguin read the equation wrong.

• How should Puzzled Penguin read the equation? 15 equals 10 plus 5

✓ **Formative Assessment: Check Understanding**

Student Summary Ask a child to name a teen number and to say it as ten ones and some extra ones. Encourage the child to state an equation for the teen number.

MATH TALK *in ACTION*   **How can you make sure that you read an equation correctly?**

Jay: We can use our arms to act out the symbols.

Evie: Yes, the equal sign is when both arms are out.

Troy: The plus sign is when one arm is up and the other is across.

Billy: The plus sign shows the numbers put together.

Jay: We can also look at the partners.

Evie: The partners come after the teen number on the Hiding Zero Gameboard.

Billy: If we do this, we can read the equation correctly.

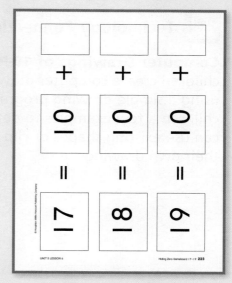

Student Activity Book page 223

▲ On Level    Tier 1
for students having success

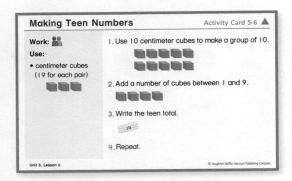

Activity Notes Encourage children to model all of the teen numbers, 11 through 19.

✏️ Math Writing Prompt

Write and Solve Have children record 10-partners for numbers 11 through 19.

 MegaMath

Software Support
Country Countdown
Block Busters, Level G

■ Challenge
for students seeking a challenge

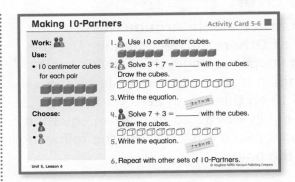

Activity Notes Children may wish to place a stick between the partners of 10.

✏️ Math Writing Prompt

Partners of 10 Have children write the partners of 10 that they know. Encourage them to use a strategy to help.

 Destination Math®

Software Support
Course I: Module 2: Unit 1: Session 3: Sums within 20, with 10 as One Addend

---

Technology Connection

Computer Drawings of 10-Partners Have children create computer drawings of 10-partners using a simple drawing program. If you wish, show children a few examples to get them started. They can use existing shapes or clip art, or they can create their own drawings.

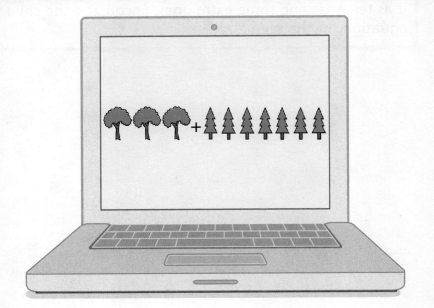

Numbers 1–20

LESSON FOCUS
- Show numbers 1–20; show the teen numbers as a group of ten ones and further ones.
- Find the unknown partner when the total and one partner are known.

VOCABULARY
partner
teen number

COMMON CORE

Mathematical Practice
CC.K–12.MP.2, CC.K–12.MP.4, CC.K–12.MP.6, CC.K–12.MP.7
Mathematical Content
CC.K.CC.3, CC.K.CC.4, CC.K.CC.4c, CC.K.CC.5, CC.K.OA.1, CC.K.OA.2, CC.K.OA.3, CC.K.OA.5, CC.K.NBT.1

The Day at a Glance

Teaching the Lesson

USE MATH TALK TODAY!

MATH BACKGROUND for this lesson is included on pp. 461JJ–461KK, 461OO.

ACTIVITY FOCUS
Activity 1   Make numbers 1–20 using 10-sticks and Centimeter Cubes.
Activity 2   Practice finding partners for 7, 8, and 9.
Activity 3   Identify and write the partners for 5.

MATERIALS
- Student Activity Book pp. 225–226 • Fluency Check 6 (Assessment Guide) • 1–20 Boards • 10-sticks • Centimeter Cubes • Number Tiles 1–9 • Break-Apart Sticks • +/– Tiles

- *i*Tools: Counters • Whiteboard

Differentiated Instruction

MATERIALS
- Activity Cards 5-7 • Centimeter Cubes • Break-Apart Sticks • Crayons • Math Journals

- Soar to Success Math Intervention • MegaMath • Destination Math®

- **RtI** Tier 1 • Tier 2 • Tier 3

Homework

MATERIALS
- Homework and Remembering pp. 95–96

QUICK PRACTICE   5 MINUTES

Repeated Quick Practice Use these Quick Practices from previous lessons.

Count to 100 by Tens and Tell How Many (See Unit 5, Lesson 3.)

Say Groups of 10 and Decade Numbers (and reverse) (See Unit 5, Lesson 3.)

Partner Peek: Tell the Unknown Partner (See Unit 5, Lesson 3.)

DAILY ROUTINES
Counting Tens and Ones
(See pp. xxxi–xxxii.)

DIGITAL RESOURCES

Use these digital resources along with your eSAB and eTE to support your students' learning experiences.

Professional Development

Whiteboard Lesson

*i*Tools

Soar to Success Math Intervention

MegaMath

Destination Math®

COMMON CORE

Mathematical Practice
CC.K–12.MP.7
Mathematical Content
CC.K.CC.4, CC.K.CC.4c, CC.K.CC.5,
CC.K.NBT.1

20 MINUTES

FOCUS Make numbers 1–20 using 10-sticks and Centimeter Cubes.

MATERIALS 1–20 Boards (TRB M36; 1 per pair), 10-sticks (12 per pair), Centimeter Cubes (90 per pair)

Whiteboard Lesson

*i*T *i*Tools: Counters

Digital Resource

*i*Tools Choose 'Counters' on the Menu. Use Activity 1 'Count' with the tab for 'Activities'. Children can use counters to count.

Teaching Note

Research This activity develops fine-motor skills and organization, as well as an understanding of numbers. See Unit 5, Lesson 5, for more information.

ACTIVITY 1

Make Numbers on the 1–20 Board

▶ **Make Numbers from 1 Through 20** PAIRS

This activity uses **Student Pairs.**

Pair children so that those who have mastered teen concepts are working with children who need additional support. Encourage discussion as children work together. The children who received help with teen concepts in Lesson 5 can work on the 11–20 side of the board this time, and the more advanced children can work on the 1–10 side. (See "Helping Community" note on page 494.)

Begin by asking each Student Pair to place the two boards beside each other. Then they work together to place the 10-sticks and Centimeter Cubes on the boards to show the numbers 1 through 20.

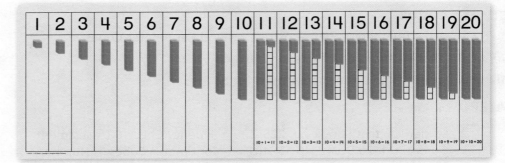

MP.7 Use Repeated Reasoning Generalize Ask children to describe what they see when they have placed the 10-sticks and cubes on all of the numbers. There are many observations they can make. Encourage discussion.

• How is each number different from the number before it? Each number is one greater (has one more cube) as you move right on the board.

• What do you notice about the teen numbers, 11 to 19? They all have one 10-stick. The 10-stick comes first in each number. The number of 10-sticks is the same as the first number in the teen numbers and in 20.

The Unknown Partner Game for 7, 8, and 9

▶ Feel the Partners on Your Fingers WHOLE CLASS

First, review partners for 7, 8, and 9 by doing finger wiggles. For each pair of partners, do the finger wiggle at least four times. Children may find some combinations of finger wiggles (such as 1 and 7) are difficult to do, but reassure children that it will get easier each time they do it.

MP.4 Model with Mathematics Start with the number 8. Have everyone hold up 8 fingers. Then, say partners for 8 (1 and 7), and ask a **Student Leader** to write the expression 1 + 7 on the board. Say and show the partners with your fingers.

• Wiggle (or bend) 1 finger. Now wiggle the other 7 fingers.

Some children may find it easier to bend their fingers than to wiggle them. You may have them bend fingers to show the first partner. But encourage them to wiggle fingers for the second partner. This helps them feel that 1 and 7 come from the 8 and together use all of the 8.

Have children wiggle 1 and 7 at least three more times. Provide encouragement.

• Let's really feel these partners. Wiggle 1, now wiggle 7. Oh, we're getting better. Wiggle 1 again, now wiggle 7. Look, it is easier! Let's do it again. Wiggle 1, and then wiggle 7.

MP.7 Look for Structure Identify Relationships Ask for different partners of 8. Wiggle fingers for each set of partners at least four times. You can extend the activity by switching the partners (for example, 7 and 1), if you wish.

Repeat the above activities, finding wiggling partners for 9 and 7.

▶ Set up *The Unknown Partner Game* PAIRS   MATH TALK

Use the **Student Pairs** structure for this activity.

The *Unknown Partner Game* was first played in Unit 3, Lesson 16, and was repeated several times in Unit 4 and then again in Unit 5, Lesson 5. Ask each child in a Student Pair to sit beside one another and face their work space. Instruct them to set up the Number Tiles in order in a horizontal row.

Activity continued ▶

COMMON CORE

Mathematical Practice
CC.K–12.MP.2, CC.K–12.MP.4, CC.K–12.MP.7

Mathematical Content
CC.K.OA.1, CC.K.OA.2, CC.K.OA.3

25 MINUTES

FOCUS Practice finding partners for 7, 8, and 9.

MATERIALS Number Tiles 1–9 (1 set per pair), centimeter cubes (9 per pair), Break-Apart Sticks (1 per pair), +/– Tiles (1 per pair)

 Whiteboard Lesson

English Language Learners

Point to 1 to 9 on a 1–20 Board. Ask: **Do these numbers have 10 in them?** no

BEGINNING

Point to 11 and 12. Say: **These numbers have 10 in them. They are** *teen numbers*. Have children repeat.

INTERMEDIATE

Ask: **Are they** *teen numbers*? no **Do 11 to 19 have 10 in them?** yes **Are they** *teen numbers*? yes

ADVANCED

Point to 11 to 19. Ask: **Do these numbers have 10 in them?** yes **What do we call them?** teen numbers

Teaching Note

Research Kindergarten children can find all the partners for numbers up to 10. By doing the kinesthetic activities in this lesson, children get experience feeling these partners. They can begin to feel the numbers inside of numbers.

Learning Community— Best Practices

Helping Community When children played *The Unknown Partner Game* in Unit 5, Lesson 5, you may have noticed that some children had difficulty figuring out the unknown partner. Pair children who need extra help with children who more firmly understand the concept. **Student Pairs** often foster learning by both children as the helper strives to adopt the perspective of the struggling learner. Helping another child almost always enables the helper to understand a concept more deeply.

It is important to take some class time to discuss what good helping is all about. Children may come up with a list that can be posted in the classroom. It is important that they understand that good helping does not mean telling answers. It means that you take other children through steps so that they come up with the answer themselves.

▶ Play *The Unknown Partner Game* PAIRS

Tell children they will start playing *The Unknown Partner Game* by finding partners for the number 8. Ask pairs to pull down Number Tile 8 and to line up eight centimeter cubes below the tile, with a space between each cube.

Explain that the first child in each **Student Pair** takes a Break-Apart Stick, while the second child closes his or her eyes, covers them, and turns away. The first child places a Break-Apart Stick to indicate any set of partners for 8 and removes the centimeter cubes for one of the 8-partners, leaving the Break-Apart Stick and the other cubes in place.

In the example below, you see the setup for 8 with the Number Tile above the 8 centimeter cubes, and then you see what it looks like after the first child has placed a Break-Apart Stick between the partners 5 and 3. Finally, you see how the materials look after the first child has removed the 3 cubes to the right of the stick. When finished, the first child asks the second child to identify the unknown partner.

• What partner of 8 did I take?

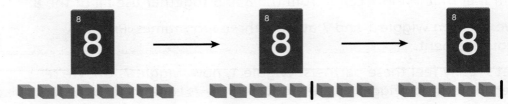

MP.2 Reason Abstractly The second child uncovers his or her eyes and looks at the cubes to find the partner that has been taken away. The child can use a variety of strategies to determine the unknown number. These include counting the cubes that are visible, counting on to 8 with the fingers, or visualizing 8 cubes and mentally "seeing" how many are missing.

The second child then arranges the Number Tiles of the two partners and the +/− Tile below the cubes. The Student Pair read the expression together, thus completing one turn.

Children then reverse roles and play the game for the numbers 7, 8, and 9 in any order. They can continue to play as time allows.

COMMON CORE

Mathematical Practice
CC.K–12.MP.6

Mathematical Content
CC.K.CC.3, CC.K.OA.1,
CC.K.OA.2, CC.K.OA.3,
CC.K.OA.5

15 MINUTES

FOCUS Identify and write the partners for 5.

MATERIALS Student Activity Book pages 225–226

 Whiteboard Lesson

ACTIVITY 3

Write 5-Partners

▶ **Identify Partners for 5** [WHOLE CLASS]

MP.6 Attend to Precision Hand out Student Activity Book pages 225 and 226. Below each set, have children write the partners for 5. Discuss the similarities and differences that children may see in the problems.

• What number does each row start with? 1
• What number does each row end with? 1
• All the pictures in the second column show what partners of 5? 2 + 3
• Where are the partners of 5 that begin with 3? the third column

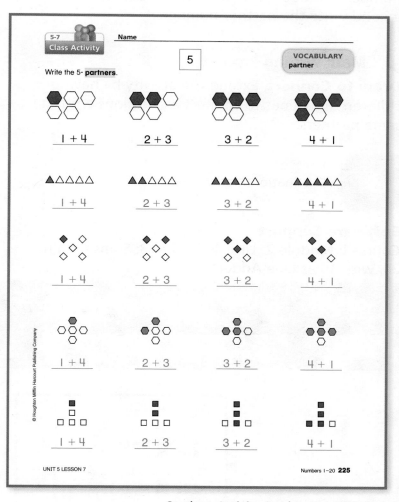

Student Activity Book pages 225–226

✅ **Formative Assessment: Check Understanding**

Student Summary Write the numbers 15–18 in a row on the board; include space between each number. Sketch a 10-stick below each number. Ask a child to finish drawing the single squares to show each number.

✓ **Fluency Check**

See Assessment Guide for Fluency Check 6 on addition/subtraction within 5.

▲ On Level · RtI · Tier 1

for students having success

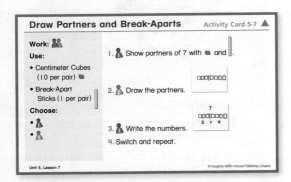

Activity Notes Model how children will use the cubes and sticks to show partners for numbers, and then draw the partners and write the numbers.

✏ Math Writing Prompt

Draw Partners Have children draw different pairs of partners for the same number and write the expressions for each.

 MegaMath

Software Support
Country Countdown
Counting Critters, Level P

■ Challenge

for students seeking a challenge

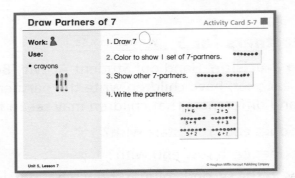

Activity Notes Demonstrate the activity using the number 5. Model how to draw the circles, color them in, and write the partner numbers.

✏ Math Writing Prompt

Draw to Connect Extend the activity by having children draw lines to connect expressions with the same partners.

 Destination Math®

Software Support
Course I: Module 2: Unit 1: Session 3: Sums within 20, with 10 as One Addend

Use the Homework activity on page 95 to provide children with more practice deconstructing teen numbers. Note that if the top row has 10 animals, some children may circle that row of 10 rather than the group of 10 on the left; this is correct but not preferred. After children have completed Homework and Remembering page 96, collect and save it. You may wish to return it to children during Lesson 11. It will provide an example of the kinds of pictures they will be making for the Unit 5 Teen Number Book.

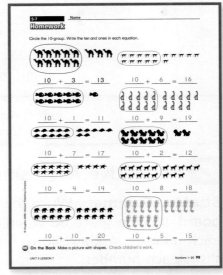

Homework and Remembering page 95

Review Partners

LESSON FOCUS
- Find all the partners of 2, 3, 4, 5, 6, and 10.
- View teen numbers as ten ones and extra ones, and practice finding 10-partners.

VOCABULARY
Tiny Tumblers
Math Mountain
known partner
unknown partner

COMMON CORE
Mathematical Practice
CC.K–12.MP.3, CC.K–12.MP.6, CC.K–12.MP.7
Mathematical Content
CC.K.CC.3, CC.K.OA.1, CC.K.OA.3, CC.K.OA.4

The Day at a Glance

Teaching the Lesson

USE MATH TALK TODAY!

MATH BACKGROUND for this lesson is included on pp. 461JJ–461KK, 461MM–461NN

ACTIVITY FOCUS

Activity 1 Find partners of the numbers 2 through 10 on Math Mountains.

Activity 2 Show 10-partners with counters and Number Tiles.

MATERIALS

📖 Student Activity Book pp. 227–228 • Counters • Number Tiles 1–10 • +/− Tiles • Night Sky display

🖥 iTools: Counters • Whiteboard

Differentiated Instruction

MATERIALS

📖 Activity Cards 5-8 • Counters • Number cubes • Math Journals

🖥 Soar to Success Math Intervention • MegaMath • Destination Math®

🔺 **RtI** Tier 1 • Tier 2 • Tier 3

Homework

MATERIALS

📖 Homework and Remembering pp. 97–98

QUICK PRACTICE ⏱ **5 MINUTES**

Repeated Quick Practice Use these Quick Practices from previous lessons.

Say Groups of 10 and Decade Numbers (and Reverse) (See Unit 5, Lesson 3.)

Partner Peek: Tell the Unknown Partner (See Unit 5, Lesson 3.)

Count to 100 by Tens and Tell How Many (See Unit 5, Lesson 3.)

DAILY ROUTINES

Counting Tens and Ones
(See pp. xxxi–xxxii.)

DIGITAL RESOURCES

Use these digital resources along with your eSAB and eTE to support your students' learning experiences.

Professional Development

Whiteboard Lesson

iTools

Soar to Success Math Intervention

MegaMath

Destination Math®

COMMON CORE

Mathematical Practice
CC.CC.K–12.MP.3

Mathematical Content
CC.K.CC.3, CC.K.OA.1, CC.K.OA.3, CC.K.OA.4

20 MINUTES

FOCUS Find partners of the numbers 2 through 10 on Math Mountains

MATERIALS Student Activity Book page 227

 *i*Tools: Counters

Whiteboard Lesson

Digital Resource

*i***Tools** Choose 'Counters' on the Menu. Use Activity 3 'Add' with the tab for 'Activities'. Children can use counters to help them add 2 numbers. Then they enter the total.

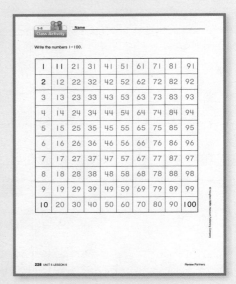

Student Activity Book page 228

ACTIVITY 1

Tiny Tumbler Partners

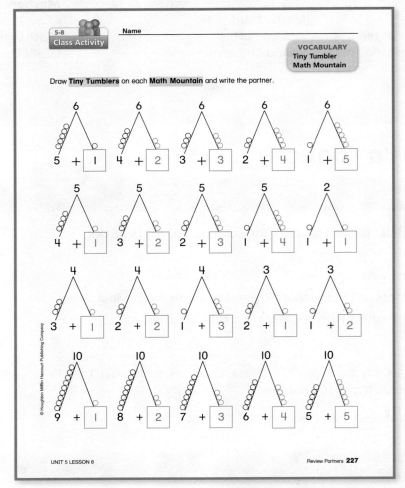

Student Activity Book page 227

▶ **Recall Tiny Tumblers**   WHOLE CLASS

Hand out Student Activity Book page 227. The drawings on the page show Tiny Tumblers playing on one side of each Math Mountain. The children will find the partner of the number shown on the left, write it in the answer box, and draw that many Tiny Tumblers on the right.

MATH TALK **MP.3 Construct a Viable Argument** Elicit strategies for how children will find the 6-partners on the mountains.

• What do you remember about the Tiny Tumblers from earlier lessons? Tiny Tumblers live on mountain tops. They tumble down one side of the Math Mountain.

• What are some ways you can figure out the unknown partner? Start with the known partner and count on to 6 while drawing circles on the right.

Ask children to complete the rest of the page independently. Then have children practice writing numbers 1 through 100 on page 228.

Play *The 10-Partners Game*

▶ Use Objects `PAIRS`

MP.6 Attend to Precision As in Unit 5, Lesson 6, children begin playing *The 10-Partners Game* in **Student Pairs** with 10 counters. They place the counters in two rows of 5 or in towers of 5 (in a 5-group pattern). One child closes and covers his or her eyes. The other child takes some of the counters and hides them. Then he or she says the rhyme below, stating how many of the counters are left. Then have both children record the equation, $10 = 6 + 4$, on a sheet of paper.

• Baa, baa, 6 sheep in the pen. Tell me, what's the partner of ten?

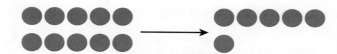

The first child looks and says the number he or she sees, before saying the end of the rhyme.

• I see 6 sheep in the pen. 6 and 4 are partners of ten.

The rhyme lets children pretend that the counters are sheep in a pen. If you wish, you or your class can choose another animal with a one-syllable name. This way, you can continue the animal theme from Unit 1 and provide opportunities for children to use their imagination.

Be sure to have children arrange their 10 counters in two rows or towers of 5 so they can see the 5-group.

▶ Use Number Tiles `PAIRS`

Then have **Student Pairs** play again, using two sets of Number Tiles and the +/− Tile. Children turn all of the tiles in one set face down and turn all of the tiles in the other set face up in order (either in two rows of five or in one long row).

MP.7 Use Structure One child turns over a face down tile, and the other child must tell the 10-partner of that number. Children may check the answers by looking on the Night Sky display or by using their fingers. When the children agree that the partner is correct, the second child uses the face up Number Tiles and the +/− Tile to show the partners (for example, $8 + 2$).

All tiles are returned to their respective places. Then the second child turns up one of the face down tiles, and the first child says the 10-partner and shows both partners using the face up Number Tiles.

✓ Formative Assessment: Check Understanding

Student Summary Show a Math Mountain for 10 on the board. Write 5 on one side of the Math Mountain. Ask a child to draw Tiny Tumblers on the Math Mountain and write the partner.

COMMON CORE

Mathematical Practice
CC.K–12.MP.6, CC.K–12.MP.7
Mathematical Content
CC.K.OA.1, CC.K.OA.3,
CC.K.OA.4

15 MINUTES

FOCUS Show 10-partners with counters and Number Tiles.

MATERIALS Counters (10 per pair), Number Tiles 1–9 (2 sets per pair), +/− Tiles (1 per pair), Night Sky display

◩ Whiteboard Lesson

English Language Learners

Write *known partner* and *unknown partner* on the board. Circle *un-*. Say: *Un-* **means "not." When a partner is unknown, we do not know it.** Write $4 = 3 + \square$. Invite a volunteer to point to the known partner. Say: **The known partner is 3.** Ask children to repeat. Ask: **Where is the unknown partner?** Prompt children to point to the box and say: **The unknown partner is here.**

Learning Community— Best Practices

Student Leaders When children are waiting in line or transitioning to and from the classroom, have them practice 10-partners. A **Student Leader** can stand at the head of the line. As each student passes by, the Student Leader will say a different partner of 10 and the passerby must say the other partner.

Student Leader: 5

Sophie: 5

Student Leader: 7

Marta: 3

▲ On Level    RtI   Tier 1
for students having success

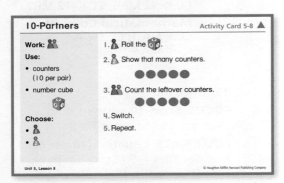

Activity Notes Model rolling the number cube and counting out that number of counters from a set of 10 to show subtraction.

 Math Writing Prompt

Subtraction Equations Encourage children to write an equation to show each subtraction, such as $10 - 5 = 5$.

 MegaMath

Software Support
Country Countdown
Counting Critters, Level G

■ Challenge
for students seeking a challenge

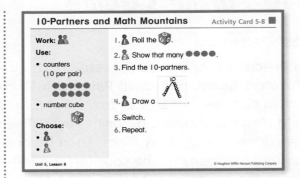

Activity Notes Model how to make a Math Mountain drawing with Tiny Tumblers on one side and the total on top.

 Math Writing Prompt

Math Mountain Numbers Ask children to write the partner equation for each Math Mountain they create.

 Destination Math®

Software Support
Course I: Module 2: Unit 1: Session 1: Combining and Joining within 10

Distribute Homework and Remembering pages 97 and 98. These pages provide children with practice using Tiny Tumblers and writing numbers through 100.

✓ Include students' completed homework page as part of their portfolios.

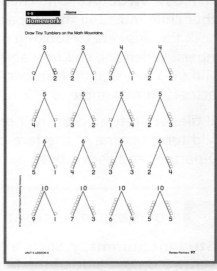

Homework and Remembering page 97

Partners of 6, 7, 8, and 9

LESSON FOCUS

- Visualize teen numbers in sequence as ten ones and extra ones and find the unknown partner when the total and one partner are known.
- Identify partners of the numbers 6 through 9.

VOCABULARY

partner

COMMON CORE

Mathematical Practice
CC.CC.K–12.MP.4, CC.K–12.MP.6, CC.K–12.MP.7
Mathematical Content
CC.K.OA.3, CC.K.OA.4, CC.K.NBT.1

The Day at a Glance

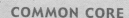

Teaching the Lesson

MATH BACKGROUND for this lesson is included on pp. 461JJ–461KK.

ACTIVITY FOCUS

Activity 1   Use 10-sticks and centimeter cubes to build the numbers 1–20 in sequence.

Activity 2   Practice finding partners of 7, 8, and 9.

Activity 3   Identify the 6-partners, and write the corresponding numbers.

MATERIALS

- Student Activity Book pp. 229–230 • 1–20 Boards • 10-sticks • Centimeter Cubes • Number Tiles 1–10 • Break-Apart Sticks • +/– Tiles

- iTools: Counters • Whiteboard

Differentiated Instruction

MATERIALS

- Activity Cards 5-9 • Centimeter Cubes • Break-Apart Sticks • Number Tiles • Crayons • Math Journals

- Soar to Success Math Intervention • MegaMath • Destination Math®

- **RtI** Tier 1 • Tier 2 • Tier 3

Homework

MATERIALS

- Homework and Remembering pp. 99–100

QUICK PRACTICE   5 MINUTES

Repeated Quick Practice Use these Quick Practices from previous lessons.

Partner Peek: Tell the Unknown Partner (See Unit 5, Lesson 3.)

Count to 100 by Tens and Tell How Many (See Unit 5, Lesson 3.)

Say Groups of 10 and Decade Numbers (and reverse) (See Unit 5, Lesson 3.)

DAILY ROUTINES

Counting Tens and Ones
(See pp. xxxi–xxxii.)

DIGITAL RESOURCES

Use these digital resources along with your eSAB and eTE to support your students' learning experiences.

Professional Development

Whiteboard Lesson

iTools

Soar to Success Math Intervention

MegaMath

Destination Math®

COMMON CORE
Mathematical Practice
CC.K–12.MP.6
Mathematical Content
CC.K.OA.3, CC.K.OA.4, CC.K.NBT.1

20 MINUTES

FOCUS Use 10-sticks and centimeter cubes to build the numbers 1–20 in sequence.

MATERIALS 1–20 Board (TRB M36; 1 per pair), 10-sticks (12 per pair), centimeter cubes (90 per pair)

 iTools: Counters

Whiteboard Lesson

Digital Resource

iTools Choose 'Counters' on the Menu. Use Activity 4 'Subtract' with the tab for 'Activities'. Children can use counters to help them subtract. Then they enter the partner.

Teaching Note

Math Background This activity develops fine-motor skills and organization, as well as an understanding of numbers.

Learning Community— Best Practices

Helping Community By pairing more advanced children with children who need support, the activity encourages children to help each other and to talk about their work. Continued discussion about how to help (for example, by not just doing it for someone, or by helping them do it their way) can lead to improved helping in all **Student Pair** situations.

ACTIVITY 1

Make Numbers on the 1–20 Board

▶ Make Numbers from 1 Through 20 [PAIRS]

This activity uses **Student Pairs.**

As in Unit 5, Lessons 3, 5, and 7, pair children so that those who have mastered teen concepts are working with children who need additional support. Have them work together to encourage discussion. Make sure that children who haven't yet worked on the 11–20 side of the board will be working on that side today.

Begin by asking each Student Pair to place the two boards beside each other. Then they will work together to place the 10-sticks and centimeter cubes on the boards to show the numbers 1 through 20.

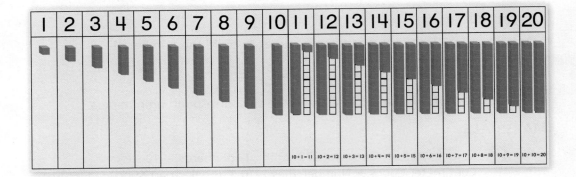

MP.6 Attend to Precision Have children discuss the changes in the numbers they see when they have placed the 10-sticks and centimeter cubes on all of the numbers. Encourage discussion.

• **What changes in the numbers can you find?** Possible responses: The numbers get one greater as we count up; the numbers get one less as we count down; all the numbers from 10 to 19 have one 10-stick; 20 has two 10-sticks.

The Unknown Partner Game
for 7, 8, and 9

▶ **Feel the Partners on Your Fingers** [WHOLE CLASS]

First review partners by doing finger wiggles. For each number—7, 8, and 9—do the finger wiggle at least four times.

Start with the number 8. Have everyone hold up 8 fingers. Then say one set of partners for 8 (for example, 1 and 7). Say and show the partners with your fingers.

• Wiggle 1 finger. Now wiggle the other 7 fingers.

Some children may still be having trouble wiggling fingers to show partners. They may find it easier to bend their fingers than to wiggle them. You may have them bend fingers to show the first partner. But encourage them to wiggle fingers for the second partner. This helps them feel that 1 and 7 come from the 8 and together make 8.

Have children wiggle 1 and 7 at least three more times. Give them encouragement.

• Let's really feel these partners. Wiggle 1, now wiggle 7. Oh, we're getting better. Wiggle 1 again, now wiggle 7. Look, it is easier! Let's do it again. Wiggle 1, and then wiggle 7.

MP.7 Look for Structure Ask for different partners of 8. Wiggle fingers for each set of partners at least four times. You can extend the activity by switching the partners (for example, 7 and 1), if you wish.

Repeat the above activities, finding wiggling partners of 9 and 7.

▶ **Set up** *The Unknown Partner Game* [PAIRS]

The Unknown Partner Game was first played in Unit 3, Lesson 16 (for totals up to 7), and then in Unit 5, Lessons 5 and 8 (for totals up to 10). Have each **Student Pair** sit beside one another facing their work space. Have them set up the Number Tiles in order in a horizontal row.

▶ **Play** *The Unknown Partner Game* [PAIRS]

Tell children they will start playing *The Unknown Partner Game* by finding partners of the number 8. Ask **Student Pairs** to pull down Number Tile 8 and to line up eight centimeter cubes below the card with space between each cube.

COMMON CORE

Mathematical Practice
CC.K–12.MP.4, CC.K–12.MP.7
Mathematical Content
CC.K.OA.3, CC.K.OA.4

15 MINUTES

FOCUS Practice finding partners of 7, 8, and 9.

MATERIALS Number Tiles 1–10 (1 set per pair), centimeter cubes (10 per pair), Break-Apart Sticks (1 per pair), +/− Tiles (1 per pair)

 Whiteboard Lesson

English Language Learners

Write *partner* on the board. Say: **Partners are two numbers that we add to make another number.** Count out 5 counters using 2 yellow counters and 3 red counters. Write 5 = 2 + 3.

BEGINNING

Say: **2 and 3 are partners of 5.** Ask children to repeat. Have children use counters to show and write other partners of 5. 1 and 4

INTERMEDIATE

Ask: **What are 2 and 3?** partners Have children use counters to show and write other partners of 5. 1 and 4

ADVANCED

Ask: **What are 2 and 3?** 2 and 3 are partners of 5. Have children use counters to find other partners of 5. Ask: **What do the counters show?** 1 and 4 are partners of 5.

Teaching Note

Research By doing the kinesthetic activities in this lesson, children feel the partners, which helps reinforce the concept of partners.

Activity continued ▶

Teaching Note

Research Kindergarten children can learn partners of numbers through 10 because they can see that a group, or total, can be broken into two groups (partners, or addends). Then by putting the two groups back together, they can prove to themselves that the two partners make up the total. In other words, children can see the *total = partner + partner* relationship, as well as the *partner + partner = total* relationship.

MP.4 Model with Mathematics Make a Model Explain that the first child in each Student Pair takes a Break-Apart Stick while the second child closes his or her eyes, covers them, and turns away. The first child places a Break-Apart Stick to indicate any set with partners of 8 and removes the cubes for one of the 8-partners, leaving the Break-Apart Stick and the other cubes in place.

In the example below, you see the set up for 8 with the Number Tile above the 8 centimeter cubes, and then you see what it looks like after the first child has placed a Break-Apart Stick between the partners 5 and 3. Finally, you see how the materials look after the first child has removed the 3 cubes to the right of the stick. When finished, the first child asks the second child to identify the unknown partner.

• What partner of 8 did I take?

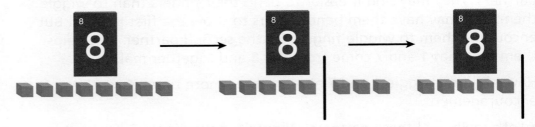

The second child uncovers his or her eyes and looks at the centimeter cubes to find the partner that has been taken. The child can use a variety of strategies to determine the unknown number. These include counting the cubes that are visible before counting on to 8 with fingers, or visualizing 8 cubes and mentally "seeing" how many are missing.

The second child then arranges the Number Tiles of the two partners and the +/− Tile below the centimeter cubes. The pair of children read the expression together, thus completing one turn.

Children then reverse roles and play the game for the numbers 7, 8, and 9 in any order. They can continue to play as time allows.

Write 6-Partners

▶ **Identify Partners of 6**   WHOLE CLASS

MP.7 Look for Structure Hand out Student Activity Book page 229. Remind children of the similar activity in Unit 5, Lesson 7, where they wrote the 5-partners. Today, have children write the 6-partners below each set of shapes. Discuss any patterns that children see.

At the top of Student Activity Book page 230 children continue to build fluency with addition within 5 and at the bottom they practice finding totals through 10.

COMMON CORE

Mathematical Practice
CC.K–12.MP.7

Mathematical Content
CC.K.OA.1, CC.K.OA.5

15 MINUTES

FOCUS Identify the 6-partners, and write the corresponding numbers.

MATERIALS Student Activity Book pages 229–230

 Whiteboard Lesson

5-9
Class Activity   Name _____

Write the 6-**partners**.

| 6 |

VOCABULARY
partner

●○○○○○   1 + 5
●●○○○○   2 + 4
●●●○○○   3 + 3
●●●●○○   4 + 2
●●●●●○   5 + 1

1 + 5   2 + 4   3 + 3   4 + 2   5 + 1

1 + 5   2 + 4   3 + 3   4 + 2   5 + 1

1 + 5   2 + 4   3 + 3   4 + 2   5 + 1

1 + 5   2 + 4   3 + 3   4 + 2   5 + 1

UNIT 5 LESSON 9   Partners of 6, 7, 8, and 9 **229**

5-9
Class Activity   Name _____

PATH to
FLUENCY

Add the numbers.

1 + 1 = 2	1 + 4 = 5	2 + 1 = 3
1 + 0 = 1	3 + 2 = 5	4 + 1 = 5
2 + 2 = 4	2 + 1 = 3	3 + 0 = 3
2 + 3 = 5	1 + 2 = 3	3 + 1 = 4
1 + 1 = 2	2 + 2 = 4	1 + 3 = 4

1 + 8 = 9	3 + 3 = 6	7 + 3 = 10
6 + 2 = 8	4 + 3 = 7	4 + 6 = 10
6 + 4 = 10	4 + 4 = 8	5 + 1 = 6
5 + 5 = 10	4 + 5 = 9	6 + 2 = 8

230 UNIT 5 LESSON 9   Partners of 6, 7, 8, and 9

Student Activity Book pages 229–230

☑ **Formative Assessment: Check Understanding**

Student Summary Write the following equations on the board: $3 + 3 = \square$, $5 + 1 = \square$, $4 + 2 = \square$. Ask a child to solve the equations and write the numbers.

▲ On Level ⬛ RtI Tier 1
for students having success

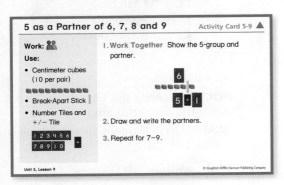

Activity Notes Explain to children that they need to show 5 plus another partner for each number 6–9.

 Math Writing Prompt

Draw the Partners Challenge children to draw the two partners for each number 6–9 using 5-groups.

 MegaMath

Software Support
Country Countdown
Counting Critters, Level G

⬛ Challenge
for students seeking a challenge

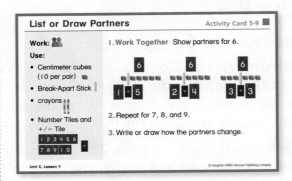

Activity Notes Explain that children need to find every partner for the numbers 6–9 and then write or draw how the partners change.

 Math Writing Prompt

Write Problems Challenge children to write subtraction problems using the cubes, tiles, and the Break-Apart stick.

 Destination Math®

Software Support
Course I: Module 2: Unit 1: Session 1: Combining and Joining within 10

Homework page 99 will give children extra practice thinking about teen numbers as ten ones and extra ones. Homework page 100 will give children the opportunity to practice addition.

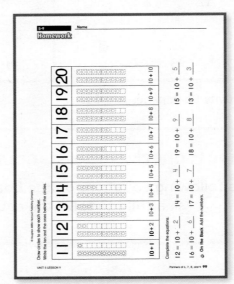
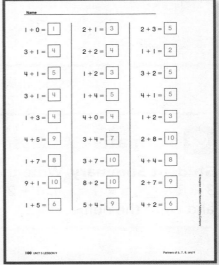

Homework and Remembering page 99   Homework and Remembering page 100

Tens in Teen Numbers: A Game

LESSON FOCUS

- Solve addition and subtraction story problems, and visualize teen numbers as ten ones and extra ones.
- Use the = and ≠ signs in comparing.

VOCABULARY

equal sign (=)
is not equal to sign (≠)
equal
unequal

COMMON CORE

Mathematical Practice
CC.K–12.MP.1, CC.K–12.MP.4, CC.K–12.MP.5, CC.K–12.MP.6
Mathematical Content
CC.K.CC.3, CC.K.OA.1, CC.K.OA.2, CC.K.OA.3, CC.K.NBT.1

The Day at a Glance

Teaching the Lesson

USE MATH TALK TODAY!

MATH BACKGROUND for this lesson is included on pp. 461JJ–461KK.

ACTIVITY FOCUS

Activity 1   Solve story problems by drawing a picture and writing an equation.
Activity 2   Look for groups of ten in teen numbers.
Activity 3   Subtract and use equal and is not equal to signs to compare.

MATERIALS

- Student Activity Book pp. 231–232 • Hiding Zero Gameboard • Number Tiles 1–10 • Giant Number Cards
- *i*Tools: Counters • Whiteboard

Differentiated Instruction

MATERIALS

- Activity Cards 5-10 • Student Activity Book p. 231 • Math Journals
- Soar to Success Math Intervention • MegaMath • Destination Math®
- **RtI**   Tier 1 • Tier 2 • Tier 3

Homework

MATERIALS

- Homework and Remembering pp. 101–102

QUICK PRACTICE   5 MINUTES

Repeated Quick Practice Use these Quick Practices from previous lessons.

Count to 100 by Tens and Tell How Many (See Unit 5, Lesson 3.)

Say Groups of 10 and Decade Numbers (and reverse) (See Unit 5, Lesson 3.)

Partner Peek: Tell the Unknown Partner (See Unit 5, Lesson 3.)

DAILY ROUTINES

Counting Tens and Ones
(See pp. xxxi–xxxii.)

DIGITAL RESOURCES

Use these digital resources along with your eSAB and eTE to support your students' learning experiences.

 Professional Development   Whiteboard Lesson   *i*Tools   Soar to Success Math Intervention   MegaMath   Destination Math®

COMMON CORE
Mathematical Practice
CC.K–12.MP.1, CC.K–12.MP.4
Mathematical Content
CC.K.OA.2, CC.K.OA.3

20 MINUTES
FOCUS Solve story problems by drawing a picture and writing an equation.

 iTools: Counters

Whiteboard Lesson

Digital Resource

iTools Choose 'Counters' on the Menu. Use Activity 4 'Subtract' with the tab for 'Activities'. Children can use counters to help them subtract. Then they enter the partner.

Learning Community—Best Practices

Helping Community Children have had opportunities to solve and retell story problems. Some children will now be proficient while others will be able to solve problems but not retell them in their own words. Provide these children with opportunities to tell and retell story problems, helping them as necessary with word prompts.

COMMON CORE
Mathematical Practice
CC.K–12.MP.5
Mathematical Content
CC.K.NBT.1

15 MINUTES
FOCUS Look for groups of ten in teen numbers.
Materials Hiding Zero Gameboard (from Unit 5, Lesson 6 or TRB M55; 1 per pair), Number Tiles 1–10 (1 set per pair), Giant Number Cards

 Whiteboard Lesson

ACTIVITY 1

Solve Story Problems

▶ **Solve Addition and Subtraction Story Problems** WHOLE CLASS MATH TALK

This activity uses **Step-by-Step** at the Board.

If necessary, refer back to Unit 5, Lessons 1, 4, and 6 to review this activity.

MP.4 Model with Mathematics Write an Equation Children tell addition and subtraction story problems, solve them with math drawings, and write equations to show the solution. Have as many children as possible work at the board while the rest of the children work at their desks. Call on two children to explain their drawings and equations for each problem. Encourage others to ask questions.

MP.1 Make Sense of Problems As in previous lessons, focus on having children retell story problems using different words that mean the same thing. In addition stories, they should be using the following words and phrases: *altogether, in all, total,* and *put them together.* The words for subtraction stories are: *left, now,* and *still.*

ACTIVITY 2

Play *The Hiding Zero Game*

▶ **Set Up and Play** *The Hiding Zero Game* PAIRS

If necessary, refer back to Unit 5, Lesson 6, for complete instructions. Have **Student Pairs** arrange their three Hiding Zero Gameboard pages in order, vertically or horizontally. Then have them work together to put a Number Tile on top of the 0 in each 10.

MP.5 Use Appropriate Tools A **Student Leader** shows the Giant Number Cards (10 plus a single-digit number) and calls out that teen number (for example, 18), and one child in each **Student Pair** picks up Number Tile 8, which is covering the 0 in the 10, and puts it in the blank rectangle. Together, the class says the following:

• "18 equals 10 plus 8. This is the ten in 18 (pointing to the 10). This is the 8 in 18 (pointing to the 8)."

The **Student Leader** continues until all of the zeroes have been uncovered.

Subtract and Use = or ≠

▶ Solve Subtraction Equations [WHOLE CLASS]

Ask children to look at the subtraction equations on page 231.

▶ Use the Signs: Equal or Unequal [WHOLE CLASS]

MP.6 Attend to Precision Discuss what children remember about the equal and is not equal to signs. Explain that children should write = or ≠ to complete the exercises at the bottom of the page.

▶ Find the Group That Has Fewer [SMALL GROUPS]

Have children turn to page 232 to count and write the numbers, circling the group that has fewer.

COMMON CORE

Mathematical Practice
CC.CC.K–12.MP.6

Mathematical Content
CC.K.CC.3, CC.K.OA.1, CC.K.OA.3

20 MINUTES

FOCUS Subtract and use equal and is not equal to signs to compare.

MATERIALS Student Activity Book pages 231–232

 Whiteboard Lesson

5-10 Class Activity   Name _____

VOCABULARY: equal, unequal   PATH to FLUENCY

Subtract the numbers. Use your fingers or draw.

$3 - 2 = 1$ $5 - 5 = 0$ $2 - 2 = 0$

$4 - 1 = 3$ $4 - 3 = 1$ $3 - 1 = 2$

$3 - 3 = 0$ $5 - 2 = 3$ $4 - 3 = 1$

$5 - 0 = 5$ $4 - 2 = 2$ $3 - 0 = 3$

$2 - 1 = 1$ $5 - 4 = 1$ $5 - 3 = 2$

Write the symbol to show **equal** or **unequal**.
= or ≠

$2 ≠$ •••   • = ✋ $10 = 2 + 8$

$5 =$ •••••   • ≠ ✋ $6 ≠ 5 + 2$

$3 =$ •••   • = ✋ $9 ≠ 3 + 4$

$1 ≠$ •••   • ≠ ✋ $7 = 1 + 6$

$4 ≠$ •••••   • = ✋ $8 = 4 + 4$

UNIT 5 LESSON 10   Tens in Teen Numbers: A Game **231**

5-10 Class Activity   Name _____

VOCABULARY: fewer

Count and write how many. Ring **fewer**.

3   2   4   5   4   2

3   4   2   4   5   3

4   5   4   2   5   3

2   3   4   3   2   5

Write the numbers from 11 through 30.

11	12	13	14	15	16	17	18	19	20
21	22	23	24	25	26	27	28	29	30

232 UNIT 5 LESSON 10   Tens in Teen Numbers: A Game

Student Activity Book pages 231–232

✅ **Formative Assessment: Check Understanding**

Student Summary Ask a child to draw two groups of objects, using = or ≠ to tell whether the groups are equal or not equal.

English Language Learners

Write **equal** and **unequal** on the board. Say: **Equal amounts have the same value.** Circle *un-*. Say: *Un-* means "not." **Unequal amounts are not equal.**

▲ On Level ⬛ RtI Tier 1

for students having success

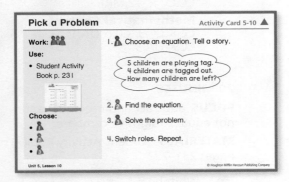

Activity Notes Encourage children to tell a story using one of the equations on Student Activity Book page 231. Other children find and solve the equations.

 Math Writing Prompt

Write Equations Challenge children to write 4 equations using the numbers 2, 3, and 5.

 MegaMath

Software Support
Country Countdown
Counting Critters, Level P

⬛ Challenge

for students seeking a challenge

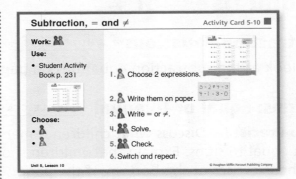

Activity Notes Explain that children will be choosing two expressions and writing them side by side for comparison.

 Math Writing Prompt

Equal Equations Encourage children to strive to make the equations equal.

 Destination Math®

Software Support
Course I: Module 2: Unit 2: Session 2: Differences within 20

Distribute Homework pages 101 and 102. Remind children, as necessary, how to draw Tiny Tumblers on the sides of Math Mountains in order to show the unknown partner. Children may need help to draw the Math Mountains on page 102.

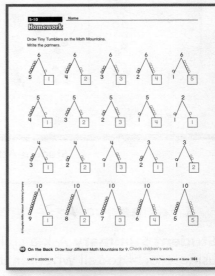

Homework and Remembering page 101

Tens in Teen Numbers Book

LESSON FOCUS

• Visualize teen numbers as ten ones and extra ones, and find 10-partners.

VOCABULARY

teen numbers
extra ones

COMMON CORE

Mathematical Practice
CC.K–12.MP.6, CC.K–12.MP.7
Mathematical Content
CC.K.CC.3, CC.K.OA.3, CC.K.OA.4, CC.K.NBT.1

The Day at a Glance

Teaching the Lesson

MATH BACKGROUND for this lesson is included on pp. 461JJ–461KK, 461MM–461NN.

ACTIVITY FOCUS

Activity 1 Illustrate teen numbers by showing ten ones and extra ones.

Activity 2 Find and show partners of 10.

MATERIALS

- Student Activity Book pp. 233–238 • Scissors • Counters • Number Tiles 1–10 • +/− Tiles • Night Sky display

- iTools: Counters • Whiteboard

Differentiated Instruction

MATERIALS

- Activity Cards 5-11 • Number Tiles 1–9 (extras of the 5-Tile) • +/− Tiles • Math Journals

- Soar to Success Math Intervention • MegaMath • Destination Math®

- RtI Tier 1 • Tier 2 • Tier 3

Homework

MATERIALS

- Homework and Remembering pp. 103–104

QUICK PRACTICE ⏱ **5 MINUTES**

Repeated Quick Practice Use these Quick Practices from previous lessons.

Say Groups of 10 and Decade Numbers (and Reverse) (See Unit 5, Lesson 3.)

Partner Peek: Tell the Unknown Partner (See Unit 5, Lesson 3.)

Count to 100 by Tens and Tell How Many (See Unit 5, Lesson 3.)

DAILY ROUTINES

Counting Tens and Ones
(See pp. xxxi–xxxii.)

DIGITAL RESOURCES

Use these digital resources along with your eSAB and eTE to support your students' learning experiences.

Professional Development

Whiteboard Lesson

iTools

Soar to Success Math Intervention

MegaMath

Destination Math®

COMMON CORE

Mathematical Practice
CC.K–12.MP.7
Mathematical Content
CC.K.CC.3, CC.K.NBT.1

20 MINUTES
FOCUS Illustrate teen numbers by showing ten ones and extra ones.
MATERIALS Student Activity Book pages 233–238 (1 set per child)

 *i*Tools: Counters

Whiteboard Lesson

English Language Learners

Write *extra ones* on the board. Display the Number Pattern Poster. Say: **A teen number is made up of a group of ten ones and extra ones.** Invite a volunteer to point out the ten ones and the extra one for 11. Guide children to say *ten ones* and *extra ones* as you point to each part of the teen numbers.

Digital Resource

*i*Tools Choose 'Counters' on the Menu. Use Activity 3 'Add' with the tab for 'Activities.' Children can use counters to help them add two numbers. Then they enter the total.

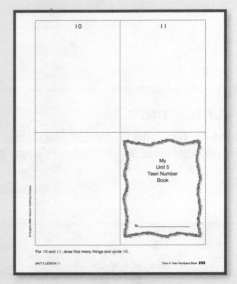

Student Activity Book page 233

ACTIVITY 1   Art Connection

Draw Teen Numbers and Group Ten Things

▶ Get Ready to Draw Teen Numbers   WHOLE CLASS

Ask for Ideas This activity builds on children's previous work in Unit 4. Ask children what they remember about making teen numbers as a group of ten and extra ones.

Distribute the three Student Activity Book pages 233, 235, and 237 children will use to make their "Unit 5 Teen Number Book." Discuss how they are to proceed. You can organize this activity in different ways. Some children can make drawings for all of the numbers 10–19, while others may only make drawings for some of the numbers. You may want to place some children in **Student Pairs.** This activity could be started today and continued on another day. If so, you could distribute only one page at a time.

- Find the page that has a space with the number 12 at the top. How many things will you draw in that box? 12 things

- After you draw 12 things, you will draw a ring around 10 of them so that anyone who looks at the drawing will see the group of ten.

Children may arrange their 10 in rows of 5 or randomly. Brainstorm with children about what they might draw that would be small and easy to draw. Help them plan ahead to make sure that 12 of the items they choose will fit in that space. You may wish to show children some of the Homework pages from this unit in which they circled 10-groups of animals.

▶ Draw Teen Numbers   INDIVIDUALS

Look for Structure Have children draw 12 things. You may want to draw an example on the board. Discuss children's results.

- What happened when you drew 12? Did you have enough space? Possible response: No, I had to crowd in the last two pictures.

- What do you need to do to draw 13 in the space at the right? Draw smaller.

Children draw 13 and circle the group of 10. Discuss the extra ones, using Giant Number Cards if necessary.

- How many extra ones do you have in 12? 2 How many in 13? 3

- How are these extra ones related to the number you see? 12 has 2 ones and 13 has 3 ones.

Children continue until they have completed all the spaces to show numbers 10 through 19.

▶ Assemble the Book INDIVIDUALS

Children are now ready to put together their books. Explain that they will cut out the four little pages from each big page by cutting on the dashed lines. The exception is Student Activity Book page 233, which has the front and back covers on the bottom half. Instruct children to fold along the solid line between the covers. After children have ordered pages 10–19, have them insert those pages between the covers.

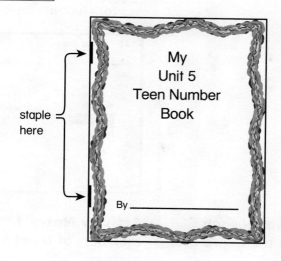

staple here

My
Unit 5
Teen Number
Book

By _____

ACTIVITY 2

Play *The 10-Partners Game*

▶ Use Objects PAIRS MATH TALK

MP.6 Attend to Precision Student Pairs play this game with 10 counters, which are arranged in two rows of 5 as shown. Children pretend the counters are sheep. One child covers his or her eyes while the other child takes away some of the counters and recites the rhyme.

   "Baa baa, 6 sheep in a pen. Tell me, what is the partner of 10?"

The first child responds by saying, "I see 6 sheep in the pen. 6 and 4 are partners of 10." Children reverse roles and play continues.

▶ Use Number Tiles PAIRS

MP.7 Use Structure Have Student Pairs play the game with two sets of Number Tiles and the +/− Tile. One set of tiles is turned face down, and the set is turned face up. One child turns a face down tile over, and the other child tells the 10-partner for that number. When both children agree that the partner is correct, the second child shows the partners with face up Number Tiles and the +/− Tile, for example, 8 + 2. Children reverse roles and continue.

 Formative Assessment: Check Understanding

Student Summary Write a teen number on the board. Ask a child to draw objects to represent the number. Repeat with another teen number.

COMPLETE CORE

COMMON CORE

Mathematical Practice
CC.K–12.MP.6, CC.K–12.MP.7
Mathematical Content
CC.K.OA.3, CC.K.OA.4

10 MINUTES

FOCUS Find and show partners of 10.
MATERIALS Counters (10 per pair), Number Tiles 1–9 (2 sets per pair), +/− Tiles (1 per pair), Night Sky display

 Whiteboard Lesson

▲ On Level    RtI   Tier 1
for students having success

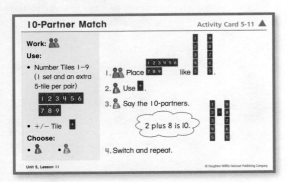

Activity Notes Ask children to name various sets with partners of 10, and write them on the board as a partner review.

 Math Writing Prompt

Partner Equations Challenge children to write two different equations using partners of 10.

 MegaMath

Software Support
Country Countdown
Counting Critters, Level P

■ Challenge
for students seeking a challenge

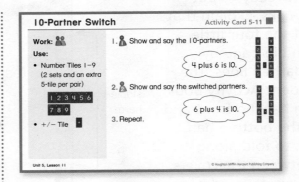

Activity Notes Model how children should arrange their sets of Number Tiles so that they show opposite partners.

 Math Writing Prompt

Draw It Ask children to draw the five equations. They show two drawings for each one.

Destination Math®

Software Support
Course I: Module 2: Unit 1: Session 3: Sums within 20, with 10 as One Addend

The Homework activities on pages 103 and 104 give children practice with using 5-groups to find totals.

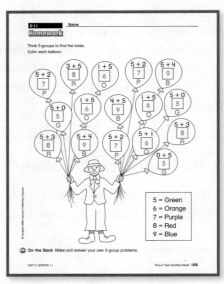

Homework and Remembering page 103   Homework and Remembering page 104

Partners of 10: Class Project

LESSON FOCUS

• Relate 10-partner drawings to addition equations and find changes in the partners of ten.

VOCABULARY

rectangle

COMMON CORE

Mathematical Practice
CC.K–12.MP.3, CC.K–12.MP.4
Mathematical Content
CC.K.OA.2, CC.K.OA.3, CC.K.OA.4, CC.K.OA.5

The Day at a Glance

Teaching the Lesson

USE
MATH TALK
TODAY!

MATH BACKGROUND for this lesson is included on p. 461JJ–461KK, 461OO.

ACTIVITY FOCUS

Activity 1   Discuss and draw 10-partners for the Showcase.

Activity 2   Explore changes in 10-partners.

MATERIALS

Student Activity Book pp. 239–242 • 10-Partner Showcase • Crayons or markers

*i*Tools: Counters • Whiteboard

Differentiated Instruction

MATERIALS

Activity Cards 5-12 • Student Activity Book p. 241 • Counters • Math Journals

Soar to Success Math Intervention • MegaMath • Destination Math®

RtI   Tier 1 • Tier 2 • Tier 3

Homework

MATERIALS

Homework and Remembering pp. 105–106

QUICK PRACTICE   5 MINUTES

Repeated Quick Practice Use these Quick Practices from previous lessons.

Partner Peek: Tell the Unknown Partner (See Unit 5, Lesson 3.)

Say Groups of 10 and Decade Numbers (and Reverse) (See Unit 5, Lesson 3.)

Count to 100 by Tens and Tell How Many (See Unit 5, Lesson 3.)

DAILY ROUTINES

Counting Tens and Ones
(See pp. xxxi–xxxii.)

DIGITAL RESOURCES

Use these digital resources along with your eSAB and eTE to support your students' learning experiences.

Professional
Development

Whiteboard
Lesson

*i*Tools

Soar to Success
Math Intervention

MegaMath

Destination
Math®

COMMON CORE

Mathematical Practice
CC.K–12.MP.4

Mathematical Content
CC.K.OA.2, CC.K.OA.3, CC.K.OA.4

20 MINUTES

FOCUS Discuss and draw 10-partners for the showcase.

MATERIALS 10-Partner Showcase (Student Activity Book pages 239–240 or TRB M58; 1 per child), crayons or markers

 *i*Tools: Counters

📝 Whiteboard Lesson

Digital Resource

*i***Tools** Choose 'Counters' on the Menu. Use Activity 3 'Add' with the tab for 'Activities.' Children can use counters to help them add two numbers. Then they enter the total.

Use Activity 4 'Subtract' with the tab for 'Activities.' Children can use counters to help them subtract. Then they enter the partner.

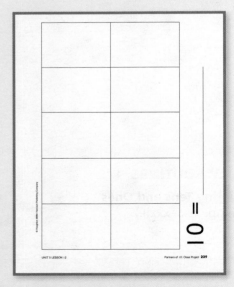

Student Activity Book page 239

ACTIVITY 1

Draw for the 10-Partner Showcase

▶ Get Ready to Draw 10-Partners   WHOLE CLASS

Distribute Student Activity Book pages 239–240. Explain that children will draw things in the rectangles on each page to show different 10-partners. Some of the pages will be put in the classroom as part of the 10-Partner Showcase. Explain that you will change the drawings that are displayed during the unit, so that all children will have a chance to see their own 10-partner drawing on display.

To make sure that all of the 10-partners are drawn, write each equation on the board along with the names of the children assigned to that set of 10-partners.

MATH TALK Brainstorm with children about what they might draw, since they will all draw the same things.

• To show the 10-partners for the showcase, we will use two colors so that the two partners are easy to see. We can draw two different things in two colors, or we can draw the same thing in two colors. What would you like to do? Let's take a vote.

Once the class decides on colors and objects, further explain that children should draw large in the spaces so that their drawings can be seen from all around the room.

▶ Draw 10-Partners for the Showcase   INDIVIDUALS

Demonstrate, if necessary, how to draw one thing in each rectangle. Also demonstrate how to write the 10-partner equation on the line. (You can go over the equations in black marker so that they can be read easily from a distance.)

MP.4 Model with Mathematics Make a Model Have children draw their 10-partners and color them in two different colors. When pages are complete, add them to the display as shown, or vertically if you prefer.

Our 10-Partner Showcase

$10 = \underline{5} + \underline{5}$ $10 = \underline{6} + \underline{4}$ $10 = \underline{7} + \underline{3}$ $10 = \underline{8} + \underline{2}$ $10 = \underline{9} + \underline{1}$

$10 = \underline{5} + \underline{5}$ $10 = \underline{4} + \underline{6}$ $10 = \underline{3} + \underline{7}$ $10 = \underline{2} + \underline{8}$ $10 = \underline{1} + \underline{9}$

Observe Changes with 10-Partners

▶ **Write 10-Partners** WHOLE CLASS

Distribute Student Activity Book pages 241–242. Make sure that children understand what was done in the first row. Do the second row together, explaining that children should write the partners shown.

• We're going to write all the 10-partners in order. Which partner set will we start with? 1 + 9

MP.3 Construct a Viable Argument Compare Representations Complete the row together in this manner. When everyone has finished, ask what is the same and what is different in the first three rows. Then continue to guide children as they write the partners for the remaining rows.

COMMON CORE

Mathematical Practice
CC.K–12.MP.3

Mathematical Content
CC.K.OA.2, CC.K.OA.3,
CC.K.OA.4, CC.K.OA.5

25 MINUTES

FOCUS Explore changes in 10-partners.

MATERIALS Student Activity Book pages 241–242

 Whiteboard Lesson

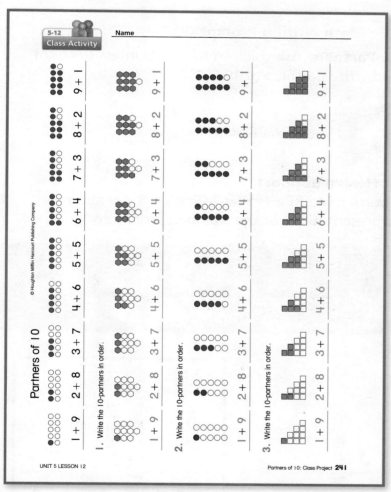

Student Activity Book pages 241–242

✅ **Formative Assessment: Check Understanding**

Student Summary Write the number 10 on the board. Ask children to write as many partners of 10 as they can.

English Language Learners

Discuss Student Activity Book page 239. Point out the rectangles on the page. Point to a side. Ask: **How many sides does a rectangle have?** 4 Point to a corner. Ask: **How many corners does a rectangle have?** 4

▲ On Level  Tier 1

for students having success

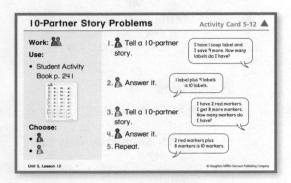

Activity Notes Using Student Activity Book page 241, model how one child tells a story using 10-partners and the other answers.

 Math Writing Prompt

Tell It Challenge children to tell subtraction stories using the same 10-partners they used previously.

 MegaMath

Software Support
Country Countdown
Block Busters, Level C

■ Challenge

for students seeking a challenge

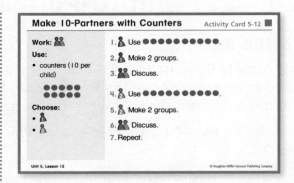

Activity Notes Explain that children need to practice counting out different groups of counters to make partners of 10.

 Math Writing Prompt

10-Partners Ask children to use counters to count and write partners of 10.

 Destination Math®

Software Support
Course I: Module 1: Unit 2: Session 3: Creating Representations of the Numbers from 5 to 10

The Homework activity on page 105 gives children additional practice with subtraction and with using the = and ≠ signs. On page 106, children practice writing the numbers 1 through 100.

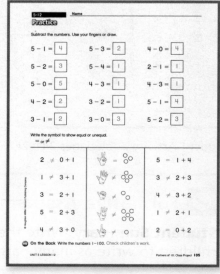

Homework and Remembering page 105

Introduction to Counting and Grouping Routines

LESSON FOCUS
- Count by ones and tens to 100.
- Find partners of 10 and write and discuss 7-partners.

VOCABULARY
one hundred

COMMON CORE

Mathematical Practice
CC.K–12.MP.4, CC.K–12.MP.6, CC.K–12.MP.7
Mathematical Content
CC.K.CC.1, CC.K.CC.2, CC.K.OA.2, CC.K.OA.3, CC.K.OA.4

The Day at a Glance

Teaching the Lesson

 USE MATH TALK TODAY!

MATH BACKGROUND for this lesson is included on pp. 461LL–461OO.

ACTIVITY FOCUS

Activity 1 Find partners of 10.

Activity 2 Count by ones and tens to 100.

Activity 3 Write and discuss 7-partners.

MATERIALS

◆ Student Activity Book pp. 243–244 • 120 Poster • Pointer • 10-Partner Showcase • Sticky notes

▢ iTools: Counters • Whiteboard

Differentiated Instruction

MATERIALS

◆ Activity Cards 5-13 • Paper strips (yellow and orange) • Paper plates • Glue • Number cube • Math Journals

▢ Soar to Success Math Intervention • MegaMath • Destination Math®

▲RtI Tier 1 • Tier 2 • Tier 3

Homework

MATERIALS

◆ Homework and Remembering pp. 107–108

QUICK PRACTICE ⏱ **5 MINUTES**

In this lesson, a new Quick Practice routine is introduced and explained in Activity 1. This routine will be used throughout the remainder of the unit: **The Partner Peek on the 10-Partner Showcase.**

┌─────────────────────────┐
│ **DAILY ROUTINES**
│ **Counting Tens and Ones**
│ (See pp. xxxi–xxxii.)
└─────────────────────────┘

DIGITAL RESOURCES

Use these digital resources along with your eSAB and eTE to support your students' learning experiences.

 Professional Development

 Whiteboard Lesson

 iTools

 Soar to Success Math Intervention

 MegaMath

 Destination Math®

COMMON CORE

Mathematical Practice
CC.K–12.MP.7

Mathematical Content
CC.K.OA.3, CC.K.OA.4

10 MINUTES

FOCUS Find partners of 10.

MATERIALS 10-Partner Showcase (from Unit 5, Lesson 12), sticky notes (5)

 Whiteboard Lesson

Class Management

Looking Ahead This Quick Practice routine will require that the 10-Partner Showcase remain on display for future lessons in this unit. During the next lesson, give **Student Leaders** a chance to lead the routine.

COMMON CORE

Mathematical Practice
CC.K–12.MP.6

Mathematical Content
CC.K.CC.1, CC.K.CC.2

15 MINUTES

FOCUS Count by ones and tens to 100.

MATERIALS 120 Poster, pointer

iT *i*Tools: Counters

 Whiteboard Lesson

Digital Resource

*i*Tool Choose 'Counters' on the Menu. Use Activity 1 'Count' with the tab for 'Activities.' Children can use counters to count.

ACTIVITY 1

Introduce the New Quick Practice

▶ The Partner Peek on the 10-Partner Showcase
WHOLE CLASS

MP.7 Look for Structure Challenge children to close their eyes as you cover one partner in five equations on the 10-Partner Showcase with a sticky note. Children can uncover their eyes as you point to one of the equations with a covered partner and read it.

- 10 is 8 and how many? Show me with your fingers. Which partner of 8 is hiding under the sticky note?

Children show 2 fingers and say (as you uncover the 2), "Now let's peek! Yes, 10 is 8 and 2."

Repeat for the next four sticky notes.

ACTIVITY 2

Count by Ones and Tens Using the 120 Poster

▶ Count to 100 by Ones and by Tens
WHOLE CLASS

Use the 120 Poster to lead the class in counting by ones and tens to 100. Some children may comment on the numbers greater than 100 in the last two columns. Children will use the part of the poster that includes numbers 101 to 120 in Grade 1.

MP.6 Attend to Precision **Count by Ones and Tens on the 120 Poster** A **Student Leader** directs the class in counting **by ones to 100** while pointing to each number.

Then children flash ten fingers each time as the Student Leader directs the **count by tens** while pointing to each decade number to 100 on the 120 Poster.

Write 7-Partners

▶ Write 7-Partners MATH TALK

MP.4 Model with Mathematics Write an Equation Have children turn Student Book Activity page 243 horizontally. Ask children to discuss the changes they see in the partners for 7 in the top row. Then do the first exercise together, writing the partner numbers. The shaded shape represents the first partner, and the unshaded shapes represent the second partner. In Exercises 3 and 4, have children write the partners below each set of shapes.

• What changes do you see in the partners for 7?

▶ Practice Addition

Ask children to complete page 244 for fluency practice.

COMMON CORE

Mathematical Practice
CC.K–12.MP.4

Mathematical Content
CC.K.OA.2, CC.K.OA.3, CC.K.OA.4

15 MINUTES

FOCUS Write and discuss 7-partners.

MATERIALS Student Activity Book pages 243–244

Whiteboard Lesson

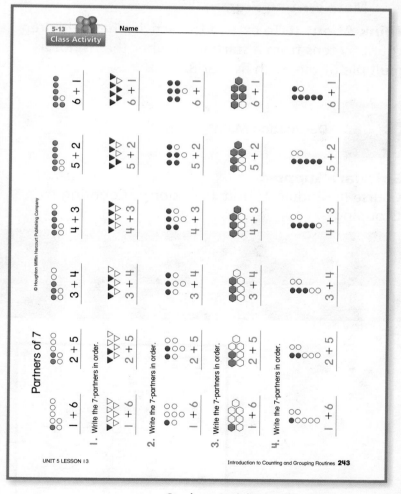

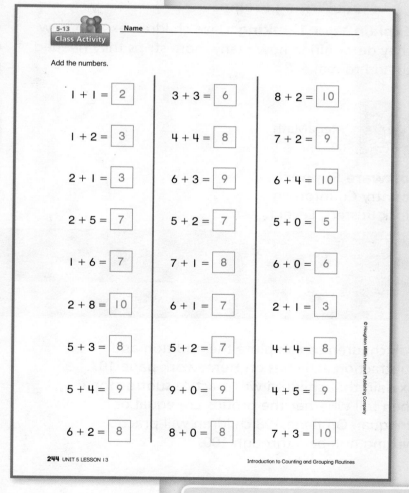

Student Activity Book pages 243–244

✓ Formative Assessment: Check Understanding

Student Summary Write the number 7 on the board. Ask children to write as many partners of 7 as they can.

English Language Learners

Write 100 and *one hundred* on the board. Display a hundred base ten block. Say: **We can count by ones to one hundred.** Lead children in counting to one hundred as you point to the ones cubes in the hundred block.

▲ On Level ▲ RtI Tier 1

for students having success

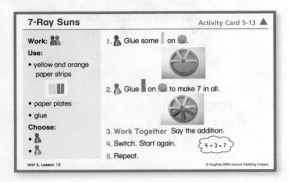

Activity Notes Prepare paper strips. Children make 7-partners by adding rays to a sun. Encourage children to make as many 7-partners as they can.

 Math Writing Prompt

Explain Your Thinking Have children explain how they determined how many more strips they needed to add to make 7.

 MegaMath

Software Support
Country Countdown
Block Busters, Level I

■ Challenge

for students seeking a challenge

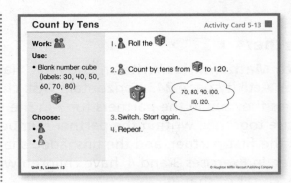

Activity Notes In this activity, children take turns counting by tens to 100. They will begin at a given tens number rather than starting at 10.

 Math Writing Prompt

Think About It To extend the activity, have children count by tens from a starting number that is not a multiple of ten, such as 4 or 8.

 Destination Math®

Software Support
Course II: Module 1: Unit 1: Session 1: Counting by Grouping

Ask children to complete the addition and subtraction activities on Homework page 107. Explain that children will practice subtraction, then tell whether the groups are equal or unequal. On page 108 children will practice writing numbers through 100.

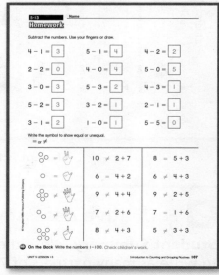

Homework and Remembering page 107

Practice: Number Activities

LESSON FOCUS

• Equalize groups by adding, and find partners of 7, 8, and 9.

VOCABULARY

more
less
equal
unequal

Mathematical Practice
CC.K–12.MP.3, CC.K–12.MP.7
Mathematical Content
CC.K.CC.3, CC.K.CC.5, CC.K.OA.1, CC.K.OA.3, CC.K.OA.5

The Day at a Glance

Teaching the Lesson

USE
MATH TALK
TODAY!

MATH BACKGROUND for this lesson is included on p. 461LL.

ACTIVITY FOCUS

Activity 1   Draw more objects to make equal groups.

Activity 2   Write numbers 1–20 and find partners of 7, 8, and 9.

MATERIALS

Student Activity Book pp. 245–246 • Fluency Check 7 (Assessment Guide)

*i*Tools: Counters • Whiteboard

Differentiated Instruction

MATERIALS

Activity Cards 5-14 • Game Cards 6–10 • Counters • Math Journals

Soar to Success Math Intervention • MegaMath • Destination Math®

RtI Tier 1 • Tier 2 • Tier 3

Home or School Activity

MATERIALS

Math-to-Math Connection p. 526

QUICK PRACTICE 5 MINUTES

Repeated Quick Practice Use these Quick Practices from previous lessons.

The Partner Peek on the 10-Partner Showcase.

DAILY ROUTINES

Counting Tens and Ones
(See pp. xxxi–xxxii.)

DIGITAL RESOURCES

Use these digital resources along with your eSAB and eTE to support your students' learning experiences.

 Professional Development

 Whiteboard Lesson

 iTools

 Soar to Success Math Intervention

 MegaMath

 Destination Math®

COMMON CORE

Mathematical Practice
CC.K–12.MP.7

Mathematical Content
CC.K.CC.3, CC.K.CC.5, CC.K.OA.5

20 MINUTES

FOCUS Draw more objects to make equal groups.

MATERIALS Student Activity Book page 245

 iTools: Counters

 Whiteboard Lesson

Digital Resource

iTools Choose 'Counters' on the Menu. Use Activity 3 'Add' with the tab for 'Activities'. Children can use counters to help them add 2 numbers. Then they enter the total.

MATH TALK *in ACTION* **How many shapes are in the first row?**

Jen: There are 6 shapes.

That's right. I will write 6 on the line next to that row.

How many shapes are in the second row?

Shawn: There are 4 in that one.

Correct! How many more shapes do I need to match the first row?

Inez: You will need 2 more.

How can I write this to show the partners?

Inez: Write the expression 4 + 2.

Good job. Let's try some more.

ACTIVITY 1

Greater Than, Less Than, or Equal

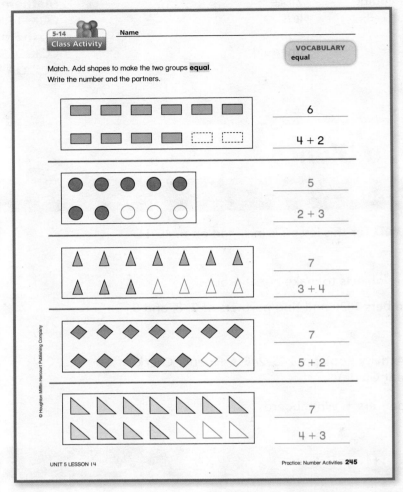

Student Activity Book page 245

▶ Add Shapes to the Smaller Group [WHOLE CLASS]

Draw the example from the top of Student Activity Book page 245 on the board without the answers.

MP.7 Look for Structure Work through the example with children, drawing and writing the numbers as you proceed. Guide children to see that the number of shapes in the second row and the additional number needed are partners. See **Math Talk in Action** in the side column for an example of classroom dialogue.

Distribute Student Activity Book page 245 and point out how the example at the top of the page is the same as the example they just did. To complete the page, children can draw lines to match objects, count sets, or just make them equal by visual correspondence. Children record their answers as in the example.

Write 1–20 and Partners of 7, 8, and 9

COMMON CORE

Mathematical Practice
CC.K–12.MP.3

Mathematical Content
CC.K.CC.3, CC.K.OA.1,
CC.K.OA.3

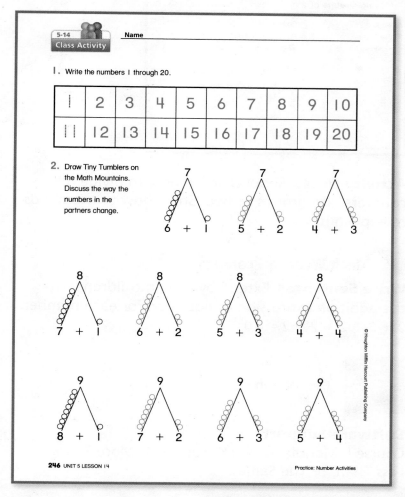

Student Activity Book page 246

15 MINUTES

FOCUS Write numbers 1–20 and find partners of 7, 8, and 9

MATERIALS Student Activity Book page 246

 Whiteboard Lesson

▶ Write 1–20 [WHOLE CLASS]

At the top of Student Activity Book page 246, children write the numbers 1 through 20. They can discuss the way the numbers change.

MP.3 Construct a Viable Argument Compare Representations Children can compare the changes in numbers going across to the changes they see on the 120 Poster, where the numbers go down.

▶ Find Partners of 7, 8, and 9 [WHOLE CLASS]

Have children discuss what they have done with Tiny Tumblers on Math Mountains in earlier lessons.

Children draw the Tiny Tumblers to show the partners of 7, 8, and 9.

✓ Formative Assessment: Check Understanding

Student Summary Write the number 8 on the board. Ask children to draw Tiny Tumblers to show the possible partners.

English Language Learners

Write **equal** on the board. Say: **When we have equal amounts, we have amounts that are the same.** Arrange 6 volunteers in rows of 4 and 2. Point out that the groups are not equal because they do not have the same number of children.

BEGINNING

Invite 2 volunteers to join the row of 2 children. Point to each group and ask: **How many in the group?** 4 Say: **The groups are equal.** Ask children to repeat.

INTERMEDIATE

Invite 2 volunteers to join the row of 2 children. Ask: **How many in each group?** 4 **What word describes the amounts in the two groups?** equal

ADVANCED

Ask: **How can we make the two groups equal?** We can add 2 children to the row of 2 to make the two groups equal. **How many in each group?** 4

✓ Fluency Check

See Assessment Guide for Fluency Check 7 on addition/subtraction within 5.

▲ On Level  Tier 1
for students having success

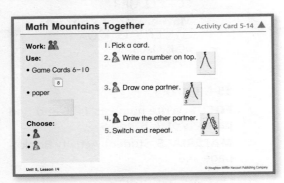

Activity Notes Review Math Mountains with children, showing that the total is at the top of the peak and the partners are on the sides.

 Math Writing Prompt

Record Partners As children make Math Mountains, have them record the expression or equation for each set of partners.

 MegaMath

Software Support
Country Countdown
Harrison's Comparisons, Level D

■ Challenge
for students seeking a challenge

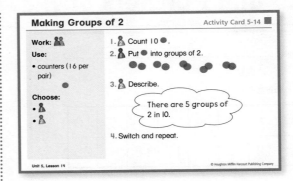

Activity Notes Show children how to divide 8 counters into groups of two. Show how to use words to explain it.

 Math Writing Prompt

Write Sentences Extend by having children write the addition expression or equation for each number.
$2 + 2 + 2 + 2 + 2 = 10$

 Destination Math®

Software Support
Course I: Module 1: Unit 4: Session 1: More Than, Less Than, or The Same

 ## Math-to-Math Connection

Many Equal Partners Choose any even number from 10 through 20. Work with children to find as many equal partners as possible for the number using counters. There cannot be any extra counters. Children should draw the equal partners on paper and say the math statements.

"There are ten 1s in 10. The 1s are all equal partners of 10."

"There are 5 groups of 2 in 10. All the 2s are equal partners of 10."

"There are 2 groups of 5 in 10. Both 5s are equal partners of 10."

LESSON FOCUS

- Show numbers 1–20; show the teen numbers as a group of ten ones and further ones.
- Find the unknown partner when the total and one partner are known and find the total of two partners.

VOCABULARY

partner
total

COMMON CORE

Mathematical Practice
CC.K–12.MP.1, CC.K–12.MP.2, CC.K–12.MP.6,
CC.K–12.MP.7, CC.K–12.MP.8
Mathematical Content
CC.K.CC.4, CC.K.CC.4c, CC.K.CC.5, CC.K.OA.1,
CC.K.OA.2, CC.K.OA.3, CC.K.OA.5, CC.K.NBT.1

The Day at a Glance

Teaching the Lesson

USE **MATH TALK** TODAY!

MATH BACKGROUND for this lesson is included on pp. 461JJ, 461OO.

ACTIVITY FOCUS

Activity 1 Make numbers 1–20 using 10-sticks and centimeter cubes.

Activity 2 Practice finding partners for 7–9 with finger activities and a game.

Activity 3 Use Tiny Tumblers to find partner totals.

MATERIALS

Student Activity Book pp. 247–248 • 1–20 Boards • 10-sticks • Centimeter cubes • Number Tiles 1–9 • Break-Apart Sticks • +/− Tiles

iTools: Counters • Whiteboard

Differentiated Instruction

MATERIALS

Activity Cards 5-15 • Number cubes • Centimeter cubes • Game Cards • Math Journals

Soar to Success Math Intervention • MegaMath • Destination Math®

RtI Tier 1 • Tier 2 • Tier 3

Homework

MATERIALS

Homework and Remembering pp. 109–110

QUICK PRACTICE 5 MINUTES

Repeated Quick Practice Use this Quick Practice from a previous lesson.

The Partner Peek on the 10-Partner Showcase (See Unit 5, Lesson 13.)

DAILY ROUTINES

Counting Tens and Ones
(See pp. xxxi–xxxii.)

DIGITAL RESOURCES

Use these digital resources along with your eSAB and eTE to support your students' learning experiences.

Professional Development

Whiteboard Lesson

iTools

Soar to Success Math Intervention

MegaMath

Destination Math®

ACTIVITY 1

Model Numbers on the 1–20 Board

▶ Make Numbers from 1 Through 20 | PAIRS |

Have **Student Pairs** place the sections of the 1–20 Board as shown below. You can use tape to hold the boards in place. Request that children place their centimeter cubes and 10-sticks on the boards to show numbers 1–20. See the Learning Community on the next page.

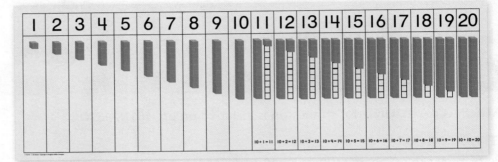

MP.8 Use Repeated Reasoning Generalize After children have finished, ask them to describe what they see, including what is alike or different between numbers and the changes they observe in the sequence of numbers.

ACTIVITY 2

Play *The Unknown Partner Game* for 7, 8, and 9

▶ Practice Finger Wiggle Partners | WHOLE CLASS |

MP.7 Look for Structure Identify Relationships Begin by doing finger wiggles to review partners for numbers 7, 8, and 9. For each pair of partners, do the finger wiggle at least four times. If desired, ask a volunteer to write the expression for each pair of partners on the board.

Have everyone hold up 8 fingers and choose partners of 8 (for example, 1 and 7). Do finger wiggles with the class.

• Wiggle (or bend) 1 finger. Now wiggle the other 7 fingers.

It is important that children wiggle all of the other fingers for the second partner. In whatever way they showed 1 finger (wiggle or bend), they should wiggle the other 7 fingers. This helps them feel that 1 and 7 come from the 8 and together make 8.

Ask children to wiggle 1 and 7 at least three more times.

• Let's really feel these partners. Wiggle 1. Now wiggle 7. Oh, we're getting better. Wiggle 1 again, now wiggle 7. Look, it's getting easier! Let's do it again. Wiggle 1. Then wiggle 7.

Continue with different partners of 8, 9, and 7.

COMMON CORE
Mathematical Practice
CC.K–12.MP.8
Mathematical Content
CC.K.CC.4, CC.K.CC.4c, CC.K.CC.5, CC.K.NBT.1

20 MINUTES

FOCUS Make numbers 1–20 using 10-sticks and centimeter cubes.

MATERIALS 1–20 Boards (TRB M36–M39; placed side by side; 1 per pair), 10-sticks (12 per pair), centimeter cubes (90 per pair)

 *i*Tools: Counters

Whiteboard Lesson

Digital Resource

***i*Tools** Choose 'Counters' on the Menu. Use Activity 1 'Count' with the tab for 'Activities.' Children can use counters to count.

COMMON CORE
Mathematical Practice
CC.K–12.MP.1, CC.K–12.MP.2, CC.K–12.MP.7
Mathematical Content
CC.K.OA.1, CC.K.OA.2, CC.K.OA.3

15 MINUTES

FOCUS Practice finding partners for 7–9 with finger activities and a game.

MATERIALS Number Tiles 1–9 (1 set per pair), centimeter cubes (18 per pair), Break-Apart Sticks (1 per pair), +/– Tiles (1 per pair)

 Whiteboard Lesson

▶ Play *The Unknown Partner Game* for 7–9 PAIRS

This is the game children played previously in Unit 5, Lesson 9. **Student Pairs** sit beside each other, facing the working space. For each turn, children take out only the number of centimeter cubes needed for the Number Tile selected.

In the example shown below, 8 centimeter cubes are placed under Number Tile 8. Then one child takes a Break-Apart Stick, while the other child covers his or her eyes and turns away. The first child places the Break-Apart Stick to make any two partners of 8. The child then removes and hides the cubes for one partner (in this example, 3), leaving the Break-Apart Stick and the other 5 cubes in place. When finished, the first child asks what partner is gone.

• What partner of 8 did I take?

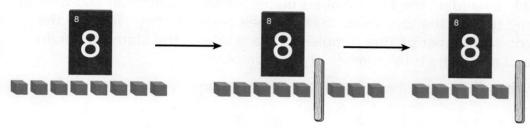

MP.2 Reason Abstractly and Quantitatively The second child now looks at the centimeter cubes to find the partner that has been taken. Children can count the cubes they see and then count on to 8 with their fingers, or they may be able to visualize 8 cubes and mentally "see" how many are missing. There may be some children who still need to place the cubes as they count on. The second child now names the two partners and puts the appropriate Number Tiles and the +/– Tile in place below the cubes. This completes one turn.

Children then reverse roles and play the game again to find several pairs of partners for numbers 7, 8, and 9, continuing as time permits.

MP.1 Make Sense of Problems You may encourage children to create simple stories to describe the situation. For example: There are 8 flowers in a vase. Five flowers are red and the rest are yellow. How many flowers in the vase are yellow?

English Language Learners

Write 3 + 5 = 8 on the board. Say: **3 and 5 are the *partners*. 8 is the *total*.**

BEGINNING

Ask: **Do we add 3 and 5?** yes Say: **We add the partners to get the total.** Ask children to repeat.

INTERMEDIATE AND ADVANCED

Say: **The numbers we add are the __.** partners Name the partners. 3 and 5 **The answer is the __.** total Say the total. 8

Learning Community— Best Practices

Helping Community Modeling numbers on the 1–20 Board in Activity 1 is a good cooperative learning opportunity. As in previous lessons (Lessons 5, 7, and 9), continue pairing children with strong teen-number concepts with children who need additional support. Have stronger learners work on the 1–10 side of the board, and encourage them to provide support and help as needed to children who are trying to master numbers on the 11–20 side of the board.

COMMON CORE
Mathematical Practice
CC.K–12.MP.2, CC.K–12.MP.6,
CC.K–12.MP.8
Mathematical Content
CC.K.OA.1, CC.K.OA.3, CC.K.OA.5

20 MINUTES
FOCUS Use Tiny Tumblers to find partner totals.

MATERIALS Student Activity Book pages 247–248

iT *i*Tools: Counters

 Whiteboard Lesson

Digital Resource

***i*Tools** Choose 'Counters' on the Menu. Use Activity 3 'Add' with the tab for 'Activities.' Children can use counters to help them add two numbers. Then they enter the total.

Use Activity 4 'Subtract' with the tab for 'Activities.' Children can use counters to help them subtract. Then they enter the partner.

ACTIVITY 3

Find Totals from Partners

▶ Partners on Math Mountains WHOLE CLASS

Instruct children to look at Student Activity Book page 247.

Ask children to talk about what kinds of games they think the Tiny Tumblers might be playing on the mountainside.

MP.2 Reason Quantitatively Review that the numbers at the bottom of each Math Mountain tell how many Tiny Tumblers are playing on each side of the mountain. Children are to find the total for each Math Mountain. They can draw the correct number of Tiny Tumblers on each side of the mountain and then count them to find the total.

Encourage advanced learners to complete Student Activity Book page 247 by adding the two numbers under the Math mountain and writing the total at the top. Then, to check their answers, they can draw the correct number of Tiny Tumblers on each side of the Math Mountain and count the total number of Tiny Tumblers.

When children have finished, discuss the page.

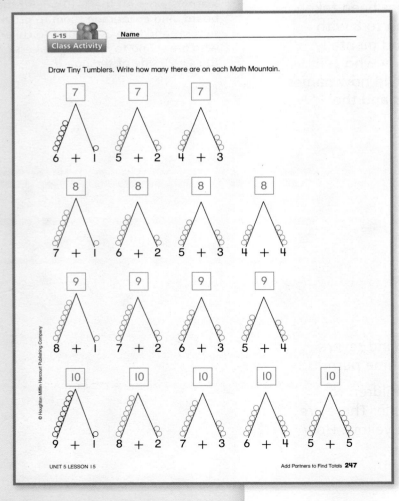

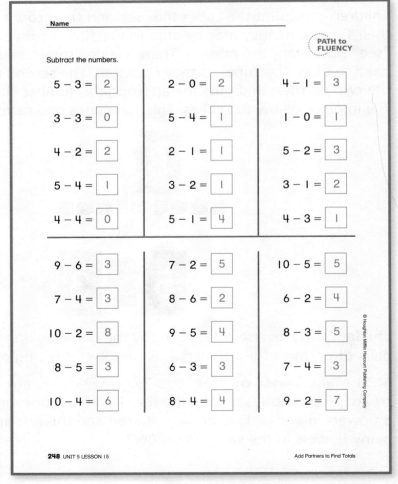

Student Activity Book pages 247–248

Let's look at the Math Mountains you've just completed. The Tiny Tumblers on the sides are a way of showing pairs of partners for the numbers at the tops of the mountains.

MP.6 Attend to Precision **Look at the first row. What are some things you notice?**

Ed: They are all 7-mountains. The number at the top is 7.

Jerry: Across the row, the number on the left side goes down by one and the number on the right side goes up by one.

That's right! Does this happen in the other rows, too?

Grace: Yes, in every row the number on one side goes down while the number on the other side goes up.

Katya: If we continued the row and showed the switched partners, we would see this too.

Ed: Yes! For 7, another Math Mountain could be 3 + 4.

There is a + between the pairs of numbers at the bottom of each mountain. What does this mean?

Jerry: The + means you can add the 2 numbers at the bottom to get the number at the top.

Grace: We can add the partner numbers to find the total, then count all the Tiny Tumblers to check the total.

Now look at the last Math Mountain in the row for 8 and in the row for 10. These are called doubles. Why do you think they are called that?

Katya: The number of Tiny Tumblers is the same on both sides. The partners are the same.

 Practice Subtraction INDIVIDUALS

MP.8 Use Repeated Reasoning Instruct children to complete Student Activity Book page 248. This page includes practice for both subtraction within 5 and subtraction within 10. Check children as they work.

 Formative Assessment: Check Understanding

Student Summary Ask children to identify the pairs of partners that equal 8, not including switched partners. 7 + 1 (or 1 + 7), 6 + 2 (or 2 + 6), 5 + 3 (or 3 + 5), 4 + 4 Instruct children to draw Math Mountains with Tiny Tumblers to show these partners.

▲ On Level    Tier 1
for students having success

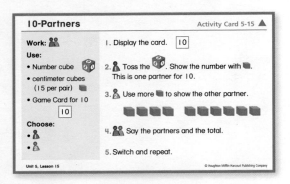

Activity Notes Explain that children will toss a number cube to name one partner for 10, and then use centimeter cubes to show both that partner and the other partner.

 Math Writing Prompt

Partners for 10 Ask children to write all the partner pairs for 10, including switched partners.

 MegaMath

Software Support
Country Countdown:
Counting Critters, Level D

■ Challenge
for students seeking a challenge

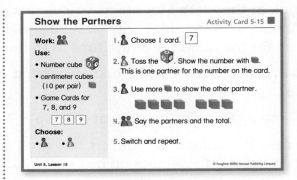

Activity Notes Suggest that children first complete the On Level Activity (10-Partners). This activity is similar, finding partners for 7, 8, and 9.

 Math Writing Prompt

Partner Pairs Ask children to write all the partner pairs for 8 and 9 including switched partners.

 Destination Math®

Software Support
Course I: Module 1: Unit 3: Session 1: Counting from 10 to 20

Distribute Homework and Remembering pages 109–110. Page 109 provides children with additional practice using Math Mountains, while page 110 reviews subtraction equations within 5 and within 10.

✓ Include children's completed homework page as part of their portfolios.

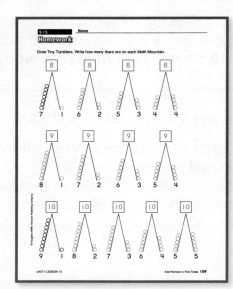 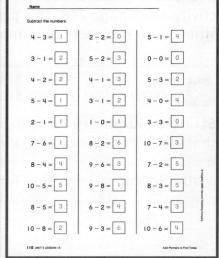

Homework and Remembering page 109   Homework and Remembering page 110

Story Problems and Comparing: Totals Through 10

LESSON FOCUS

- Tell, retell, and solve addition and subtraction stories.
- Compare the number of objects in two groups, and take away objects to make groups equal.

VOCABULARY

add
subtract
greater than
less than
equal

COMMON CORE

Mathematical Practice
CC.K–12.MP.1, CC.K–12.MP.3, CC.K–12.MP.6, CC.K–12.MP.8
Mathematical Content
CC.K.CC.3, CC.K.CC.5, CC.K.CC.6, CC.K.OA.1, CC.K.OA.2

The Day at a Glance

Teaching the Lesson

MATH BACKGROUND for this lesson is included on pp. 461GG–461II, 461PP.

ACTIVITY FOCUS

Activity 1 Tell, retell, and solve addition and subtraction story problems with drawings and equations.

Activity 2 Compare groups, and cross out objects to make equal groups.

MATERIALS

Student Activity Book pp. 249–250

*i*Tools: Counters • Whiteboard

Differentiated Instruction

MATERIALS

Activity Cards 5-16 • Centimeter cubes • Construction paper • Math Journals

Soar to Success Math Intervention • MegaMath • Destination Math®

RtI Tier 1 • Tier 2 • Tier 3

Homework

MATERIALS

Homework and Remembering pp. 111–112

QUICK PRACTICE 5 MINUTES

Repeated Quick Practice Use this Quick Practice from a previous lesson.

The Partner Peek on the 10-Partner Showcase (See Unit 5, Lesson 13.)

DAILY ROUTINES

Counting Tens and Ones
(See pp. xxxi–xxxii.)

DIGITAL RESOURCES

Use these digital resources along with your eSAB and eTE to support your students' learning experiences.

Professional Development

Whiteboard Lesson

*i*Tools

Soar to Success Math Intervention

MegaMath

Destination Math®

30 MINUTES

FOCUS Tell, retell, and solve addition and subtraction story problems with drawings and equations.

 *i*Tools: Counters (see below)

 Whiteboard Lesson

25 MINUTES

FOCUS Compare groups, and cross out objects to make equal groups.

MATERIALS Student Activity Book pages 249–250

 Whiteboard Lesson

Digital Resource

*i***Tools** Choose 'Counters' on the Menu. Use Activity 3 'Add' with the tab for 'Activities.' Children can use counters to help them add two numbers. Then they enter the total.

Use Activity 4 'Subtract' with the tab for 'Activities.' Children can use counters to help them subtract. Then they enter the partner.

ACTIVITY 1 🔤 Language Arts Connection

Tell, Retell, and Solve Story Problems

▶ Tell and Solve Addition and Subtraction Stories WHOLE CLASS

MP.1 Make Sense of Problems Ask children to tell addition and subtraction story problems, solve them with math drawings, and write the corresponding expressions or equations. Encourage children to use numbers with totals up to 10 (5 + 4 , 9 − 7, 10 − 4, and so on).

ACTIVITY 2

Greater Than, Less Than, or Equal

▶ Compare Groups and Take Away to Make Groups Equal WHOLE CLASS

Distribute Student Activity Book page 249. Remind children that in an earlier lesson (Unit 5, Lesson 14), they compared two groups to find which had the greater number and which had the lesser number of objects. Then they drew more objects to make the two groups equal.

Today, they will compare the numbers in two groups and cross out (take away) objects to make the groups equal. Note that by crossing objects out, they can see how many more the group with the greater number has. After going over the example, allow children to continue on their own.

When completed, review the page with the class. For each pair, have a volunteer name which number is greater and which is less, and say how many were crossed out to make the groups equal.

▶ What's the Error? WHOLE CLASS

MP.3, MP.6 Construct Viable Arguments/Critique Reasoning of Others Puzzled Penguin This Puzzled Penguin activity addresses the error of incorrectly identifying which number is *greater* and which is *less* when comparing two numbers.

 Discuss with children whether Puzzled Penguin's work is correct and how they can help.

- Puzzled Penguin counted groups of objects and compared the numbers as we have just done.

- Let's look at Puzzled Penguin's work. For each pair of groups, we should check that both the counting and comparison are correct.

- Count the number of objects in both rows of Exercise 7. Did Puzzled Penguin count correctly? yes Did Puzzled Penguin correctly show which number is greater and which is less? yes

Ask a volunteer to say the two comparisons. 6 is less than 7 and 7 is greater than 6.

• Yes! Now cross out the extra object to make the groups equal.

MP.8 Use Repeated Reasoning Continue in this way with the remaining problems. Ask: What two steps are needed each time to check Puzzled Penguin's work? Count the objects in the groups and then see whether the numbers were compared correctly.

Children should determine that Exercises 8 and 10 have incorrect comparisons. Ask them to cross out the incorrect letters and rewrite them to the side.

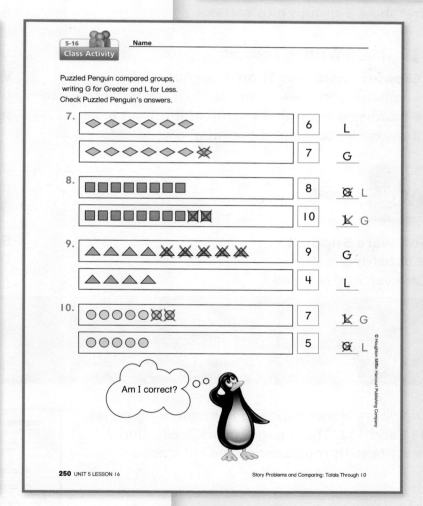

Student Activity Book pages 249–250

✅ **Formative Assessment: Check Understanding**

Student Summary Draw a row of 6 circles on the board and a row of 9 circles below it. Ask children to count each group and write the number beside the row. Ask children to write G and L and to say the two comparisons. 6 is less than 9; 9 is greater than 6.

▲ On Level  Tier 1
for students having success

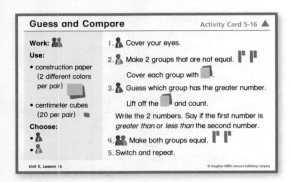

Activity Notes Encourage children to make groups that show 5-groups plus extras.

 Math Writing Prompt

Greater Than/Less Than Ask children to write the number 6 and draw 6 circles. Then ask them to write a number greater and a number less than 6, and draw circles to show those numbers.

 MegaMath

Software Support
Numberopolis:
Carnival Stories, Level C

■ Challenge
for students seeking a challenge

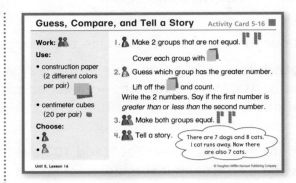

Activity Notes Have children practice the On Level Activity, and then include storytelling.

 Math Writing Prompt

Write Equations Extend the activity by having children write the equations that go with their subtraction stories.

 Destination Math®

Software Support
Course I: Module 2: Unit 1: Session 1: Combining and Joining within 10

Distribute Homework and Remembering pages 111 and 112. These pages provide additional practice with comparisons and subtraction.

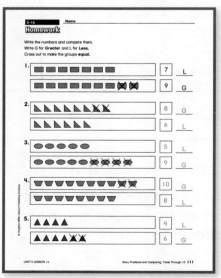

Homework and Remembering page 111   Homework and Remembering page 112

Subtract to Make Equal Groups

LESSON FOCUS
- Visualize teen numbers as ten ones and further ones.
- Compare the number of objects in groups, and compare numbers.

VOCABULARY
add
subtract
greater
greater than
less
less than
equal

COMMON CORE
Mathematical Practice
CC.K–12.MP.2, CC.K–12.MP.3, CC.K–12.MP.6,
CC.K–12.MP.7, CC.K–12.MP.8
Mathematical Content
CC.K.CC.3, CC.K.CC.5, CC.K.CC.6,
CC.K.CC.7, CC.K.NBT.1

The Day at a Glance

USE
MATH TALK
TODAY!

Teaching the Lesson

MATH BACKGROUND for this lesson is included on pp. 461JJ–461KK, 461PP.

ACTIVITY FOCUS

Activity 1   Visualize a group of ten in a teen number using *The Hiding Zero Game*.

Activity 2   Compare the number of objects in two groups, and make groups equal.

Activity 3   Compare two numbers.

MATERIALS

📖 Student Activity Book pp. 251–252 • Hiding Zero Gameboard • Number Tiles 1–10 • Giant Number Cards 1–10 • Number Parade (optional)

💻 *i*Tools: Counters • Whiteboard

Differentiated Instruction

MATERIALS

📖 Activity Cards 5-17 • Small bags of classroom objects • Index cards • Math Journals

💻 Soar to Success Math Intervention • MegaMath • Destination Math®

 **RtI**   Tier 1 • Tier 2 • Tier 3

Homework

MATERIALS

📖 Homework and Remembering pp. 113–114

QUICK PRACTICE 🕐 5 MINUTES

Repeated Quick Practice Use this Quick Practice from a previous lesson.

The Partner Peek on the 10-Partner Showcase Beginning today, tell children they can choose whether to open their eyes or to keep them closed while showing the partners with their fingers. (See Unit 5, Lesson 13.)

DAILY ROUTINES

Counting Tens and Ones
(See pp. xxxi–xxxii.)

DIGITAL RESOURCES

Use these digital resources along with your eSAB and eTE to support your students' learning experiences.

Professional Development

Whiteboard Lesson

*i*Tools

Soar to Success Math Intervention

MegaMath

Destination Math®

COMMON CORE

Mathematical Practice
CC.K–12.MP.7

Mathematical Content
CC.K.NBT.1

10 MINUTES

FOCUS Visualize a group of ten in a teen number using *The Hiding Zero Game.*

MATERIALS Hiding Zero Gameboard (from Unit 5, Lesson 6 or TRB M55–M57; 1 set per pair), Number Tiles 1–10 (TRB M19–M20; 1 set per pair), Giant Number Cards 1–10 (TRB M7–M18)

 Whiteboard Lesson

Learning Community— Best Practices

Building Concepts As children learn to see the 10 in a teen number, they are developing their mental math skills. Later on, children will make the leap to recognizing the tens place, which is the beginning of understanding place value.

ACTIVITY 1

Play *The Hiding Zero Game*

▶ **Set Up and Play the Game**

This activity uses **Student Pairs** and **Whole Class Practice with Student Leaders** structures.

Children were introduced to this activity in Unit 5, Lesson 6. Remind them that the goal of *The Hiding Zero Game* is to see the ten in the teen number. They will do this by putting a single digit over the 0 of the 10 to make the teen number.

MP.7 Look for Structure Ask Student Pairs to arrange their three Hiding Zero Gameboard pages in order, vertically or horizontally. Then have them work together to put the correct Number Tile on top of the 0 in each 10.

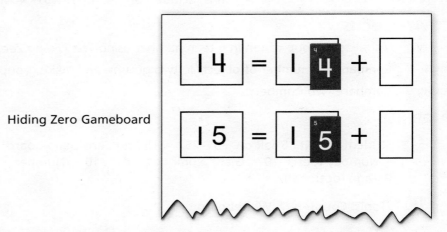

Hiding Zero Gameboard

A Student Leader calls out a teen number (for example, 15) and shows the number with the Giant Number Cards (holding the 5 over the 0 of the 10). One child in each Student Pair picks up Number Tile 5, which is covering the 0 of the 10, and puts it in the blank rectangle. Together, the class says the following:

• 15 equals 10 plus 5.

• This is the ten in 15 (pointing to the 1).

• This is the 5 in 15 (pointing to the 5.)

The Student Leader should pull apart the Giant Number Cards as the class is saying "15 equals 10 plus 5." The Student Leader continues calling out different numbers until all of the zeroes have been uncovered on the gameboards.

You can have children play the game again, if there is time. Both the visual and auditory components are important in this activity. Invite children to discuss their observations.

• **What do you notice about each number?** Each teen number is made by replacing the zero in 10 with the number that tells how many more ones there are.

Greater Than, Less Than, or Equal

▶ **Compare Groups and Add or Subtract to Make Groups Equal** [INDIVIDUALS]

Distribute Student Activity Book page 251.

MP.2 Reason Abstractly and Quantitatively In this activity, children will first count the number of objects in two groups and compare the numbers. Then they will make equal groups by adding (drawing) more objects to the smaller group or by taking away (crossing out) objects from the larger group. Children can determine how many to add or subtract by drawing lines to match, by counting, or by visual correspondence.

MP.8 Use Repeated Reasoning Conclude Children will realize they can make two groups equal either by adding to the group that has less or by taking away from the one that has the greater number. It is important for children to experience both processes. While completing the activity, children will be exposed to the partner relationships that are embedded (the group that has less plus the difference between the groups are partners of the greater number).

COMMON CORE

Mathematical Practice
CC.K–12.MP.2, CC.K–12.MP.8
Mathematical Content
CC.K.CC.3, CC.K.CC.5, CC.K.CC.6

20 MINUTES

FOCUS Compare the number of objects in two groups, and make groups equal.

MATERIALS Student Activity Book page 251

 *i*Tools: Counters

Whiteboard Lesson

5-17 Class Activity   Name _____

Write the numbers and compare them. Write **G** for **Greater** and **L** for **Less**. Add (draw more) to make the groups **equal**.

VOCABULARY
greater
less
equal

1. ▢▢▢▢⬚⬚ | 4 | L
    ▢▢▢▢▢▢ | 6 | G

2. ●●●●●●●○ | 8 | L
    ●●●●●●●●● | 9 | G

3. ▲▲▲▲▲▲▲ | 7 | G
    ▲▲▲▲▲△△ | 5 | L

Write the numbers and compare them. Write **G** for **Greater** and **L** for **Less**. Subtract (cross out) to make the groups **equal**.

4. ▨▨▨▨▨▨▨ | 7 | G
    ▨▨▨▨ | 4 | L

5. ◆◆◆◆◆◆ | 6 | L
    ◆◆◆◆◆◆✕✕✕✕ | 10 | G

6. ◉◉◉⊗⊗⊗ | 6 | G
    ◉◉◉ | 3 | L

© Houghton Mifflin Harcourt Publishing Company

UNIT 5 LESSON 17   Subtract to Make Equal Groups **251**

Student Activity Book page 251

English Language Learners

Draw a box with 2 stars and a box with 3 stars. Ask: **Are the number of stars** *equal*? no Say: **Let's make them** *equal*.

BEGINNING

Erase one of the 3 stars. Ask: **Did I add a star?** no **Did I subtract**? yes **Are the number of stars equal now**? yes

INTERMEDIATE

Point to the 3 stars. Ask: **Do I add or subtract a star to make this equal to the other group?** subtract

ADVANCED

Ask children to describe two ways they can make the stars equal.

Digital Resource

*i***Tools** Choose 'Counters' on the Menu. Use Activity 1 'Count' with the tab for 'Activities.' Children can use counters to count.

COMMON CORE

Mathematical Practice
CC.K–12.MP.2, CC.K–12.MP.3,
CC.K–12.MP.6

Mathematical Content
CC.K.CC.7

20 MINUTES

FOCUS Compare two numbers.

MATERIALS Student Activity Book page 252, Number Parade (optional)

Whiteboard Lesson

Teaching Notes

Watch For! The comparison of numerals may confuse some children because direction (first number/second number) is involved. If you notice a child is having difficulty, suggest that he or she refer to the Number Parade. Point out that numbers on the right are *greater than* numbers to their left.

Math Symbols When the two numbers are equal, some children may write the equal sign (=) rather than E on the Student Activity Book page. Accept the answer as correct, but point out that E was requested. The comparison symbols for greater than (>) and less than (<), however, may be confusing to many Kindergarten children. These will be introduced in Grade 1.

ACTIVITY 3

Compare Numbers

▶ Compare Numbers Written as Numerals | WHOLE CLASS |

Ask the class to look at Student Activity Book page 252. Explain that children will continue to practice comparing numbers, but this time without the groups of objects showing the numbers.

In the activity they just completed, children showed which group had the greater number of objects and which had the lesser number of objects, comparing the numbers by writing *both* G and L next to the groups.

MP.2 Reason Abstractly and Quantitatively In this activity, children are comparing the first number to the second number, and writing one comparison letter between the two numbers. Stress that direction is important in writing this comparison. They must determine whether the number on the left is *greater than, equal to,* or *less than* the number on the right.

Write 5 ___ 4, 8 ___ 10, and 6 ___ 6 on the board. Ask volunteers to write the correct comparison letter for each pair of numbers. G; L; E Ask the others in the class whether they agree with the comparisons, and discuss as needed. Reinforce the order by having the class say each comparison aloud. Then instruct children to complete the top of the Student Activity Book page.

Student Activity Book page 252

▶ What's the Error? `WHOLE CLASS`

MP.3, MP.6 Construct Viable Arguments/Critique Reasoning of Others Puzzled Penguin This Puzzled Penguin activity addresses the error of incorrectly identifying whether the first number is greater than or less than the second number when comparing two numbers.

 Discuss with children whether Puzzled Penguin's work is correct or not, and how they can help.

• Puzzled Penguin compared pairs of numbers, as we have just done.

• Let's look at Puzzled Penguin's work.

Write **6 L 4** on the board. Ask children to read the comparison aloud.

• Is this correct? No. Why? 6 is greater than 4.

• What letter should be shown instead of the L? G

Ask a volunteer to come to the board to cross out L and write G. Direct children to make the change on their papers.

• What are some ways we could check the comparison?

MP.6 Attend to Precision Describe Methods Encourage children to discuss methods of comparing the two numbers. They may suggest drawing groups of shapes, using objects, or referring to the Number Parade.

Continue with the remaining problems. Children should determine that the last comparison is incorrect and change this to 6 L 8.

✓ Formative Assessment: Check Understanding

Student Summary Write the following number pairs on the board. Ask children to write the letter (G, L, or E) for each comparison and then say the comparison aloud.

5 _L_ 9   10 _G_ 6   8 _E_ 8   4 _G_ 2   7 _G_ 3   4 _L_ 5

 We have been comparing both groups of objects and numbers to see whether one is greater than, equal to, or less than the other.

What are different ways we can compare groups of objects?

LaDonna: One way is to match the objects in the two groups. If the objects are in drawings, we can draw lines to match them up.

Oscar: And if the objects are real, we can line them up side by side. That way we can see which group has more.

Yes! What is another way to compare groups?

Connie: Another way is to count the number of things in the groups and compare the numbers. That's a good way to compare the number of objects in drawings, if it's hard to draw lines between the groups.

LaDonna: Yes, if the groups are far apart or if the objects aren't in a row, it would be hard to draw lines to match them.

Joe: You have to be careful when you count. You could make a mark on each object as you count it. That way you wouldn't count something two times or miss something.

That's a good idea, Joe. Now let's talk about comparing numbers when we don't see the groups.

MP.2 Reason Abstractly and Quantitatively How do we compare two numbers?

Connie: We should look at the first number and decide if it's greater than, less than, or equal to the second number.

Oscar: It might help to visualize the numbers as groups. If we had to, we could draw the groups to show the numbers.

Joe: It might also help to look at the Number Parade. As you go right on the Number Parade, the numbers get bigger. They are greater than the numbers before them.

▲ On Level ▲ RtI Tier 1

for students having success

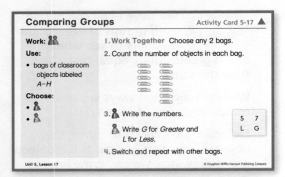

Activity Notes Prepare 8 small plastic bags with different numbers of small objects, such as paper clips. Label the bags *A* through *H*.

✎ Math Writing Prompt

Compare Groups Ask each child to draw 2 rows with different numbers of circles. Children then write the numbers and G and L to compare.

 MegaMath

Software Support
Country Countdown:
Harrison's Comparisons, Level H

■ Challenge

for students seeking a challenge

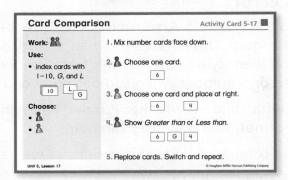

Activity Notes Prepare a set of index cards with the numbers 1–10 and the letters *G* and *L*. Demonstrate selecting two cards and comparing them.

✎ Math Writing Prompt

Compare Two Ways Ask children to write each comparison and draw to check it. Encourage children to say the comparison aloud.

 Destination Math®

Software Support
Course I: Module 1: Unit 3: Session 1: Counting from 10 to 20

Distribute Homework and Remembering pages 113 and 114. Page 113 provides children with subtraction practice, while on the back children draw equal groups of triangles.

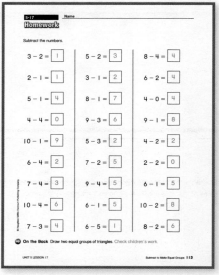

Homework and Remembering page 113

Tens and Ones

LESSON FOCUS
- Visualize teen numbers as a group of ten ones and further ones.

VOCABULARY
teen number

COMMON CORE

Mathematical Practice
CC.K–12.MP.2, CC.K–12.MP.7, CC.K–12.MP.8
Mathematical Content
CC.K.OA.3, CC.K.OA.4, CC.K.OA.5, CC.K.NBT.1

The Day at a Glance

USE MATH TALK TODAY!

Teaching the Lesson

MATH BACKGROUND for this lesson is included on pp. 461JJ, 461MM–461OO.

ACTIVITY FOCUS

Activity 1   Show teen numbers as a group of ten and extra ones by drawing.

Activity 2   Record partners for 10 and 6.

MATERIALS

📖   Student Activity Book pp. 253–256 • Crayons or markers

💻   *i*Tools: Counters • Whiteboard

Differentiated Instruction

MATERIALS

📖   Activity Cards 5-18 • Connecting cubes • Math Journals

💻   Soar to Success Math Intervention • MegaMath • Destination Math®

🔺 **RtI**   Tier 1 • Tier 2 • Tier 3

Home or School Activity

MATERIALS

💻   Technology Connection p. 548

QUICK PRACTICE ⏱ 5 MINUTES

Repeated Quick Practice Use this Quick Practice from a previous lesson.

The Partner Peek on the 10-Partner Showcase (See Unit 5, Lesson 17.)

DAILY ROUTINES

Counting Tens and Ones
(See pp. xxxi–xxxii.)

DIGITAL RESOURCES

Use these digital resources along with your eSAB and eTE to support your students' learning experiences.

 Professional Development

 Whiteboard Lesson

 *i*Tools

 Soar to Success Math Intervention

 MegaMath

 Destination Math®

COMMON CORE

Mathematical Practice
CC.K–12.MP.7, CC.K–12.MP.8

Mathematical Content
CC.K.NBT.1

15 MINUTES

FOCUS Show teen numbers as a group of ten and extra ones by drawing.

MATERIALS Student Activity Book page 253, crayons or markers

iT *iTools:* Counters

 Whiteboard Lesson

Digital Resource

iTools Choose 'Counters' on the Menu. Use Activity 1 'Count' with the tab for 'Activities.' Children can use counters to count.

Learning Community— Best Practices

MATH TALK What types of questions are you asking your students? Are you only asking questions that elicit a short answer, or do you probe to learn more about children's thinking as they tell about their work? If possible, make a video or audio recording of yourself leading a math lesson. Play it back and make notes about the types of questions you ask. Reflect on any changes you would like to make. Write a date in your planning book to do this again and see if you observe changes.

ACTIVITY 1

See Teens as Ten Ones and Further Ones

▶ Show Teen Numbers   WHOLE CLASS

MP.7 Use Structure Student Activity Book page 253 offers children another opportunity to see and make teen numbers with a group of ten and some extra ones. Children will draw circles or dots to show each teen number in order.

Student Activity Book page 253

Instruct children to use a different color for each row to help each teen number stand out as a group of ten and some extra ones. Tell children that it is all right to repeat colors, if needed, in the lower rows.

Circulate around the room as children work. Ask questions such as these: Which teen number will you (did you) show here? How many extra ones are in this teen number? How is this teen number different from the one before it?

MP.8 Use Repeated Reasoning When children have finished the page, have everyone point to each number and read the equation together (for example, $11 = 10 + 1$). Invite several children to show the circles they drew.

Switch the Partners for 10 and 6

▶ **Complete Partner Equations** | INDIVIDUALS |

MP.7 Look for Structure Identify Relationships Student Activity Book page 254 is an opportunity for children to review some equations in which partners are switched and reinforces the fact that the partners can appear in either order in an equation without changing the total.

When looking at the 10-partners (first two columns), focus children's attention on the 5-groups, which allow children to "see" the numbers rapidly. Equations in which the partners for 10 are switched are beside each other. For space considerations, equations in which partners of 6 are switched are positioned vertically.

After children have completed the page, practice 10-partners and 6-partners by saying one partner and asking children to say the other.

If desired, you may say both partners as an expression (9 + 1) and ask children to say the switched partners as an expression (1 + 9).

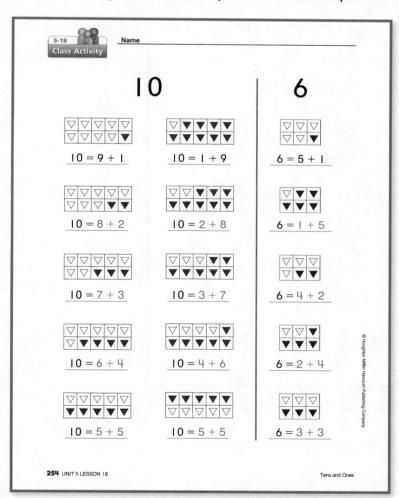

Student Activity Book page 254

COMMON CORE

Mathematical Practice
CC.K–12.MP.2, CC.K–12.MP.7, CC.K–12.MP.8
Mathematical Content
CC.K.OA.3, CC.K.OA.4, CC.K.OA.5

25 MINUTES

FOCUS Record partners for 10 and 6.

MATERIALS Student Activity Book pages 254–256

 *i*Tools: Counters

Whiteboard Lesson

English Language Learners

On the board, write the equation 10 = 6 + 4 and the equation 10 = 4 + 6 directly below. Say: **When we switch the partners, we write the partners in a different order.**

BEGINNING

Say: **Both equations have 10 as the total. We have switched the partners from the first equation to the second. Draw or motion how the 6 and 4 have traded places.** Say: **Repeat after me, switch the partners.**

INTERMEDIATE

Say: **What number is the total in these two equations.** 10 **Are the same two numbers partners in both equations?** yes **What are the partner numbers?** 4 and 6 **The partners are switched from one equation to the other.**

ADVANCED

Say: **Both equations have the same two partners, but the order of the partners is different. This is called ___.** switching the partners

Learning Community— Best Practices

Building Concepts Activities like Student Activity Book page 254 help children learn to recognize that a collection of objects is composed of two subcollections and by combining their cardinalities the cardinality of the collection is found (conceptual subitizing).

Activity continued ▶

Differentiated Instruction

Special Needs For children who have difficulty reading problems line by line, provide a strip of paper that they can use to uncover one line of problems at at time.

Digital Resource

***i*Tools** Choose 'Counters' on the Menu. Use Activity 4 'Subtract' with the tab for 'Activities.' Children can use counters to help them subtract. Then they enter the partner.

▶ **PATH to FLUENCY** **Practice Subtraction Within 5 and Within 10** INDIVIDUALS

MP.8 Use Repeated Reasoning Instruct children to complete Student Activity Book pages 255 and 256. These pages continue practice for subtraction within 10. Check children as they work.

If desired, you may include any or all of the following activities as children work on these subtraction equations:

Instruct children to find and solve all of the – 0 problems first. Ask what is true about – 0 problems. Children should indicate that the answer is the same as the starting number. Ask them to discuss why this is true.

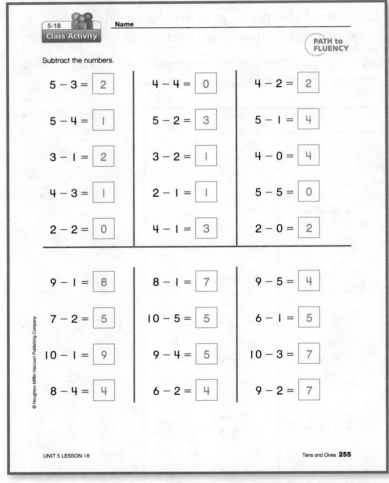

Student Activity Book page 255

Next, instruct children to find and solve all of the −1 problems. Ask them to describe the location of the beginning number and the answer on the Number Parade. Children should indicate that the answer is one place to the left of the beginning number.

MP.2 Reason Abstractly and Quantitatively Connect Symbols and Words Ask for volunteers to select a problem from the bottom 4 rows and tell a story problem using those numbers.

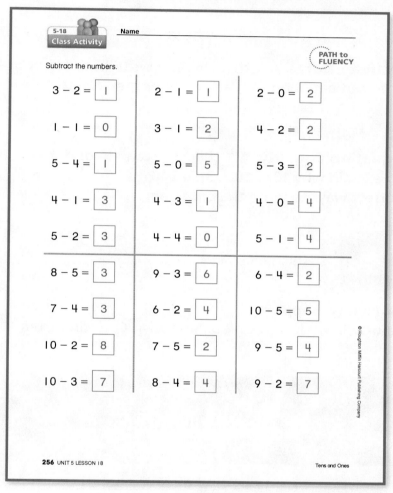

Student Activity Book page 256

✅ **Formative Assessment: Check Understanding**

Student Summary Ask children whether switching addition partners changes the total. They should indicate that the order of the numbers added together has no effect on the total. If desired, you may ask children to verify this by drawing 2 small groups of circles on the board. Ask children to count the total twice, first by starting with one group and then by starting with the other group.

▲ On Level  Tier 1
for students having success

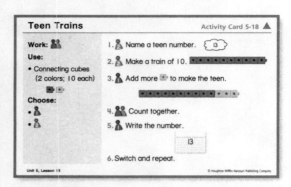

Activity Notes One child picks the teen number, and then both build it using connecting cubes.

 Math Writing Prompt

Write Addition Sentences Encourage children to write addition expressions or equations to go along with each teen number created.

 MegaMath

Software Support
Country Countdown:
Block Busters, Level G

■ Challenge
for students seeking a challenge

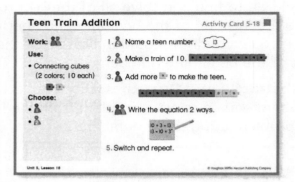

Activity Notes Ask that children write both forms of the teen equation for each number they create.

 Math Writing Prompt

Equation Equality Ask children to write or draw to explain why $13 = 10 + 3$ and $10 + 3 = 13$ are both correct ways to write the equation.

 Destination Math®

Software Support
Course I: Module 1: Unit 3: Session 1: Counting from 10 to 20

 ## Technology Connection

Make Teen Number Pictures Help children use a drawing program to make pictures (either with clip art or drawings of their own) that represent teen numbers as a group of ten ones and extra ones. For example, a child might use 10 red apples and 4 green apples to show the number 14.

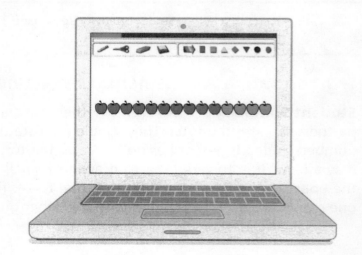

Teen Numbers, Partners, and Equations

LESSON FOCUS
- Tell, retell, and solve addition and subtraction stories.
- Show teen numbers as a group of ten ones and further ones.

COMMON CORE

Mathematical Practice
CC.K–12.MP.4, CC.K–12.MP.5, CC.K–12.MP.6
Mathematical Content
CC.K.CC.4, CC.K.CC.5, CC.K.OA.1, CC.K.OA.2, CC.K.NBT.1

The Day at a Glance

USE MATH TALK TODAY!

Teaching the Lesson

MATH BACKGROUND for this lesson is included on pp. 461GG–461JJ.

ACTIVITY FOCUS

Activity 1   Tell, retell, and solve addition and subtraction story problems with drawings and equations.

Activity 2   Make drawings to show teen numbers as a group of ten ones and extra ones.

MATERIALS

- Student Activity Book pp. 257–258
- *i*Tools: Counters • Whiteboard

Differentiated Instruction

MATERIALS

- Activity Cards 5-19 • Centimeter cubes • 10-sticks • Math Journals
- Soar to Success Math Intervention • MegaMath • Destination Math®
- **RtI** Tier 1 • Tier 2 • Tier 3

Home or School Activity

MATERIALS

- Science Connection p. 552

QUICK PRACTICE ◔ 5 MINUTES

Repeated Quick Practice Use this Quick Practice from a previous lesson.

The Partner Peek on the 10-Partner Showcase (See Unit 5, Lesson 17.)

DAILY ROUTINES

Counting Tens and Ones
(See pp. xxxi–xxxii.)

DIGITAL RESOURCES

Use these digital resources along with your eSAB and eTE to support your students' learning experiences.

Professional Development

Whiteboard Lesson

iTools

Soar to Success Math Intervention

MegaMath

Destination Math®

30 MINUTES

FOCUS Tell, retell, and solve addition and subtraction story problems with drawings and equations.

 iTools: Counters

 Whiteboard Lesson

Digital Resource

iTools Choose 'Counters' on the Menu. Use Activity 3 'Add' with the tab for 'Activities.' Children can use counters to help them add two numbers. Then they enter the total.

Use Activity 4 'Subtract' with the tab for 'Activities.' Children can use counters to help them subtract. Then they enter the partner.

Teaching Note

Language and Vocabulary Some common words and phrases that indicate addition or subtraction are as follows: *altogether, total, in all, put them together, left, still,* and *now.* Help children use these words and phrases as they tell and retell math stories.

10 MINUTES

FOCUS Make drawings to show teen numbers as a group of ten ones and extra ones.

MATERIALS Student Activity Book pages 257–258

 Whiteboard Lesson

ACTIVITY 1

Tell, Retell, and Solve Story Problems

▶ Tell Math Story Problems WHOLE CLASS   MATH TALK

Use **Solve and Discuss** for this activity.

MP.4 Model with Mathematics Write an Equation Have children tell addition or subtraction story problems, solve them with math drawings, and write the corresponding equations. Try to have as many children as possible work at the board, while other children work on paper.

MP.6 Attend to Precision Explain Solutions For each story problem, select two children to explain their drawings and equations. Encourage the other children to ask them questions.

As they did in earlier lessons, have children retell each story using different words that mean the same thing. Focus on having children ask the story problem question in different ways.

Children have done this story-problem activity several times in Unit 5 (Lessons 4, 6, 10, and 16). By the end of this lesson, all children should have had multiple turns at the board, at telling their own stories, and at retelling someone else's story. At this point, concentrate on the greater numbers with totals up to 10. Modify the numbers in children's stories as necessary, to include these more challenging numbers ($5 + 4$, $9 - 7$, $10 - 4$, and so on).

To assure that children have experience solving different kinds of problems, you may want to tell a couple of story problems with the types of situations that children don't often create, such as a take apart problem and a problem with both addends unknown. Children can then retell the story problem with different numbers.

ACTIVITY 2

Show Teen Numbers

▶ Complete a Teen Board WHOLE CLASS   MATH TALK

Distribute Student Activity Book page 257 and discuss the layout on the page. It is similar to the 11–20 side of the 1–20 Board. Remind children that they made a similar Teen Board previously (Unit 5, Lesson 3).

MP.5 Use Appropriate Tools Model the Math Be sure children understand that they will draw as they did when they made their Unit 4 Teen Number Books. They can draw circles, dots, triangles, or anything they wish in the 10-sticks. Then, under each pair of 10-sticks, children will write the partners needed to make the teen total.

Under the Teen Board, children should complete the equations showing teen partners.

When children have finished the page, do some oral practice linking the teen number at the top of each column to the expression at the bottom, for example:

• Put your finger on 15. 15 is 10 plus how many? 5

• Let's say it together: 15 is 10 + 5.

MP.6 Attend to Precision Continue by asking children to discuss their observations about the table. Encourage children to note what is alike or different about the numbers, changes in the numbers from left to right, and so on.

▶ **Practice Subtraction** INDIVIDUALS

On Student Activity Book page 258, children build fluency within 5 and practice subtraction within 10.

English Language Learners

Hold up an incomplete *Teen Board*.

BEGINNING

Say: **This is a Teen Board.** Ask children to repeat. Say: **We draw circles to show teen numbers on this board.**

INTERMEDIATE

Ask: **Does this board show all the teen numbers?** yes **Is it a Teen Board?** yes

ADVANCED

Ask: **What kind of numbers are on this board?** teen numbers **What kind of board is it?** Teen Board

Student Activity Book pages 257–258

✓ **Formative Assessment: Check Understanding**

Student Summary Write the numbers 11–19, each followed by an equal sign, in a column on the board. Ask children to name and write the partners for 11. 10 + 1 Continue with the remaining teen numbers.

▲ On Level    Tier 1
for students having success

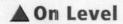

Teen Equations   Activity Card 5-19 ▲

Work: 👥   1. Show a teen number like 19 using ▪.
Use:
• centimeter cubes
  (10 per pair)   2. Say the teen number.

• 10-sticks
  (1 per pair)   3. Write both equations for the   19 = 10 + 9
                         teen number.   10 + 9 = 19

Choose: 4. Say both equations out loud.
• 👤
• 👤   5. Switch and repeat with other teen numbers.

Unit 5, Lesson 19   © Houghton Mifflin Harcourt Publishing Company

Activity Notes Model each step of the activity.

 Math Writing Prompt

Teen Equations Ask children to write both equations showing a teen number and then draw circles in columns to show the two partners.

 MegaMath

Software Support
Numberopolis:
Carnival Stories, Level M

■ Challenge
for students seeking a challenge

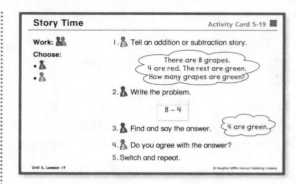

Story Time   Activity Card 5-19 ■

Work: 👥   1. Tell an addition or subtraction story.
Choose:
• 👤   *There are 8 grapes.*
• 👤   *4 are red. The rest are green.*
                      How many grapes are green?

                      2. Write the problem.
                         8 – 4

                      3. Find and say the answer.   *4 are green.*

                      4. Do you agree with the answer?
                      5. Switch and repeat.

Unit 5, Lesson 19   © Houghton Mifflin Harcourt Publishing Company

Activity Notes Encourage children to tell both addition and subtraction stories with totals to 10. Children may also write an equation like $4 + \_\_ = 8$.

 Math Writing Prompt

Solving Problems Ask each child to write or draw a story problem. Have children exchange their stories. Ask them to show the solution with an equation.

 Destination Math®

Software Support
Course I: Module 1: Unit 3: Session 1: Counting from 10 to 20

 ## Science Connection

Animal Addition Ask children to say the number of legs various animals have. You may want to pass around some of the Sorting Card pictures from Student Activity Book pages 119 and 125. Show children how to make a table. A dog has 4 legs, a bird has 2 legs, an insect has 6 legs, a spider has 8 legs, and so on. Then have children do "animal addition" to find the number of legs on 2 dogs. $4 + 4 = 8$ legs Review the term doubles.

Animal	Legs
Dog	4
Bird	2
Insect	6
Spider	8

More Tens in Teen Numbers: A Game

LESSON FOCUS
- Compare the number of objects in groups and compare numbers.
- Visualize teen numbers as ten ones and further ones.

VOCABULARY
subtract
greater
less
equal
teen number

COMMON CORE
Mathematical Practice
CC.K–12.MP.2, CC.K–12.MP.6, CC.K–12.MP.7, CC.K–12.MP.8
Mathematical Content
CC.K.CC.3, CC.K.CC.5, CC.K.CC.6, CC.K.CC.7, CC.K.NBT.1

The Day at a Glance

 USE MATH TALK TODAY!

Teaching the Lesson

MATH BACKGROUND for this lesson is included on pp. 461JJ–461KK, 461PP.

ACTIVITY FOCUS

Activity 1   Compare the number of objects in two groups and make the groups equal.

Activity 2   Visualize a group of ten in a teen number using *The Hiding Zero Game.*

MATERIALS

Student Activity Book pp. 259–262 (includes Family Letter) • Hiding Zero Gameboard • Number Tiles 1–10 • Giant Number Cards 1–10

*i*Tools: Counters • Whiteboard

Differentiated Instruction

MATERIALS

Activity Cards 5-20 • Giant Number Cards 1–10 • Connecting cubes • Math Journals

Soar to Success Math Intervention • MegaMath • Destination Math®

RtI   Tier 1 • Tier 2 • Tier 3

Home and School Connection

MATERIALS

Family Letter (Student Activity Book pp. 259–260)

QUICK PRACTICE   5 MINUTES

Repeated Quick Practice Use this Quick Practice from a previous lesson.

The Partner Peek on the 10-Partner Showcase (See Unit 5, Lesson 17.)

DAILY ROUTINES

Counting Tens and Ones
(See pp. xxxi–xxxii.)

DIGITAL RESOURCES

Use these digital resources along with your eSAB and eTE to support your students' learning experiences.

 Professional Development

 Whiteboard Lesson

 *i*Tools

 Soar to Success Math Intervention

 MegaMath

 Destination Math®

COMMON CORE
Mathematical Practice
CC.K–12.MP.2, CC.K–12.MP.6,
CC.K–12.MP.8
Mathematical Content
CC.K.CC.3, CC.K.CC.5, CC.K.CC.6,
CC.K.CC.7

20 MINUTES

FOCUS Compare the number of objects in two groups and make groups equal.

MATERIALS Student Activity Book pages 261–262

 *iTools: Counters

Whiteboard Lesson

Digital Resource

*i*Tools Choose 'Counters' on the Menu. Use Activity 1 'Count' with the tab for 'Activities.' Children can use counters to count.

ACTIVITY 1

Greater Than, Less Than, or Equal

▶ Compare Groups and Add or Subtract to Make Groups Equal WHOLE CLASS

Distribute Student Activity Book page 261. This page is similar to the Student Activity Book page completed in Unit 5, Lesson 17. Today, children will again compare two groups of objects and add or subtract to make the two groups equal.

Review that children will first count the number of objects in two groups and compare the numbers. They will then make the groups equal by adding and subtracting objects. Children can determine how many to add or subtract by drawing lines to match objects, by counting, or by visual correspondence.

MP.8 Use Repeated Reasoning Conclude The goal is for children to realize that they can make two groups equal by taking away from the larger group or by adding to the smaller group. When children have completed the page, review the answers. Ask how many objects were added or subtracted each time.

MP.6 Attend to Precision Ask children to discuss and compare these methods for making groups equal.

5-20
Class Activity   Name _____

VOCABULARY
greater
less
equal

Write the numbers and compare them. Write G for **Greater** and L for **Less**. Add (draw more) to make the groups **equal**.

1. ⊙⊙⊙⊙⊙⊙⊙ | 7 | G
   ⊙⊙⊙⊙○○○ | 4 | L

2. ▲▲▲▲▲▲▲▲▲▲ | 10 | G
   ▲▲▲▲▲▲▲▲△△ | 8 | L

3. ■■■□□□□ | 3 | L
   ■■■■■■■■ | 8 | G

Write the numbers and compare them. Write G for **Greater** and L for **Less**. Subtract (cross out) to make the groups **equal**.

4. ▽▽▽▽ | 4 | L
   ▽▽▽▽⊠ | 5 | G

5. ⬡⬡⬡⬡⬡⊗⊗⊗⊗ | 9 | G
   ⬡⬡⬡⬡⬡ | 5 | L

6. ◆◆◆◆◆◆ | 6 | L
   ◆◆◆◆◆◆⊗⊗ | 8 | G

UNIT 5 LESSON 20   More Tens in Teen Numbers: A Game **261**

5-20
Class Activity   Name _____

VOCABULARY
greater than
less than
equal

Compare the numbers.
Write G if the first number is **Greater than** the second number.
Write L if the first number is **Less than** the second number.
Write E if the numbers are **Equal**.

5	E	5		7	G	6
2	L	7		2	E	2
10	G	4		9	G	4
3	L	4		5	L	8
8	E	8		2	L	3
5	L	9		6	L	10
8	G	6		4	E	4
7	G	1		6	G	2

262 UNIT 5 LESSON 20   More Tens in Teen Numbers: A Game

Student Activity Book pages 261–262

▶ **Compare Numbers Written as Numerals** WHOLE CLASS

MP.2 Reason Abstractly and Quantitatively Ask children to turn to Student Activity Book page 262. Explain that children will continue to practice comparing numbers, but without the groups of objects showing the numbers. Remind them that they should show whether the first number is greater than, equal to, or less than the second number. If desired, show some sample comparisons on the board before beginning the page.

Circulate around the classroom as children work, assisting as needed. When children have finished, review each answer with the class.

ACTIVITY 2

Play *The Hiding Zero Game*

▶ **Set Up and Play the Game** PAIRS

Direct children to work in **Student Pairs** to play the game. If necessary, refer to Unit 5, Lesson 6 for complete instructions. Remind children that the goal of *The Hiding Zero Game* is to see the 10 in the teen number by putting a single digit over the zero of the 10 to make the teen number.

MP.7 Look for Structure Ask Student Pairs to arrange their three Hiding Zero Gameboard pages in order, either vertically or horizontally. Then have them work together to put their Number Tiles on top of the 0 in each 10 to make the equations.

A Student Leader calls out a teen number (for example, 18), and children pick up Number Tile 8, which is covering the 0 in the 10, and put it in the blank rectangle. Together, children say the following while using Finger Flashes:

• 18 equals 10 plus 8.

• This is the 10 in 18 (pointing to the 1).

• This is the 8 in 18 (pointing to the 8.)

Ask the Student Leader to construct the number 18 using the Giant Number Cards 10 and 8. He or she can place the 8 over the 0 in the 10, replicating what children have done on their gameboards. Then the Student Leader can pull apart the cards as the class is saying "18 equals 10 plus 8."

> ✓ **Formative Assessment: Check Understanding**
>
> **Student Summary** Hold up any two Giant Number Cards (1–10). Ask whether the first number is greater than or less than the second number. Repeat with other pairs of numbers.

COMMON CORE
Mathematical Practice
CC.K–12.MP.7
Mathematical Content
CC.K.NBT.1

10 MINUTES

FOCUS Visualize a group of ten in a teen number using *The Hiding Zero Game.*

MATERIALS Hiding Zero Gameboard (from Unit 5, Lesson 6 or TRB M55–M57; 1 set per pair), Number Tiles 1–10 (1 set per pair), Giant Number Cards 1–10

Whiteboard Lesson

Class Management

Looking Ahead In Lesson 22, the class will be comparing the weights of objects and the capacities of containers. The weight comparisons include using a beach ball and tennis ball. If you cannot provide these objects, consider substitutes like an inflated balloon and a golf ball. Assemble several containers with different capacities and a "pourable" material like sand or rice. See the lesson for details.

▲ On Level ▲ RtI Tier 1
for students having success

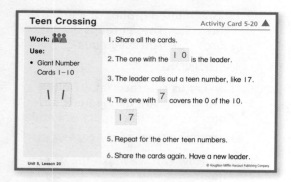

Activity Notes Review with children how to cover the zero on the 10 card. Explain that the leader will decide each teen to make.

 Math Writing Prompt

Write Equations Ask children to write both equations for each teen number that is created, such as 17 = 10 + 7 and 10 + 7 = 17.

 MegaMath

Software Support
Country Countdown:
Counting Critters, Level P

■ Challenge
for students seeking a challenge

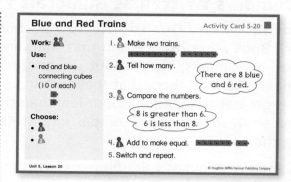

Activity Notes Model making two unequal trains with the connecting cubes. Then demonstrate saying the comparison of the two numbers.

 Math Writing Prompt

Write Comparisons Extend the activity by having children write the comparison two ways, such as 8 G 6 and 6 L 8.

Destination Math®

Software Support
Course I: Module 2: Unit 2: Session 2: Differences within 20

Family Letter Remind children to take home the Family Letter on Student Activity Book page 259. This letter explains how comparison of the attributes length, height, weight, and capacity will be developed in the next two lessons of *Math Expressions*. It gives parents and guardians a better understanding of the learning that goes on in math class and creates a bridge between school and home. A Spanish translation of this letter is on the following page in the Student Activity Book.

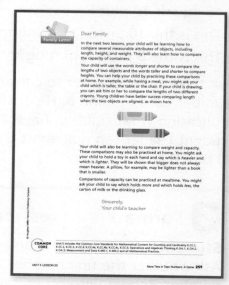

Student Activity Book page 259

Compare Length and Compare Height

LESSON FOCUS	**VOCABULARY**	**COMMON CORE**
• Compare two objects and identify which is longer or shorter.	longer shorter taller length height	**Mathematical Practice** CC.K–12.MP.1, CC.K–12.MP.3, CC.K–12.MP.6 **Mathematical Content** CC.K.MD.1, CC.K.MD.2
• Compare two objects and identify which is taller or shorter.		

The Day at a Glance

USE MATH TALK TODAY!

Teaching the Lesson

MATH BACKGROUND for this lesson is included on p. 461PP.

ACTIVITY FOCUS

Activity 1   Compare 2 objects and identify which is longer or shorter.

Activity 2   Compare 2 objects and identify which is taller or shorter.

MATERIALS

- Pencils and other objects for comparing length and height
- Whiteboard

Differentiated Instruction

MATERIALS

- Activity Cards 5-21 • Index cards • Math Journals
- Soar to Success Math Intervention • MegaMath • Destination Math®
- **RtI** Tier 1 • Tier 2 • Tier 3

Home or School Activity

MATERIALS

- Science Connection p. 560

QUICK PRACTICE   **5 MINUTES**

Repeated Quick Practice Use this Quick Practice from a previous lesson.

The Partner Peek on the 10-Partner Showcase (See Unit 5, Lesson 17.)

DAILY ROUTINES

Counting Tens and Ones
(See pp. xxxi–xxxii.)

DIGITAL RESOURCES

Use these digital resources along with your eSAB and eTE to support your students' learning experiences.

Professional Development

Whiteboard Lesson

Soar to Success Math Intervention

MegaMath

Destination Math®

COMMON CORE

Mathematical Practice
CC.K–12.MP.1, CC.K–12.MP.6

Mathematical Content
CC.K.MD.1, CC.K.MD.2

15 MINUTES

FOCUS Compare 2 objects and identify which is longer or shorter.

MATERIALS Pencils (2 per pair), other pairs of classroom objects

 Whiteboard Lesson

Teaching Note

Language and Vocabulary
Distinguishing between the use of *taller* (for comparing vertical dimensions) and *longer* (for comparing horizontal dimensions) will, in many cases, require teacher guidance. At this point, the distinction is not critical.

Alternate Approach

To help children who may have difficulty comparing lengths, demonstrate how to compare lengths by cutting pieces of string or strips of paper to represent each length and then placing them side by side with one end aligned to see which length is longer.

ACTIVITY 1

Identify Longer and Shorter

▶ Determine Longer or Shorter [PAIRS]   MATH TALK

In this activity, children will be learning about length by comparing the lengths of two objects. To introduce the concept of length to children, guide them to see that length is the idea of how long something is. Length is how far it is from one end of the object to the other end.

Ask for Ideas Ask children to share what they know about the words *longer* and *shorter*. Then demonstrate for them how to compare the length of a hand to the length of a foot. Guide children to align the base of the palm with the heel.

• Let's find out which is longer, your foot or your hand.

Have each child place a hand next to a foot to see which is longer and which is shorter.

• Which is longer, your hand or your foot? Explain your answer.
  My foot is longer because it goes farther than my hand.

MP.1 Make Sense of Problems Analyze Relationships Give each **Student Pair** two pencils. Demonstrate how to compare the lengths of two pencils by placing them side by side and aligned at one end. Ask pairs to work together to determine which of the pencils is longer and which is shorter.

• Which pencil is shorter? How do you know? When we line up the eraser ends, the point on the brown pencil does not go as far as the point on the green pencil.

• Which pencil is longer? How do you know? When we line up the eraser ends, the point on the green pencil goes farther than the point on the brown pencil.

Ask if any of the Student Pairs has a set of pencils that is about the same length. Invite them to show how the pencils are about the same length.

Distribute sets of 2 classroom objects for children to compare lengths. Objects might include paper clips, crayons, erasers, paint brushes, and strips of paper. Remind children to align objects to compare.

MP.6 Attend to Precision Circulate among the groups and ask them to say which object is longer and which is shorter. Urge them to explain their reasoning.

Identify Taller and Shorter

▶ Determine Taller or Shorter `WHOLE CLASS`

Ask children to share what they know about *taller* and *shorter*.

MP.6 Attend to Precision Invite a volunteer to stand next to the door so that children may compare the heights. Have the child stand on his or her toes or bend down. Ask children whether these actions change the comparison of the child's height to that of the door.

- Which is taller, the door or (child's name)? Explain how you know. The door is taller because the door goes up above (child's name).

- Suppose I ask each child to take a turn standing next to the door. What can you say about the heights? Explain. Each child is shorter than the door because the top of each child does not reach to the top of the door.

Place a pencil cup on the table. Invite a volunteer to find an object in the classroom that is shorter than the pencil cup. Have him or her place the object next to the pencil cup and compare the heights. Point out that it helps to compare heights if objects are aligned, for example if both are placed on the floor or the same table.

MP.3 Critique the Reasoning of Others Ask if everyone agrees that the object is shorter. Invite a child to explain why (or why not).

Continue comparing heights to determine objects that are shorter or taller than other objects. (Avoid comparing one child's height to that of another child.)

▶ Determine Several Attributes `WHOLE CLASS`

Choose two classroom objects such as a pencil cup and a tape dispenser. Point out that objects can be measured in more than one way. An object can be measured for its length as well as its height. Ask children to describe the objects in terms of lengths as well as heights.

- You know about longer and shorter. You also know about taller and shorter. Compare these two objects. What can you say about their lengths? What can you say about their heights? The tape dispenser is longer than the pencil cup. The pencil cup is taller than the tape dispenser.

✓ Formative Assessment: Check Understanding

Student Summary Choose a classroom object, such as a cube. Ask children to name another object in the classroom to compare to the cube. Then have children describe how the object chosen compares to the cube in length and height. Place the objects together for the comparisons.

COMMON CORE

Mathematical Practice
CC.K–12.MP.3, CC.K–12.MP.6
Mathematical Content
CC.K.MD.1, CC.K.MD.2

15 MINUTES

FOCUS Compare 2 objects and identify which is taller or shorter in a pair.

MATERIALS Classroom objects

 Whiteboard Lesson

 MATH TALK *in ACTION*

Describe some things in the room that are taller or shorter, or longer or shorter, or about the same length or height as this backpack.

Marta: The trash can next to the door is taller than this backpack.

Alex: But the trash can next to the teacher's desk is shorter than the backpack.

Glenn: The big counting book is bigger than the backpack. It will not fit in the backpack.

Mai: That is because the big counting book is taller than the backpack.

Alex: The puppy book fits in the backpack just right.

Marta: That is because the puppy book is about the same length and height as the backpack.

Mai: I am taller than the backpack.

Glenn: So am I. We all are taller than the backpack!

English Language Learners

On the board, draw a *taller* building, labeled *A*, and a *shorter* building, labeled *B*.

BEGINNING

Point and say: **Building A is taller. Building B is shorter.** Ask children to repeat.

INTERMEDIATE AND ADVANCED

Ask: **Is building A shorter?** No, it is taller. **Building B is __.** shorter

---

▲ On Level  Tier 1

for students having success

Longer Line, Shorter Line — Activity Card 5-21 ▲

Work: 👥

Use:
- 2 index cards labeled *shorter* and *longer*

  shorter   longer

Choose:
- 👤
- 👤

1. Put both cards face down.

2. 👤 Draw a line. ————

3. 👤 Pick a card.   shorter

4. 👤 Draw a line as the card describes. Label both lines, L for Longer and S for Shorter.

   ————— S

5. Switch and repeat.

Unit 5, Lesson 21   © Houghton Mifflin Harcourt Publishing Company

Activity Notes Label one card *shorter* and one card *longer.* Remind children to draw their line below the first line.

✏ Math Writing Prompt

Compare the Lengths Ask children to trace 2 crayons, and then draw a circle around the longer tracing.

 **MegaMath**

Software Support
Shapes Ahoy:
Made to Measure, Level A

■ Challenge

for students seeking a challenge

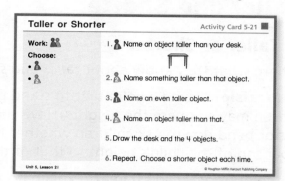

Taller or Shorter — Activity Card 5-21 ■

Work: 👥

Choose:
- 👤
- 👤

1. 👤 Name an object taller than your desk.

   🪑

2. 👤 Name something taller than that object.

3. 👤 Name an even taller object.

4. 👤 Name an object taller than that.

5. Draw the desk and the 4 objects.

6. Repeat. Choose a shorter object each time.

Unit 5, Lesson 21   © Houghton Mifflin Harcourt Publishing Company

Activity Notes Stress that objects may not be taller if they are sitting on something else. Remind children to compare the new object to the prior item.

✏ Math Writing Prompt

Order Objects Ask children to draw 3 or 4 objects that are different lengths. Then have them write S by the shortest object and L by the longest.

Destination Math®

Software Support
Course I: Module 3: Unit 1: Session 1: Length

Science Connection

Compare Heights of Plants Provide two plants, either potted or from nature, for children to compare heights. Place the plants side by side and have children tell which plant is taller and which is shorter. Ask them to justify their answer. It may be such that one plant has more leaves or stems, but children should focus on the heights of the plants.

Compare Weight and Compare Capacity

LESSON FOCUS

- Compare two objects and identify which is heavier or lighter.
- Compare two containers and identify which has more or less capacity.

VOCABULARY

weight
heavier
lighter
capacity
more
less

COMMON CORE

Mathematical Practice
CC.K–12.MP.1, CC.K–12.MP.3, CC.K–12.MP.6
Mathematical Content
CC.K.MD.1, CC.K.MD.2

The Day at a Glance

Teaching the Lesson

MATH BACKGROUND for this lesson is included on p. 461PP.

ACTIVITY FOCUS

Activity 1 Compare 2 objects and identify which is heavier or lighter.

Activity 2 Compare 2 containers and identify which has more or less capacity.

MATERIALS

Classroom objects (including bottle of glue and glue stick) • Beach ball • Tennis ball • Containers of various sizes • Water, rice, or sand • Spill tray

*i*Tools: Measurement • Whiteboard

Differentiated Instruction

MATERIALS

Activity Cards 5-22 • Classroom objects • Containers of various sizes • Water, rice, or sand • Math Journals

Soar to Success Math Intervention • MegaMath • Destination Math®

RtI Tier 1 • Tier 2 • Tier 3

Home or School Activity

MATERIALS

Science Connection p. 564

QUICK PRACTICE 5 MINUTES

Repeated Quick Practice Use this Quick Practice from a previous lesson.

The Partner Peek on the 10-Partner Showcase (See Unit 5, Lesson 17.)

DAILY ROUTINES

Counting Tens and Ones
(See pp. xxxi–xxxii.)

DIGITAL RESOURCES

Use these digital resources along with your eSAB and eTE to support your students' learning experiences.

 Professional Development

 Whiteboard Lesson

 iTools

 Soar to Success Math Intervention

 MegaMath

 Destination Math®

COMMON CORE

Mathematical Practice
CC.K–12.MP.1

Mathematical Content
CC.K.MD.1, CC.K.MD.2

20 MINUTES

FOCUS Compare 2 objects and identify which is lighter or heavier.

MATERIALS Classroom objects (including books, pencils, bottle of glue, glue stick), beach ball, tennis ball

iT *i*Tools: Measurement

◥ Whiteboard Lesson

Digital Resource

*i*Tools Choose 'Measurement' on the Menu. Use Activity 1 'Balance and Scale' with the tab for 'Activities.' Children can use the balance option to compare the weights of objects.

 MATH TALK *in ACTION*

What are some ways you can describe how to measure this book I am holding?

Amy: You can hold it to feel if it is heavy or light.

Paco: Yes, that is talking about its weight.

Chase: I think you can look at it to see if it is long or short.

Nina: We did that, too. It is called length.

Paco: I think there is another way.

Nina: You can hold it like this to see how tall it is.

Chase: It is not very tall. It is short.

ACTIVITY 1

Compare Weight

▶ Determine Heavier or Lighter `PAIRS`

Ask for Ideas Ask children to share what they know about the words *heavier* and *lighter*. Display a classroom book and a pencil. Provide the same two objects for each child.

- Let's find out which object is heavier by holding the book in one hand and the pencil in the other.

Pick them up, one object in each hand. Demonstrate how to compare the weights.

- Which is heavier, the book or the pencil? Explain your answer. The book is heavier because it pulls down more than the pencil.

MP.1 Make Sense of Problems Analyze Relationships Give each **Student Pair** two classroom objects with which to compare weights. Remind children to hold one object in each hand. Have them determine the lighter object and the heavier object. Ask if both agree.

- Which is lighter, the glue stick or the bottle of glue? The glue stick is lighter. **How do you know?** The glue stick feels lighter than the glue bottle when I hold them both.

Continue with other objects of various weights for children to compare.

Ask if anyone has two objects that are about the same weight. Invite them to describe how both objects feel when they are about the same weight. Encourage volunteers to examine the objects for themselves.

After they have compared the weights of several objects, present children with the opportunity to compare a tennis ball and a beach ball.

- I think bigger things are heavier and smaller things are lighter. Is that always true? Can you show me how you know that? A beach ball is bigger than a tennis ball, but it does not feel as heavy.

Allow children to share and discuss their ideas. They may believe the beach ball should be heavier because it is larger. Allow each child to hold both balls, and then describe and compare their weights. Encourage children to conclude that a bigger object is not always heavier.

Compare Capacity

▶ Determine More or Less WHOLE CLASS

• When you are very thirsty, what size glass do you use? Why?

Talk about why a larger glass holds more than a smaller one. Hold up 2 different sized containers.

• Which container holds more? Which container holds less?

Explain that you can check by filling the container you think holds more and then pouring the contents into the other container. If it spills over, you were correct and the container you're pouring from holds more. Demonstrate the activity using water, sand, or rice. You may want to work over a box or sink to catch anything that spills.

Repeat, but pour the contents from the smaller container into the larger container to show the larger one isn't filled. Repeat a few times with different sized containers.

MP.6 Attend to Precision Encourage children to explain why one container holds more than another.

▶ Determine Several Attributes WHOLE CLASS

Choose two containers with lids that have different measurable attributes for weight, capacity, length, and height.

• What are the different ways we can measure these objects?

Point out that objects can be measured in more than one way. Invite children to describe the containers in terms of weight, capacity, height, and length.

• You know about heavier and lighter. You also know about more and less and taller and shorter. Compare these two objects. What can you say about their weights? What can you say about their capacities? What can you say about their heights? The white container holds more than the red container. The white container is also taller and heavier.

MP.3 Critique the Reasoning of Others Request that a child explain how he or she knows that the conclusions that one container is taller or heavier are correct. If the child disagrees, ask why. The child may move or hold the objects to support the explanation.

✓ Formative Assessment: Check Understanding

Student Summary Choose two objects that have several measurable, comparable attributes. Ask children to find more than one way to compare and measure those objects. Have them explain their answers.

COMMON CORE

Mathematical Practice
CC.K–12.MP.3, CC.K–12.MP.6
Mathematical Content
CC.K.MD.1, CC.K.MD.2

20 MINUTES

FOCUS Compare 2 containers and identify which has more or less capacity.

MATERIALS Containers, water, rice, or sand, spill tray

 Whiteboard Lesson

English Language Learners

Write **heavy, heavier, light,** and **lighter** on the board. Pick up a box and pretend it is heavy. Say: **Oh! It is heavy!** Hold another box above your head. Ask: **Is it heavy?** no Say: **It is light.** Place the boxes side by side.

BEGINNING

Pointing to two boxes, say: **This box is heavier than that box. That box is lighter than this box.** Ask children to repeat.

INTERMEDIATE AND ADVANCED

Say: **This box is heavy. It is not __.** light **That box is light. It is not __.** heavy Say: **Let's compare the boxes. Is this box heavier than that box?** yes **How does that box compare to this one?** It is lighter.

Class Management

Looking Ahead In Lesson 23, children will use sets of numbered index cards. See page 568 for a description.

▲ On Level  RtI Tier 1
for students having success

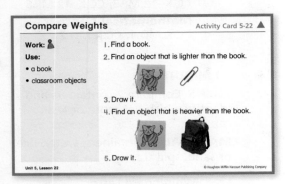

Activity Notes Remind children to hold one object in each hand at the same time, in order to compare the weights of both objects.

 Math Writing Prompt

Explain Your Thinking Ask children to explain how you tell which object is heavier and which is lighter.

 MegaMath

Software Support
Country Countdown:
Harrison's Comparisons, Level F

■ Challenge
for students seeking a challenge

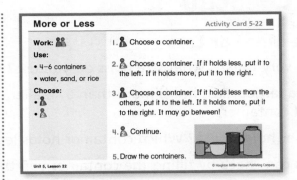

Activity Notes Provide 4–6 different sized containers. Some should be close in size. Children may use water, rice, or sand to help them compare the capacities while ordering.

 Math Writing Prompt

Explain and Draw Ask children to explain how a shorter container can hold more than a taller one. Have them draw a picture to demonstrate.

 Destination Math®

Software Support
Course I: Module 3: Unit 1: Session 2: Weight

 Science Connection

Compare Weights of Fruits and Vegetables
Provide several kinds of fruits and vegetables for children to compare weights. You may choose to have a variety of sizes, shapes, and densities for children to explore. Some pairs to compare might be a grape and an apple, an apple and a potato, a grapefruit and a lime, and an avocado and a tomato. Remind children to hold one piece in each hand to compare.

Focus on Mathematical Practices

LESSON FOCUS

- Apply mathematical concepts and skills in meaningful contexts.
- Reinforce the Common Core Mathematical Content Standards and Mathematical Practices with a variety of problem solving situations.

COMMON CORE

Mathematical Practice
CC.K–12.MP.1, CC.K–12.MP.2, CC.K–12.MP.3, CC.K–12.MP.4, CC.K–12.MP.5, CC.K–12.MP.6, CC.K–12.MP.7, CC.K–12.MP.8
Mathematical Content
CC.K.CC.3, CC.K.CC.4, CC.K.NBT.1, CC.K.MD.1, CC.K.MD.2

The Day at a Glance

USE MATH TALK TODAY!

Teaching the Lesson

MATH BACKGROUND for this lesson is included on pp. 461LL, 461PP.

ACTIVITY FOCUS

Activity 1 Mathematical Practices

2 Reason abstractly and quantitatively.

3 Construct viable arguments and critique the reasoning of others.

6 Attend to precision.

7 Look for and make use of structure.

Activity 2 Mathematical Practices

4 Model with mathematics.

5 Use appropriate tools strategically.

6 Attend to precision.

8 Look for and express regularity in repeated reasoning.

Activity 3 Mathematical Practices

1 Make sense of problems and persevere in solving them.

3 Construct viable arguments and critique the reasoning of others.

6 Attend to precision.

MATERIALS

 Student Activity Book pp. 263–264 • Fluency Check 8 (Assessment Guide) • Crayons • Index cards

▢ Whiteboard

Differentiated Instruction

MATERIALS

 Activity Cards 5-23 • Classroom objects • Index cards

▢ Soar to Success Math Intervention • MegaMath • Destination Math®

◢ **RtI** Tier 1 • Tier 2 • Tier 3

Home or School Activity

MATERIALS

 Science Connection p. 570

QUICK PRACTICE ⏲ 5 MINUTES

Repeated Quick Practice Use this Quick Practice from a previous lesson.

The Partner Peek on the 10-Partner Showcase (See Unit 5, Lesson 17.)

DAILY ROUTINES

Counting Tens and Ones
(See pp. xxxi–xxxii.)

DIGITAL RESOURCES

Use these digital resources along with your eSAB and eTE to support your students' learning experiences.

Professional Development

Whiteboard Lesson

Soar to Success Math Intervention

MegaMath

Destination Math®

COMMON CORE

Mathematical Practice
CC.K–12.MP.2, CC.K–12.MP.3,
CC.K–12.MP.6, CC.K–12.MP.7
Mathematical Content
CC.K.MD.1, CC.K.MD.2

30 MINUTES

FOCUS Compare heights and lengths of animals or objects.
MATERIALS Student Activity Book pages 263–264, crayons

Whiteboard Lesson

ACTIVITY 1

Math and Animals

▶ Discuss Animals WHOLE CLASS

Ask for Ideas Invite volunteers to share any experiences they may have had at an animal park or what they might have read or seen about wild animals in books or movies, or on television. Encourage children to describe some of the animals they have seen.

▶ Identify Shorter and Taller in Pictures
INDIVIDUALS   MATH TALK

Direct children to look at Student Activity Book page 263. Children will circle the taller animal and underline the shorter animal in each pair. They should use crayons to mark their papers.

MP.6 Attend to Precision Allow time for children to study all the animals on the page before beginning.

• What kinds of animals do you see? giraffes, deer, zebras, elephants

• What does each picture show? mother and baby animals; a large animal and a small animal

• Have you ever seen any of these animals live?

• We will compare the animals to see which is taller and which is shorter.

MP.7 Look for and Make Use of Structure
Review the meaning of *taller* and *shorter* by holding up two different classroom objects, with one clearly taller than the other. Hold the objects so they are aligned at the bottom. Explain why that is important when comparing how tall they are. Encourage a volunteer to compare the objects using the words *taller* and *shorter*.

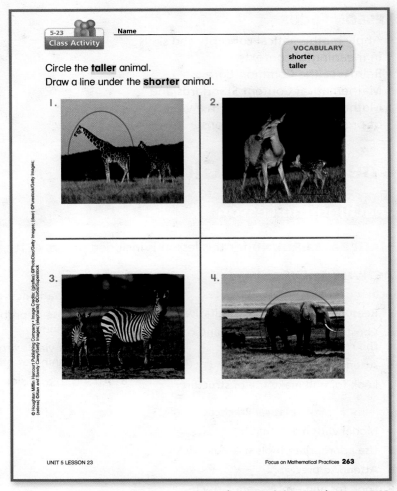

Student Activity Book page 263

Now ask children to look at the giraffes in Exercise 1.

• Look at the giraffes. How many do you see? two giraffes

• How are the giraffes alike? They both have spots and long necks.

• How are they different? One is taller (bigger) than the other; they have different heights.

• With a crayon, circle the taller giraffe. Draw a line under the shorter giraffe.

Check children as they work. Repeat with similar questioning for the other pairs of animals.

MP.2 Reason Quantitatively Ask children to explain why they have circled the animal they did. Children should be able to explain how they know that the one animal is taller/shorter without seeing the live animal or measuring it.

MP.3 Construct a Viable Argument Justify Conclusions Extend the questioning to include another measurable attribute, such as weight.

- Which animal do you think is heavier, the mother elephant or the baby deer?
- Explain your answer.

MP.2 Reason Quantitatively Stress that size does not always determine weight. You may point out that a balloon is larger than an orange, but an orange is heavier than a balloon. Encourage children to come up with other examples. pillow / bowling ball; bag of popped popcorn / can of soup

▶ **Discuss the Picture** [WHOLE CLASS] (MATH TALK)

Let children share what they see on Student Activity Book page 264. Encourage children to share any experiences they may have had with fish, fish tanks, trips to an aquarium, fishing trips, or anything else they may know about fish.

▶ **Longer or Shorter** [INDIVIDUALS]

MP.7 Look for Structure Direct children's attention to the fish on Student Activity Book page 264.

- Look at the 2 pink fish at the top. What do you see? How are they alike? They are both pink. They both have fins and tails.
- How are they different? One is longer (shorter) than the other.
- With a crayon, circle the longer pink fish. Draw a line under the shorter pink fish.

Check that children have marked the fish correctly.

- How do you know which fish is longer? The longer fish goes farther right than the shorter fish.

- Look at the 2 fish at the top on the right, in Exercise 6. What do you see? How are the fish alike? They are both orange. They have the same shape.

- How are they different? One is longer (shorter) than the other.

- Circle the longer orange fish. Draw a line under the shorter orange fish.

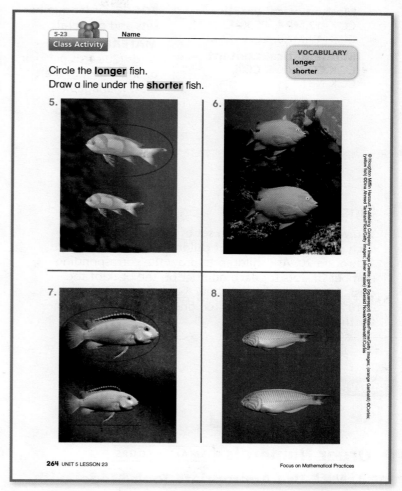

Student Activity Book page 264

Repeat, using similar questioning for the pairs of yellow and silver fish.

Encourage children to explain their answers. Get children to talk about things that determine size (such as length and weight) and things that do not determine size (such as color).

Teaching Note

Watch For! Some children may look for height or plumpness of the fish rather than length. Remind them that on this page they are looking for length. Demonstrate how to compare the lengths of two objects by aligning them on the left. Point out that both objects start at the same place, and the one that goes farther to the right is longer. The other object is shorter.

COMMON CORE

Mathematical Practice
CC.K–12.MP.4, CC.K–12.MP.5,
CC.K–12.MP.6, CC.K–12.MP.8

Mathematical Content
CC.K.CC.3, CC.K.CC.4,
CC.K.NBT.1

15 MINUTES

FOCUS Order number sets and numerals.

MATERIALS Index cards (20 cards per pair or small group; see Class Management)

 Whiteboard Lesson

Class Management

You will need to prepare a set of 20 index cards for each pair or small group of children. Number the cards 1 through 20. Ask children to draw the corresponding number of dots for each number on the back of the card. Remind children to draw 5-groups for the numbers 6–10 and to draw a set of ten ones and some extra ones for the numbers 11–19.

ACTIVITY 2

Use Reasoning

▶ Order Numerals SMALL GROUPS

MP.4, MP.5 Use Appropriate Tools/Model with Mathematics Instruct children to put the cards in order from 1–20 by looking at the number of dots. Ask questions about how the numbers change from one number to the next.

Children should verbalize the following ideas:

▶ Each card has one more dot than the one before it.

▶ Each number is one more than the number before it.

Have children mix up the cards and place the cards in order again, either by dots or by numerals. Allow each child in the group to order the cards, but not every child in the group should order them the same way.

As children work, ask questions such as these:

• Which number has 10 ones and 2 extra ones? 12

• Which number has 10 ones and 8 extra ones? 18

• Which number has 2 groups of 10? 20

Continue with similar questions.

▶ Missing Numerals SMALL GROUPS

MP.8 Use Repeated Reasoning Tell children that next they will find which numbers have been removed from their set of cards. Observe the groups as you explain each step. Assist them as needed.

• Everyone will get a turn removing number cards. Decide who in your group will go first.

• The first person in your group will remove two cards from the set without anyone else seeing what the cards are. The rest of you should close and cover your eyes.

• The person who took out the two cards will hide them and give the remaining cards to the group. The group will then decide which two cards are missing.

• When the group has figured out the missing cards, the person who has them will give them back to the group. They will replace those cards correctly in the set.

Children should repeat the activity until everyone in the group has had a turn.

MP.6 Attend to Precision Ask children to share how they determined which cards had been removed and how they knew where to place the cards correctly in the set. Encourage the class to discuss different strategies that were used.

English Language Learners

Write **order** on the board. Explain that when we arrange numbers one after another, we are putting them in order. Write the numbers 1–5 on the board. Invite 5 volunteers to hold up a different number of fingers from 1–5. Work together to put the children in order by number of fingers from 1–5. Point out that each child is holding up one more finger than the child before them. Say: **We put the numbers in order.** Ask children to repeat.

COMMON CORE

Mathematical Practice
CC.K–12.MP.1, CC.K–12.MP.3,
CC.K–12.MP.6
Mathematical Content
CC.K.MD.1, CC.K.MD.2

15 MINUTES

FOCUS Use logical reasoning to support or disprove a given statement.

MATERIALS Classroom objects

 Whiteboard Lesson

ACTIVITY 3

Establish a Position

▶ Is the Statement True? | WHOLE CLASS |

 MATH TALK

Select an object and ask children to suggest something in the classroom that is longer or taller, (whichever word is appropriate), shorter, or about the same length. Ask some questions that require children to establish a position, while allowing other children to react to it.

• How do you know that you have selected an object that is [longer/taller than, shorter than, or about the same length/height as] this object?

Ensure that if the comparison is about height that children understand that both objects should be aligned at one end. Unless both objects are on the floor or the same table, for example, children may believe one object is taller simply because its top is above the top of the other object.

MP.3 Construct a Viable Argument Justify Conclusions Children should be able to explain how they know they are correct. They may present a logical argument (using indirect comparison, for example) or they may put the objects side by side, for a direct comparison.

• Do you agree or disagree with your classmate's choice? Hold up your hand if you agree.

• [Child's name], you agreed [disagreed]. Please tell us why.

On the board, write the name of the original object. Then write either *Longer* or *Taller* (depending on the object), *Shorter,* and *Same* to create columns. Write the object the child named in the appropriate column.

Ask volunteers to name other objects that are longer, shorter, or the same length.

• Do you agree with this choice?

MP.1 Make Sense of Problems Analyze the Problem Children should be able to explain why they agree that a statement is true or why they think it is false. Allow class discussion for children to present their thoughts.

MP.6 Attend to Precision Children should include accurate words and facts in their explanation. They can use models or drawings to support their position.

When all children have agreed with the description, add the object to the correct list. Children should name 5 or 6 objects for each category, if possible.

MP.3 Construct a Viable Argument Justify Conclusions Ask about another attribute of the objects that have been listed.

• Which of these objects do you think are heavier than [the original object]? Which do you think are lighter?

• Explain your thinking.

MP.3 Critique the Reasoning of Others Invite volunteers to share their positions and explanations with the class and allow the class to ask questions of the volunteers. They may verify the conclusion or change reasoning errors by holding the two objects. Stress that disagreements should be polite and thoughtful.

 Formative Assessment: Check Understanding

Student Summary Ask children if it is true that bigger objects are always heavier than smaller objects. Ask for an example that supports their position.

 Fluency Check

See Assessment Guide for Fluency Check 8 on addition and subtraction within 5.

▲ On Level  Tier 1
for students having success

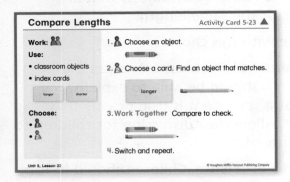

Activity Notes Write *longer* and *shorter* on 2 index cards. You may wish to review how to align objects to compare their lengths.

 Math Writing Prompt

Draw a Picture Ask children to draw the pairs of objects and circle the longer one.

 MegaMath

Software Support
Shapes Ahoy:
Made to Measure, Level A

■ Challenge
for students seeking a challenge

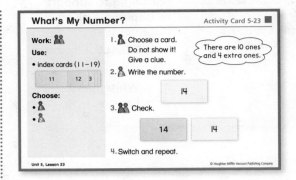

Activity Notes Number nine index cards 11 through 19. Remind children not to show the card they've chosen, but just to give clues about the number.

 Math Writing Prompt

Draw a Picture Ask children to find 3 objects and draw the objects in order from longest to shortest.

 Destination Math®

Software Support
Course I: Module 3: Unit 1:
Session 1: Length

 Science Connection

Ask children to name some animals that are very tall. Then ask them to name some animals that are very short. Repeat with animals that are very long and very short. Discuss these animals.

Tell children to think of two animals that have different lengths or heights. Ask them to draw pictures of the animals. Have them compare the lengths or heights of the animals using the words *taller* and *shorter* or *longer* and *shorter*. Provide the words for them to copy.

Unit Review and Test

UNIT TEST OBJECTIVES

5A Count objects and compare the number of objects in groups. [CC.K.CC.1, CC.K.CC.2, CC.K.CC.3, CC.K.CC.4, CC.K.CC.4a, CC.K.CC.4b, CC.K.CC.4c, CC.K.CC.5, CC.K.CC.6, CC.K.CC.7]

5B Add and subtract within 10 by composing and decomposing numbers. [CC.K.OA.1, CC.K.OA.2, CC.K.OA.3, CC.K.OA.4, CC.K.OA.5]

5C Decompose teen numbers into a group of ten ones and extra ones. [CC.K.NBT.1]

5D Identify and compare measurable attributes. [CC.K.MD.1, CC.K.MD.2]

The Day at a Glance

Today's Goals

ASSESSING THE UNIT: SUMMATIVE ASSESSMENT

• Review and assess progress on unit test objectives.

DIFFERENTIATED INSTRUCTION

• Use activities from unit lessons to reteach content.

• Use prescriptions for common errors.

ONLINE PRACTICE

• Additional practice is provided online at www.thinkcentral.com.

MATERIALS

Student Activity Book pp. 265–268 • Unit 5 Test Form A (open response) and Form B (multiple choice), Assessment Guide (optional) • Unit 5 Performance Assessment with rubric, Assessment Guide (optional) • Math Journals (optional)

USING THE ASSESSMENT

You can use this Unit Review/Test as an end-of-unit review to determine if children have mastered all the unit objectives.

You can assess children's knowledge with a secure, formal assessment that is provided in the Assessment Guide.

VOCABULARY

Choose a vocabulary activity from the Teacher Resources section (page T10) to review words from the unit.

Assess Unit Objectives

45 MINUTES (more if schedule permits)

FOCUS Review and assess progress on unit objectives.

MATERIALS Student Activity Book pp. 265–268

▷ Review and Assessment

If children are ready for assessment on the unit test objectives, you may use either the Unit Review/Test in the Student Activity Book or one of the forms of the Unit 5 Test in the Assessment Guide.

If children would benefit from review, use the Student Activity Book pages to review the content, and then use one of the forms of the Unit 5 Test in the Assessment Guide.

Scoring To provide a numerical score for this assessment, assign 4 points for each item.

▷ Reteaching Resources

The chart below lists the objectives for each test item.

Reteaching The lesson activities in which the objective is covered are provided so you may revisit these activities with children who do not show mastery of the objectives.

Common Errors You will find common errors and prescriptions on page 575 of this Unit Review.

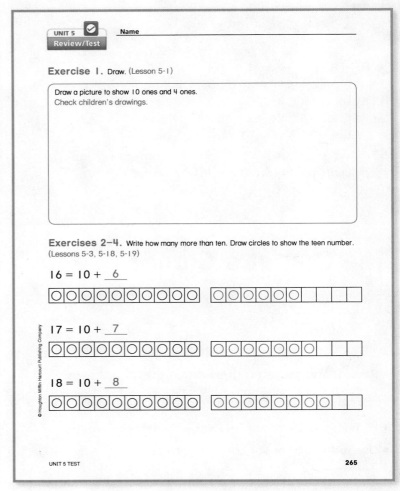

Student Activity Book page 265

Test Items	Unit Test Objective	Reteaching Activities
1	**5C** Decompose teen numbers into a group of ten ones and extra ones.	Lesson 1 Activity 2
2–4	**5C** Decompose teen numbers into a group of ten ones and extra ones.	Lesson 3 Activity 3 Lesson 18 Activity 1 Lesson 19 Activity 2

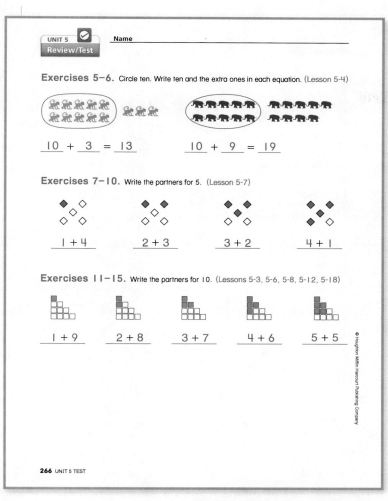

Student Activity Book page 266

▶ Assessment Options

SUMMATIVE ASSESSMENT

Open Response Test
Unit 5 Test, Form A, is provided in the Assessment Guide.

Multiple Choice Test
Unit 5 Test, Form B, is provided in the Assessment Guide.

Performance Assessment
Unit 5 Performance Task, with rubric, is provided in the Assessment Guide.

Online Assessment
www.thinkcentral.com

FORMATIVE ASSESSMENT

Portfolio Assessment

> **Teacher Selected Items:**
> Homework for Lessons 8, 15
> Class Activity work for Lessons 4, 7, 10, 17

> **Student Selected Items:** Allow children to choose a favorite Home or School Activity and a best writing prompt.

Check Understanding: in every lesson

Fluency Check: for every Big Idea

Test Items	Unit Test Objective	Reteaching Activities
5–6	**5C** Decompose teen numbers into a group of ten ones and extra ones.	Lesson 4 Activity 2
7–10	**5B** Add and subtract within 10 by composing and decomposing numbers.	Lesson 7 Activity 3
11–15	**5B** Add and subtract within 10 by composing and decomposing numbers.	Lesson 3 Activities 1 and 2 Lesson 6 Activity 2 Lesson 8 Activity 2 Lesson 12 Activities 1 and 2 Lesson 18 Activity 2

Assessing the Unit continued ▶

Assessing the Unit

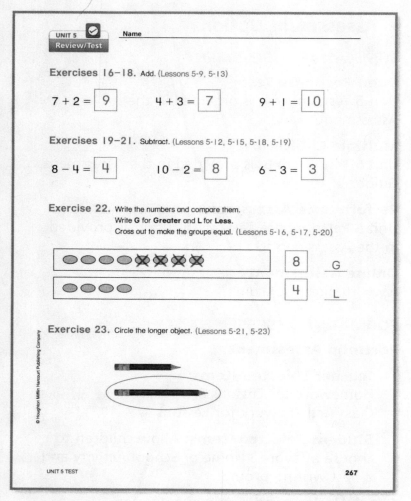

Student Activity Book page 267

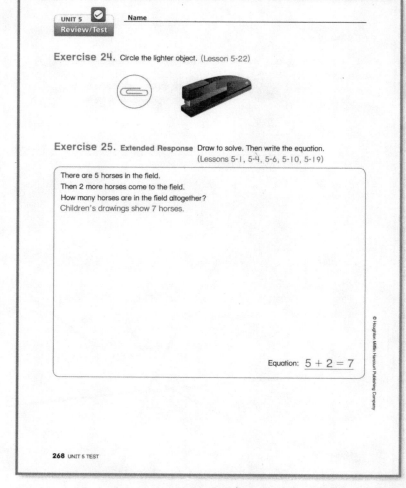

Student Activity Book page 268

Test Items	Unit Test Objective	Reteaching Activities
16–18	**5B** Add and subtract within 10 by composing and decomposing numbers.	Lesson 9 Activity 3 Lesson 13 Activity 2
19–21	**5B** Add and subtract within 10 by composing and decomposing numbers.	Lesson 15 Activity 3 Lesson 18 Activity 2 Lesson 19 Activity 2
22	**5A** Count objects and compare the number of objects in groups.	Lesson 16 Activity 2 Lesson 17 Activity 2
23	**5D** Identify and compare measurable attributes.	Lesson 21 Activity 1 Lesson 23 Activity 1
24	**5D** Identify and compare measurable attributes.	Lesson 22 Activity 1
25	**5B** Add and subtract within 10 by composing and decomposing numbers.	Lesson 1 Activity 1 Lesson 4 Activity 1 Lesson 6 Activity 1 Lesson 19 Activity 1

Differentiated Instruction

Common Errors and Prescriptions

Items	Common Error	Prescription
1	May not draw the correct number of objects	Suggest that children draw 10 objects, count them to check, and then draw the extra objects.
2–4	May not draw the correct number of circles	Encourage children to count softly to themselves as they draw the circles.
5–6	May not write the equation correctly	Remind children to circle 10 and write 10 on the first line. Then have them count the remaining ones and write that number on the second line. Suggest that children count all the figures and write the total.
7–10	May write the partners incorrectly	Suggest that children count the shapes with color first and write that partner. Then have them count the white shapes and write the other partner.
11–15	May write the partners incorrectly	Suggest that children count the shapes with color first and write that partner. Then have them count the white shapes and write the other partner.
16–18	May add incorrectly	Encourage children to draw simple objects to represent the partners. Then have them count the objects they drew.
19–21	May subtract incorrectly	Encourage children to draw objects to show the starting number and then break apart the objects to show the two partners.
22	May be confused about the meanings of *greater* and *less*	Use tiles to demonstrate for children how to compare two groups. Remind them that *greater* means *more* and *less* means *fewer*.
23–24	May be confused about how to compare objects	Review the meanings of the comparison words. Provide children with real world objects with which to compare measurable attributes.
25	May be confused about how many objects to draw	Slowly read one sentence at a time and pause to allow children time to process the information. Then read the problem again one sentence at a time, encouraging children to draw to represent the information.

Online Practice

Additional practice is provided online at www.thinkcentral.com.

NOTES:

_____

_____

_____

_____

_____

_____

_____

_____

_____

_____

_____

_____

_____

_____

_____

_____

_____

_____

_____

Appendix Contents

Posters

Teacher Resources

1 2 3 4 5 6 7 8 9 10

POSTERS

Number Patterns

0	
1	•
2	••
3	•••
4	••••
5	•••••
6	••••••
7	•••••••
8	••••••••
9	•••••••••

10	▦	
11	▦	•
12	▦	••
13	▦	•••
14	▦	••••
15	▦	•••••
16	▦	••••••
17	▦	•••••••
18	▦	••••••••
19	▦	•••••••••

1	11	21	31	41	51	61	71	81	91	101	111
2	12	22	32	42	52	62	72	82	92	102	112
3	13	23	33	43	53	63	73	83	93	103	113
4	14	24	34	44	54	64	74	84	94	104	114
5	15	25	35	45	55	65	75	85	95	105	115
6	16	26	36	46	56	66	76	86	96	106	116
7	17	27	37	47	57	67	77	87	97	107	117
8	18	28	38	48	58	68	78	88	98	108	118
9	19	29	39	49	59	69	79	89	99	109	119
10	20	30	40	50	60	70	80	90	100	110	120

Materials and Manipulatives in Grade K

Grade K Material or Manipulative	Pages in Student Activity Book	Blackline Masters in Teacher's Resource Book
Counting Tens and Ones Flip Chart*		
120 Poster*		M44
Number Parade*		M1–M5
Number Pattern Poster*		M40
Anno's Counting Book (Big Book)		
Giant Number Cards*		M7–M18, M23–M30
Number Cards*	103–104	
Number Tiles*	3–4	M19–M20
Square-Inch Tiles*	3–4	M19–M20
5-Square Tiles*		M31–M32
2-Dimensional Shapes*	9–10, 15–16	M77–M84
3-Dimensional Shapes*		
+/− Tiles and =/≠ Tiles*	55–56	M33–M34
1—20 Board*		M36–M39, M63
Counting Mats (Plastic Trays)		
Sticky Board		
Pointer		
Base Ten Blocks (centimeter cubes and 10-sticks)		
Connecting Cubes		
Two-Color Counters		
Number Cubes		
Counters		

* These materials were developed specifically for this program during the Children's Math Worlds Research Project.

Using Materials and Manipulatives for Each Unit

Grade K Material or Manipulative	Daily Routines	1	2	3	4	5
Counting Tens and Ones Flip Chart*	•			•	•	
120 Poster*	•			•	•	•
Number Parade*		•	•	•	•	•
Number Pattern Poster*			•	•		
Anno's Counting Book (Big Book)		•	•			•
Giant Number Cards*		•	•	•	•	•
Number Cards*		•				
Number Tiles*		•	•	•	•	•
Square-Inch Tiles*		•	•	•	•	
5-Square Tiles*			•	•		
2-Dimensional Shapes*		•	•	•	•	
3-Dimensional Shapes*					•	
+/− Tiles and =/≠ Tiles*			•	•	•	•
1—20 Board*			•		•	•
Counting Mats (Plastic Trays)		•	•	•	•	
Sticky Board			•			
Pointer		•	•	•	•	•
Base Ten Blocks (centimeter cubes and 10-sticks)		•	•	•	•	•
Connecting Cubes				•		•
Two-Color Counters		•				•
Number Cubes		•		•		•
Counters		•	•	•		•

All materials for each unit (including those not in the kits) are listed in the Planning Guide for that unit.

Vocabulary Activities  MathWord Power

► Word Wall

At the beginning of the school year, start a word wall in your classroom. As you work through each lesson, put the math vocabulary words on index cards and place them on the word wall. Children can add illustrations to the words. In small or large groups, children can choose a word and give a definition.

► Word Web

Make a word web for vocabulary words in a unit. Ask children to fill in the web with words, phrases, or examples that are related to the vocabulary word.

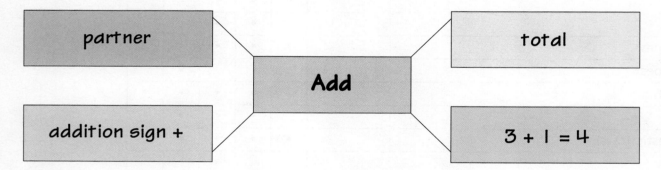

partner	Add	total
addition sign +		3 + 1 = 4

► Alphabet Challenge

Ask children to take an alphabet challenge. Choose 3 letters from the alphabet. Children then think of three vocabulary words for each letter. Write the words on the board. Children can provide definitions and draw an example for each word.

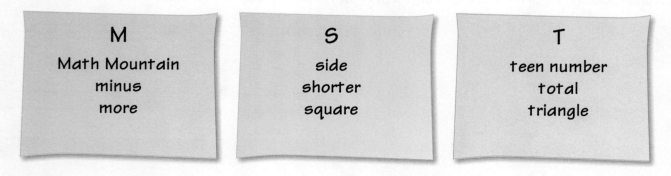

M	S	T
Math Mountain	side	teen number
minus	shorter	total
more	square	triangle

► Concentration

Write the vocabulary words and related words from a unit on index cards. Write examples or illustrations on a different set of index cards. Children can help make the sets of cards, too. Children mix up both sets of cards. Then they place the cards face down on a table in an array, for example, 3 by 4. They take turns turning over two cards. If one card is a word and one card is an example that matches the word, the child takes the pair. Children continue until each word has been matched with its definition.

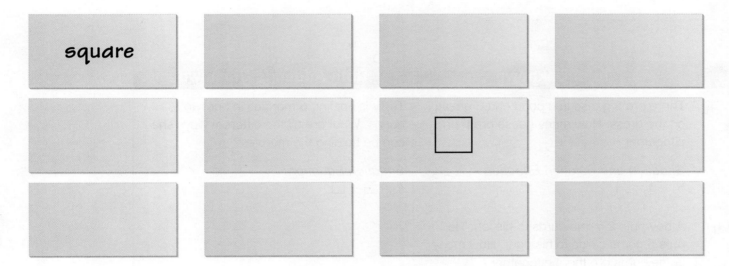

► Math Journal

As children learn new words, they can add them to their Math Journals. They can write or draw about each new word.

Problem Types

	Result Unknown
Add To	7 girls are playing tag. 2 boys join them. How many children are playing tag now? *Situation and Solution Equation:* $7 + 2 = \square$
Take From	9 joggers are running in the park. 3 of the joggers stop to rest. How many joggers are still running? *Situation and Solution Equation:* $9 - 3 = \square$

	Total Unknown	Both Addends Unknown
Put Together/ Take Apart	There are 5 geese in a pond and 3 geese on the grass. How many geese are there altogether? *Situation and Solution Equation:* $5 + 3 = \square$ A boy puts 2 game cards to his left. He puts 5 game cards to his right. How many game cards are there altogether? *Situation and Solution Equation:* $2 + 5 = \square$	Terry is holding 6 marbles in her two hands. What are all the different ways she can be holding the marbles? *Situation Equation:* $6 = \square + \square$

Teacher Glossary

1–20 Board

 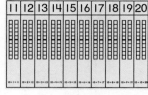

1–20 Board (front)   1–20 Board (back)

5-Counter Strip A double-sided strip of paper or cardboard displaying the number 5 on one side and 5 counters on the other side.

front   back

5-group A building block to help children understand 6 through 10 (6 = 5 +1, 7 = 5 + 2, 8 = 5 + 3, and so on).

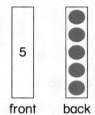 ← 5-group

5-Square Tiles A strip of five square-inch tiles. Children use the 5-Square Tiles to help them visualize 5 in numbers 6 through 10.

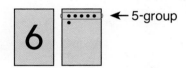

10-Counter Strip A double-sided strip of paper or cardboard displaying the number 10 on one side and 10 counters on the other side.

front   back

10-group A building block to help children visualize teen numbers.

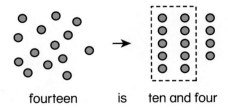

fourteen   is   ten and four

10-stick A 10-group of centimeter cubes from the set of Base Ten Blocks.

120 Poster A visual aid that displays numbers 1–120 arranged vertically in columns of ten.

1	11	21	31	41	51	61	71	81	91	101	111
2	12	22	32	42	52	62	72	82	92	102	112
3	13	23	33	43	53	63	73	83	93	103	113
4	14	24	34	44	54	64	74	84	94	104	114
5	15	25	35	45	55	65	75	85	95	105	115
6	16	26	36	46	56	66	76	86	96	106	116
7	17	27	37	47	57	67	77	87	97	107	117
8	18	28	38	48	58	68	78	88	98	108	118
9	19	29	39	49	59	69	79	89	99	109	119
10	20	30	40	50	60	70	80	90	100	110	120

+/− Tiles Tiles that display the addition and subtraction symbols.

=/≠ Tiles Tiles that display the "is equal to" and "is not equal to" symbols.

A

add Combine partners to find the total.

addition sign (+) The symbol used to show the operation of addition.

arrangement A way to display objects to represent numbers. A number can be arranged in different ways and look different, but it is still that number.

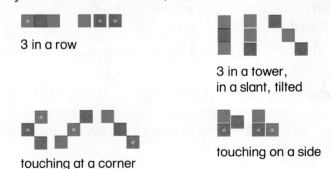

3 in a row

3 in a tower, in a slant, tilted

touching at a corner

touching on a side

Arrangements of 3 Objects

attribute A characteristic or feature of an object or person.

B

break apart (noun or verb)
You can break apart (verb) a larger number to get two smaller amounts called break-aparts (noun), also called partners.

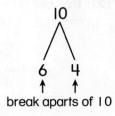

break aparts of 10

Break-Apart Stick A simple stick (such as a coffee stirrer) children can use to help break apart numbers. Children lay out a certain number of counters and then use the Break-Apart Stick to separate the counters into two groups.

Break-Apart Stick

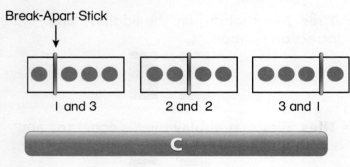

1 and 3   2 and 2   3 and 1

C

capacity A measure describing the maximum amount a container can hold.

category A classification group an object belongs to based on particular similar characerics; almonds, walnuts, and pecans would all be members of the *nut* category.

centimeter cubes The unit (ones) cubes from a set of Base Ten Blocks.

circle A two-dimensional shape with all points the same distance from a fixed point called the center.

classify Assign to categories based on one or more attributes.

combine Put together; form one group from two or more groups.

compare To examine amounts or numbers to decide if one amount or number is greater than another, less than another, or if the amounts or numbers are equal.

Comparing Mat A chart displaying two rows (or columns if used vertically) of ten square-inch boxes. Children use the Comparing Mat to represent and compare numbers.

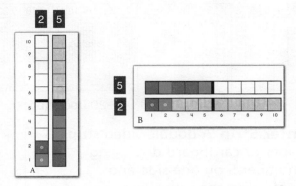

compose Put together.

conceptual subitizing Recognizing that a collection of objects is composed of two subcollections.

cone A three-dimensional shape with a curved surface that comes to a point.

corners Points where line segments meet.

Counting Mat A space children use to contain their work. The Counting Mat can be anything from a plain piece of paper (11" by 17" is a good size to use) to a cookie sheet. The white plastic trays in the *Math Expressions* Materials Kit are intended to be used as Counting Mats.

cube A three-dimensional shape that has six congruent square faces.

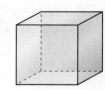

curved A segment that is not straight.

cylinder A three-dimensional shape with two circular congruent bases.

D

decade numbers Numbers that are multiples of 10 (10, 20, 30, 40, 50, 60, 70, 80, 90).

decompose Take apart.

difference The result of subtraction. In the subtraction equation $5 - 2 = 3$, 3 is the difference.

digit Any one of these symbols: 0, 1, 2, 3, 4, 5, 6, 7, 8, 9.

doubles Two of the same addend, or partner. In the equation $5 + 5 = 10$, the two fives are doubles.

E

equal Having the same value as another quantity or expression.

equal sign A symbol that shows two quantities or expressions have the same value.

equation A mathematical sentence that uses an equal sign to show that two expressions, or values, are equal.
$$3 + 1 = 4 \qquad 6 = 8 - 2 \qquad 10 + 4 = 14$$

expression A number or any combination of numbers, operation signs, and grouping symbols.
$$3 + 3 \qquad 8 - 5$$

F

face A flat surface of a three-dimensional shape.

fewer *Fewer* is used to compare two quantities that can be counted. *There are fewer red books than blue books. Less is used to compare two quantities that can be measured. There is less water than juice.*

flat A way to describe a two-dimensional shape.

G

Game Cards Cards displaying the numerals 0–10. These are on TRB M21.

Giant Number Cards A larger version of the Number Tiles for classroom use. The Giant Number Cards include decade numbers 20–90 as well as numbers 1–10.

(fronts)   (backs)

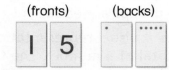

greater A word used in comparisons to show a quantity or a number is larger than another. *Greater than* is used when comparing numbers on their own, for example 8 is greater than 6.

H

heavier A word used in comparing weight to show that one item has a greater weight than another.

height The measure of how tall something is.

hexagon A two-dimensional shape with six sides.

horizontal Parallel to the horizon; going straight across.

horizontal mat A comparing mat that is horizontal.

K

known partner

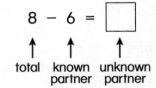

L

length The measure of how long something is.

less A word used to show a quantity is smaller than another. *Less* is used to compare quantities that cannot be counted individually: less milk, less traffic. *Less than* is used when comparing numbers on their own, for example 6 is less than 8.

lighter A word used in comparing weight to show that one item has less weight than another.

longer A word used in comparing length to show that one item has a greater length than another.

M

matching A strategy of pairing objects from different groups to determine which group has more or if the groups are equal.

Math Mountain A visual representation of the partners and total of a number. The total appears at the top, and the two partners that are added to produce the total are below to the left and right.

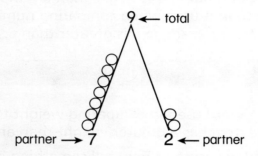

minus sign (−) The symbol used to show the operation of subtraction.

more An amount or quantity greater than another.

N

not equal Not having the same value as another quantity or expression.

not equal sign (≠) The symbol that shows two quantities or expressions do not have the same value.

number The word used to describe value (cardinal number: 1, 2, 3). Note: Mathematically, the words *number* and *numeral* are not interchangeable. *Numeral* is the word for the symbol (1, 2, 3, 4) that represents a number. However, at the kindergarten level, the mathematical distinction between the words is not made and the word *number* is also used to refer to numerals.

Number Parade A large connected sequence of numbers from 1 to 10 that is displayed permanently in the classroom. Above each number is a 5-structured grouping of dots designed to help children form mental pictures of quantity.

Number Pattern Poster A visual aid that displays the numerals 1–19 and the number of dots to represent each numeral. The numerals 6–9 are shown using 5-groups and the numerals 10–19 are shown using 10-groups.

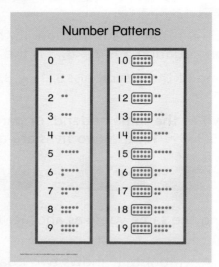

Number Tiles A set of tiles for child use that displays the numbers 1 through 10 with a numeral on one side and the corresponding number of dots on the other side.

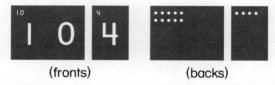

(fronts)   (backs)

numeral A symbol used to represent a number. 7 is the numeral for *seven*.

O

ones Individual units that make up a quantity. 12 is 10 ones and 2 more ones.

order (verb) Arrange numbers according to value, from least to greatest or from greatest to least.

P

pair A group of two, such as a pair of shoes; also a matching strategy when comparing the number of objects in two groups

partners A pair of numbers in an equation or expression. When 10 is broken apart into the equation 10 = 3 + 7, 3 and 7 are partners.

perceptual subitizing Visualizing quantities without counting individual units.

plus sign (+) Symbol used to show the operation of addition.

Puzzled Penguin A character shown on Student Activity Book pages and as a puppet; used to introduce critical thinking activities. The Puzzled Penguin's work contains errors that the children must identify and correct.

R
---

rectangle A quadrilateral with four right angles.

S
---

shorter A word used to compare length or height to show that one item has a lesser length or height than another.

side One of the line segments that make up a shape.

solid A way to describe a three-dimensional shape.

sort To include items in particular groups based on attributes.

Sorting Cards Shape and picture cards used to practice sorting by various attributes. These cards are located in the Student Activity Book.

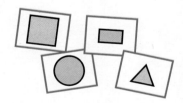

sphere A three-dimensional figure that is shaped like a round ball.

square A quadrilateral with four equal sides and four right angles.

Square-Inch Tiles Tiles that measure one inch on each side. The tiles are blank on one side and have one dot on the other side. Children use the Square-Inch Tiles to compare numbers and show arrangements and partners of a number.

story problem A math problem using a narrative, including topics from daily life and the math that is being studied.

subitize Perceive the number of items in a group or the total in two groups at a glance without counting.

subtraction sign (−) The symbol used to show the operation of subtraction.

Switch the Partners To change the order of the partners in an addition equation. Used to demonstrate the Commutative Property of Addition.

$$6 + 4 = 10 \qquad 4 + 6 = 10$$
$$\uparrow \quad \uparrow \qquad\qquad \uparrow \quad \uparrow$$

partners   partners

T
---

taller A word used to compare height to show that one item has a greater height than another.

teen number A number made up of ten ones and some more ones. The numbers 11–19 are referred to as teen numbers.

Teen Equation Cards Cards from the Student Activity Book that display addition equations with sums that are teen numbers. In Set A, the teen total is first and on the left in the equation; in Set B, the teen number is last and on the right in the equation.

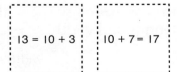

Teen Total Cards Cards from the Student Activity Book that display the numerals 11 through 19 and the corresponding expressions that can be found by adding 10 and any other number from 1 through 9.

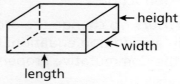

Ten Bug A cutout device used to introduce 10-groups. The teacher "flies" the Ten Bug around the classroom and speaks as the Ten Bug. The Ten Bug encourages children to make groups of ten to help them see the 10 inside teen numbers.

three-dimensional figure A figure with three dimensions: length, width, and height.

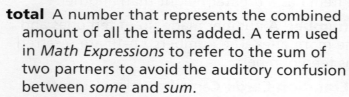

Tiny Tumblers Used with Math Mountains, Tiny Tumblers represent an imaginative way for children to visualize the partners of a number. If the total represented on a Math Mountain is 10, 7 Tiny Tumblers might play on the left side of the mountain and 3 play on the right side to show 7 and 3 as partners of 10.

total A number that represents the combined amount of all the items added. A term used in *Math Expressions* to refer to the sum of two partners to avoid the auditory confusion between *some* and *sum*.

triangle A closed two-dimensional figure with three sides.

two-dimensional shape A shape with two dimensions: length and width.

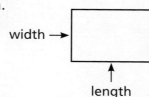

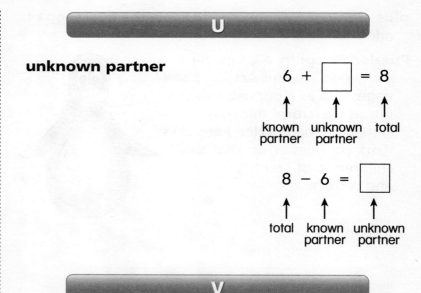

unknown partner

vertical Straight up and down.

weigh Determine how heavy an object is.

weight The measure of how heavy an object is.

Recommended Books

Unit 1

What Comes in 2's, 3's and 4's? by Suzanne Aker, illustrated by Bernie Karlin (Simon & Schuster, 1990)

Anno's Counting Book by Mitsumasa Anno (HarperCollins Publishers, 1977, or Big Book edition, 1992)

The Three Little Pigs by Paul Galdone (Clarion Books, 1984)

Unit 2

How Many Birds? by Don L. Curry and Johanna Kaufman (Capstone Curriculum Publishing, 1999)

Unit 3

Swan Harbor by Laura Rankin (Dial Books for Young Readers, 2003)

Unit 4

One Less Fish by Kim Michelle Toft and Allan Sheather (Charlesbridge Publishing, Inc., 1998)

The Very Hungry Caterpillar by Eric Carle (Philomel, 1981)

Unit 5

Rumble Bus by Larry Dane Brimmer, illustrated by Ronnie Rooney (The Child's World, 2006)

Anno's Counting Book by Mitsumasa Anno (HarperCollins Publishers, 1977, or Big Book edition, 1992)

A

Activities for Reaching All Learners.
See Differentiated Instruction; English
Language Learners; Home or School
Activity; Intervention; Math Center
Challenges; Special Needs

Add
Fluency Checks, 341, 371, 377, 415, 449,
525, 569, 573
fluency practice, 228, 236, 243, 247,
279, 289, 305, 310, 419, 521,
531, 546
fluently within 5, 1LL, 203MM, 228,
236, 243, 247, 279, 289, 305, 310,
329MM, 419, 434, 461OO, 495, 505,
517, 521, 531, 546
plus 0 pattern, 166
plus 1 pattern, xxxi–xxxii, 1BB,
155–158, 165–168

Addition
acting it out, 36–37, 73–74, 114, 124,
146, 149, 152, 170, 222, 386
add to, 36, 103EE, 157, 539, 554
equal, 103X, 146, 157, 167, 539, 554
is equal to, 132, 140, 143, 289
equations, 103T, 103U, 103X, 103AA,
111, 128, 146, 152, 157, 158, 166,
167, 399, 401, 417–418, 426, 434,
441, 478, 486, 508, 521
expressions, 227, 360, 386, 406–407
model
acting out, 36–37, 114, 124, 146,
149, 152, 170, 222
drawings, 1GG, 93, 94, 103X, 103HH,
105, 106, 108, 112, 114, 121, 129,
167, 227, 228, 231, 235–237,
239–243, 246–247, 258–259,
269–271, 273–274, 278–279, 282,
288, 292, 294, 296, 298–299, 316,
320–322, 360, 472, 475, 478,
508, 516
fingers, 1LL 3, 103AA, 103DD, 103EE,
106, 110, 111, 146, 167, 170, 203,
206, 209, 210, 214, 217, 220–223,
225, 226, 228, 231, 233, 234, 236,
237, 239–243, 245, 245, 249, 251,
253, 263, 269, 270, 272, 274, 275,
281, 283, 284, 287, 291, 293, 295,
296, 299, 300, 315, 316, 328, 344,
472, 493

mental image, 25, 103FF, 128,
190, 348
objects, 36–37, 62, 103Y, 122, 186,
203GG, 206, 216, 267, 277, 298,
306, 311, 313, 315, 321, 338
sounds, 36–37, 66
partners, 462–463
scenarios
Act Out Addition and Subtraction
Stories, 124, 128, 350, 386
Act Out and Tell Math Stories, 146
Act Out Family Experiences,
114–115, 170
Add and Subtract Fruits, 348–350
Addition and Subtraction Stories,
114–115, 128, 152, 206, 226–227,
246, 270, 296
Garden, 152
Grocery Store Problems, 348–350,
360–361, 386
Park Scene, 204–206, 226–227, 246,
270, 296
Use Addition and Subtraction to Tell
Math Stories, 128, 152
Scene, 13, 16, 21, 24–25
sign, 157, 349
stories, 74–75, 114, 115, 124, 128, 146,
152, 170, 206, 226, 463
story problems, 1LL, 152, 203GG,
206, 246, 270, 296, 329GG, 416,
461GG–461II 486, 534, 550
subtraction and, 9, 29–32, 227, 394

Advanced Learners.
See Challenge activity, Math Writing
Prompt, and technology Software
Support in Differentiated Instruction
for every lesson; See Math Center
Challenges

Algebra
Addition
compose numbers, 227, 394
decompose numbers, 353, 365
equations, 103T, 103U, 103X, 103AA,
111, 128, 146, 152, 157, 158, 166,
167, 401, 417–418, 426, 434, 441,
478, 486, 508, 521
partners (number pairs), 146, 152,
462–463
represent problems, 345, 349–350
subtraction and, 9, 124, 128, 152,
227, 394

equations
model, 111, 146, 152, 157, 167, 478,
486, 521, 550
write, 399, 430, 434, 473, 475, 486,
521, 550
expressions, 349, 360, 361, 386, 406–407
subtraction
addition and, 9, 124, 128, 152, 227,
394
equations, 111, 175, 188, 189,
345, 434
represent problems, 345, 349–350
symbols
addition/plus (+), 111, 157, 167, 349
equal (=), 111, 132, 134, 140, 157,
167, 278, 288, 509
minus (−), 111, 175, 349
not equal (≠),132, 134, 140, 278, 288

Anno's Counting Book, 1S, 1W, 1Y, 1CC,
1EE–1FF, 1JJ, 2, 12, 56, 62, 70, 81–82,
103Q, 106, 462

Argument, construct, 95, 195, 453, 568,
756. See also Puzzled Penguin

Art Connection
Build Triangles, 164
Create Shapes, 96
Draw a Scene with Groups of 1–5, 44
Draw a Scene with Groups of 5, 22
Draw Circles, 38
Draw Scenes with Groups of 2 or 3, 13
Draw Scenes with Groups of 4 and
5, 21
Drawing to Show Positions, 322
Learn to Make Dot-to-Dot Pictures, 88,
206, 211
Picture Pieces, 18
Prepare Fruits and Vegetables for
Sorting and Classifying, 331
Shapes in the Environment, 268
Story of the Tiny Tumblers, 373–375
Ten Bug, 211

Ask for Ideas, 24, 26, 56, 92, 106, 135,
147, 153, 192, 204, 210, 266, 331,
450–452, 463, 479, 512, 558, 564, 566

Assessment
Assessment Resources, 1O, 97–102,
103R, 197–202, 203E, 323–328, 329E,
455–460, 461E, 571–576
Formative Assessment, In every lesson
Check Understanding, In every
lesson

INDEX

H

I

L

INDEX

Q

Z

INDEX